G C S E

Foundation
Science
CLASSBOOK

David Baylis
Graham Booth
Bob McDuell

Letts

EDUCATIONAL

First published 1998

Reprinted 1998

Letts Educational
Schools and Colleges Division
9–15 Aldine Street
London W12 8AW
Tel 0181 740 2270
Fax 0181 740 2280

Text: © David Baylis, Graham Booth, Bob McDuell 1998

Design and illustrations © BPP (Letts Educational) Ltd 1998

Design and page layout: Ken Vail Graphic Design

Illustrations: Graeme Morris (Ken Vail Graphic Design)

Colour reproduction by PDQ Repro Ltd, Bungay, Suffolk

British Library Cataloguing-in-Publication Data

A CIP record for this book is available from the British Library

ISBN 1 84085 029 9

Printed and Bound in Great Britain by Bath Press Ltd.

Letts Educational is the trading name of
BPP (Letts Educational) Ltd

Acknowledgements

The authors would like to thank Sheila Hands for her work in reviewing and adapting the text to meet the needs of Foundation level students.

The authors and publishers are grateful to the following for permission to reproduce photographs:

Action Plus 17.1; 17.4; 19.3; 100.3; The Ancient Art & Architecture Collection 65.4; Biophoto Associates 1.2b; 4.1; 4.8; 6.4; 14.2; 20.3a; 20.3b; 25.1b; 37.1; 39.4; 42.2; Graham Booth 87.2; 87.3; 117.3; Aron Carr 4.3; Bruce Coleman Limited 1.2a; 1.2c; 1.2d; 1.2e; 4.2; 4.5; 17.3; 25.1a; 38.2; 38.3; 40.1; 40.2; 40.3; 42.1; 62.1; 64.2c; 65.2; 66.2; 69.4; 79.1; 95.3; Wayne Davies 105.2; John Dixon 18.3; 86.4; 122.1; Dorling Kindersley Limited 4.7; Electricity Association 88.1; 94.2; Eye Ubiquitous Picture Library 96.3; Ford Motor Company Limited 74.2; Mark Gadd 18.1; Geoscience Features Picture Library 64.2a; 64.2b; 64.3; Health Education Authority 29.1; Holt Studios International 32.1; 33.1; 33.3; 43.1; 77.3; ICI Plc. 77.1; The Kobal Collection 21.4; 39.1; Frank Lane Picture Agency Limited 33.2; Milepost 921/2 Picture Library 61.1; 91.3; Natural History Photographic Agency 4.4; Oxford Scientific Films Limited 94.1; Philips Electronics UK Limited 111.4; Quadrant Picture Library 99.2; 101.1; Rex Features Limited 69.5; 84.4; 89.4; Royal Albert Hall 104.1; Science & Society Picture Library 10.1; Science Photo Library 4.6; 6.4; 6.5; 12.1; 14.1a; 14.1b; 18.2; 21.2; 21.3; 24.1; 24.2; 26.3; 28.1a; 28.1b; 28.2; 31.2; 34.3a; 34.3b; 39.2; 41.3; 41.4; 57.1; 63.4; 64.1; 67.1; 69.1; 69.2; 76.1; 78.1; 93.3; 104.4; 111.2; 112.2; 113.1; 113.3; 114.2; 117.1; 122.2; 125.3; Spectrum Colour Library 60.1; 69.3; 91.4; Shout Picture Company 29.2; Tony Stone Images 18.4; 27.2; United Distillers 52.

CONTENTS

INTRODUCTION	**1**
LIFE PROCESSES AND LIVING THINGS	**2**

Life processes and cell activity

1	Classification – 1	2
2	Classification – 2	4
3	Making and using keys	6
4	Life processes	8
5	Organ systems	10
6	Plant and animal cells	12
7	Chromosomes and mitosis	14
8	Meiosis	16

Humans as organisms

9	Nutrients – the chemistry of food	18
10	Human diet	20
11	The human digestive system	22
12	Absorption and assimilation	24
13	The heart and circulation	26
14	Blood	28
15	Breathing	30
16	Gas exchange and lung structure	32
17	Aerobic respiration	34
18	Anaerobic respiration	36
19	Senses	38
20	The eye	40
21	Reflex action	42
22	Hormonal control	44
23	Insulin and sex hormones	46
24	Medical uses of hormones	48
25	Homeostasis	50
26	The kidney	52
27	Skin and homeostasis	54
28	Defence mechanisms of the body	56
29	Solvents and drugs	58

Green plants as organisms

30	Photosynthesis	60
31	Plant mineral mutrition	62
32	Control of plant growth	64
33	Uses of plant hormones	66
34	Transpiration	68

Variation, inheritance and evolution

35	Variation	70
36	Reproduction and mutation products	72
37	Inheritance and disease	74
38	Cloning and selective breeding	76
39	Evidence for evolution	78

Living things in their environment

40	Adaptation and competition	80
41	Environment	82
42	Feeding relationships	84
52	The carbon cycle	86

MATERIALS AND THEIR PROPERTIES 88

Classifying materials

44 Materials   88
45 Solids, liquids and gases   90
46 Structure of the atom   92
47 Bonding   94
48 Ionic bonding   96
49 Elements, mixtures & compounds   98
50 Separating mixtures – 1   100
51 Separating mixtures – 2   102
52 Separating mixtures – 3   104
53 Separating mixtures – 4   106

Changing materials

54 Solubility   108
55 Change   110
56 Oxidation and reduction   112
57 Crude oil and its refining   114
58 Uses of alkanes   116
59 Cracking hydrocarbons   118
60 Polymerisation   120
61 Reactivity series   122
62 Extraction of metals – 1   124
63 Extraction of metals – 2   126
64 Types of rock   128
65 Uses of rocks   130
66 The rock cycle   132

Patterns of behaviour

67 The Periodic Table   134
68 The alkali metals   136
69 Noble gases   138
70 The halogens – 1   140
71 The halogens – 2   142
72 Rates of chemical reactions – 1   144
73 Rates of chemical reactions – 2   146
74 Rates of chemical reactions – 3   148
75 Enzymes   150
76 The Haber process   152
77 Fertilisers   154
78 Acids and alkalis   156
79 Neutralisation   158
80 Salt formation – 1   160
81 Salt formation – 2   162

PHYSICAL PROCESSES 164

Electricity and magnetism

82 Measuring current 164
83 Circuits and energy transfer 166
84 Current and its control 168
85 Measuring resistance 170
86 Power in circuits 172
87 Using electricity safely 174
88 Paying for electricity 176
89 Static charge 178
90 Electromagnetism 180
91 The d.c. motor 182
92 Electromagnetic induction 184
93 Transformers 186
94 Power transmission 188

Forces and motion

95 Changing shape 190
96 Under pressure 192
97 Hydraulics 194
98 How fast? 196
99 Coming to a halt 198
100 Forces in and out 200
of balance
101 Acceleration 202
102 Falling down 204
103 Turning forces 268

Waves

104 Sound reflections 208
105 Reflecting light 210
106 Different waves 212

107 Wave measurements 214
108 Refraction of light 216
109 Using total internal 218
reflection
110 A family of waves 220
111 At home with waves 222
112 Using X-rays and 224
gamma rays

The Earth and beyond

113 The Earth and the Universe 226
114 Gravitational forces 228

Energy resources and energy transfer

115 Using convection currents 230
116 Thermal conduction 232
117 Radiant energy 234
118 Evaporation and insulation 236
119 Insulating a house 238
120 Using energy resources 240
121 Forces and work 242
122 Power 244

Radioactivity

123 Radioactive emissions 246
124 Radioactive decay 248
125 Using radioactivity 250

GLOSSARY 253

INDEX 261

INTRODUCTION

This Letts GCSE Foundation Science classbook has been developed from the very successful Letts GCSE Science classbook. It is designed to cover the Foundation tier of all GCSE syllabuses. It is intended to help you achieve the highest grades in the Foundation tier. Remember you can achieve a grade C by entering the Foundation tier, but you will have to perform well on the examination papers, achieving in excess of 70%.

This book covers all of the key concepts required by Key Stage 4 Foundation tier, and also covers some of the important topics of Key Stage 3 that will appear on GCSE papers at Foundation tier.

The book is suitable for all Double Science syllabuses. If you are doing Single Science, your teacher will be able to tell you which parts of the book you should study.

This classbook has been written in three co-ordinated sections:

1 Life processes and living things
2 Materials and their properties
3 Physical processes

It has also been split into 125 topics called 'units'. Each unit covers two pages and begins with a list of questions which will introduce you to the ideas in that unit. Each is clearly and simply written in such a way that the Science in not made more difficult. In each unit there are questions for you to think about which will help you to understand the ideas involved, and certain 'key words' are listed at the end of each unit. Success in GCSE Science requires knowing and using the correct scientific language. Each of these words is defined in the Glossary at the end of the book.

ideas introduced in the unit

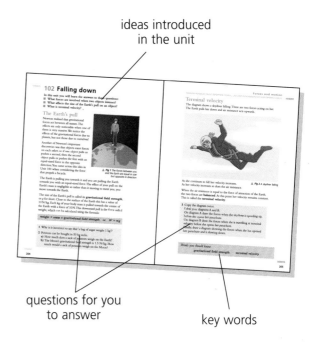

questions for you to answer

key words

This classbook is written by three experienced teachers, authors and examiners. We hope that it will help you understand the important concepts of Science and help you to achieve your best grade. In using this classbook we hope you will get an insight into and enjoyment of Science, which is vital to an understanding of the modern world.

1 Classification – 1

In this unit you should learn the answers to these questions:
- How are living things and non-living things different?
- How can living things be grouped?
- What are vertebrates and invertebrates?
- What are the five groups of vertebrates?

Plant and Animal Kingdoms

You can easily tell the difference between living things like a plant or an animal and non-living things like a rock or a plastic box.

Large numbers of things can often be split into smaller groups. This is called **classification**.

All living things can be divided into **kingdoms**. Two of these kingdoms are the **plant kingdom** and the **animal kingdom**

Fig 1 shows a picture of a pond.

1 Make a list of the differences between living and non-living things. For example a living thing grows and a non-living thing does not.

2 Look at Fig 1. Six living things have been lettered A–F. Which are in the plant kingdom and which in the animal kingdom?

▲ **Fig 1** Life in and around a pond

Animals can be divided into two groups, the **vertebrates** and the **invertebrates**. Vertebrates (such as humans, fish and snakes) have a backbone. Animals without a backbone (such as worms and insects) are called invertebrates.

Five classes of vertebrates

We can divide vertebrates into five groups.

These are

amphibians   birds   fish   mammals   reptiles

Fig 2 shows five different animals.

◀ **Fig 2b** *Frog*

Fig 2a
Pigeon ▼

Fig 2d
Crocodile ▼

▲ **Fig 2c** *Shark*

◀ **Fig 2e** *Dog; bitch suckling pups*

3 Which group of vertebrates does each animal in Fig 2 belong to? There is one example of each.

4 Here are two descriptions. One is a description of an amphibian and one is of a reptile. Which is which?

A
• backbone
• soft and moist skin
• tadpoles have gills, adults have lungs
• eggs laid in water
• larvae live in water, adults live on land and in water

B
• backbone
• skin is covered with dry scales or bony plates
• lungs
• lay eggs with leathery shells

Words you should know
amphibian   bird   fish   invertebrate   mammal   reptile   vertebrate

2 Classification – 2

In this unit you should learn the answers to these questions:
■ Into what groups can animals be divided?
■ How can plants be grouped?

Family tree of animals

In Unit 1 we looked at five groups of vertebrates – animals with backbones. If we think of the animal kingdom as a tree, we have looked at only one branch of it.

Fig 1 shows the animal kingdom drawn as a tree. You will see many different groups of animals. The number shown with each name is the number of different **species** of each of the groups. For example, there are 3200 different species of mammals

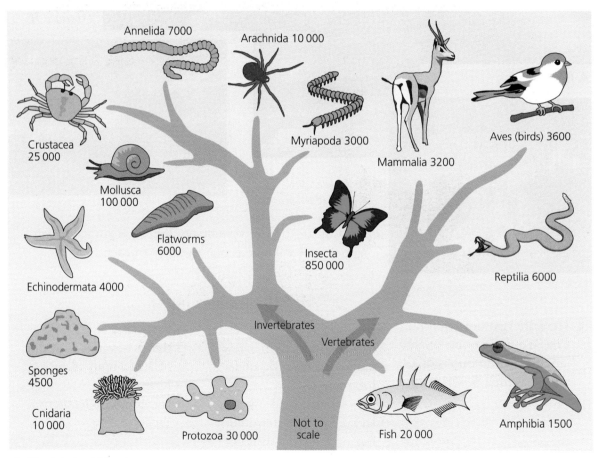

Annelida 7000

Arachnida 10 000

Myriapoda 3000

Mammalia 3200

Aves (birds) 3600

Crustacea 25 000

Mollusca 100 000

Flatworms 6000

Insecta 850 000

Reptilia 6000

Echinodermata 4000

Sponges 4500

Cnidaria 10 000

Protozoa 30 000

Invertebrates

Vertebrates

Not to scale

Fish 20 000

Amphibia 1500

▲ **Fig 1** Animal kingdom drawn as a tree

1 To which group do each of the following belong?
crab   spider   snail   starfish   butterfly

2 Which group of animals has the most species?

The plant kingdom

Plants can be grouped in a similar way to the way animals were grouped. Fig 2 shows a way of grouping plants according to whether or not they make seeds.

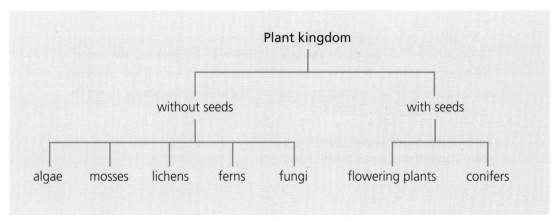

▲ *Fig 2* Grouping plants

Fig 3 shows some different plants.

◀ *Fig 3*

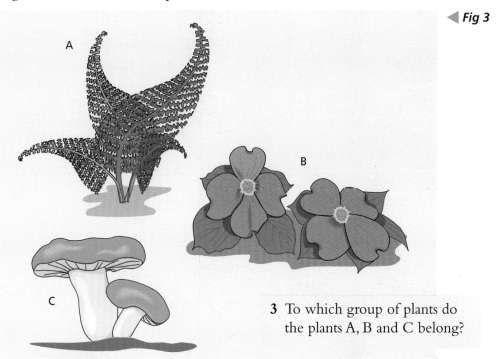

3 To which group of plants do the plants A, B and C belong?

Words you should know

arachnid   crustacean   insect   mollusc   species

3 Making and using keys

In this unit you should learn the answers to these questions:
- How can a key be used to classify organisms?
- How can you make a key using the differences between organisms?

Keys

We may need to classify or identify an individual organism. We could use keys to help us. A key is a series of questions. To use it we need to look carefully at an organism. Then we can answer questions about its appearance and characteristics.

Here is a key which can be used to identify the groups which the four organisms shown below belong to.

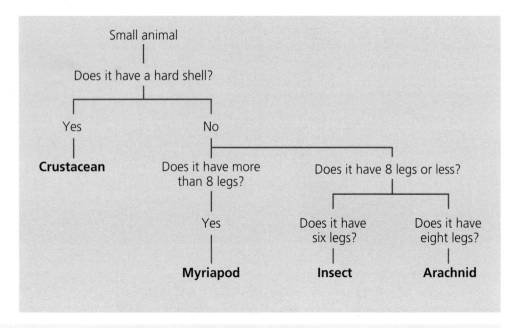

1 Use the key to identify the groups for organisms A, B, C and D.

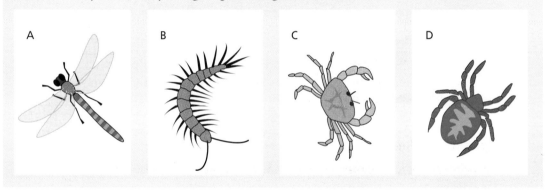

In Unit 1 (on page 3) five animals belonging to different groups are shown in Fig 2.

The following key can be used to identify these organisms.

1 Legs present . . . . go to 2
  No legs . . . . **Fig 2c**

2 Four legs . . . . go to 3
  Two legs, and a pair of wings . . . . . **Fig 2a**

3 Body not covered in hair . . . . go to 4
  Body covered in hair . . . . **Fig 2e**

4 Body not covered in scales . . . . . . **Fig 2b**
  Body covered in scales . . . . **Fig 2d**

2 Here are pictures of six different fish.

goldfish

pike

eel

spine

stickleback

plaice

perch

The pictures are not to scale.
Look for differences, e.g. the eel does not have a tail fin.
Make your own key to identify these fish.

Words you should know
  arachnid   crustacean   insect   key   mollusc   species

4 Life processes

In this unit you will learn the answer to this question:
- What are the life processes of plants and animals?

Living things carry out **seven processes** to stay alive.

Look at Figs 1 and 2. An oak tree starts off its life as an acorn. Fifty years later it may look like the tree in Fig 2. It has made a permanent increase in size. You too will have got much bigger since your birth.

1 All living things grow.

▲ **Fig 1**   ▲ **Fig 2**

Plants and animals need energy to stay alive. Food materials contain energy. Chemical reactions release this energy. The process of releasing energy from food chemicals is called **respiration**.

2 All living things respire.

1 Suggest one way in which energy from respiration might be used **a)** by you and **b)** by an oak tree.

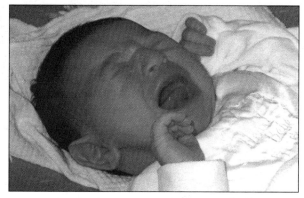

▲ **Fig 3**

Fig 3 shows a crying baby. When do babies cry? They cry if they are hungry or perhaps upset by a loud noise. Potted plants left on a window sill may grow towards the light coming into the room. Each of these living things is aware of changes in and around them.

3 All living things show **sensitivity** or irritability.

Most of the plants we see around us are usually firmly rooted to the ground. Even these move as they grow. The shoot tip of a climbing plant moves around its support as it grows. Movement shown by animals is easily seen.

2 Why is movement in animals easier to see than movement in plants?

4 All living things move.

Processes such as respiration produce waste products. Some wastes are harmful and have to be got rid of. The hyena in Fig 4 is getting rid of a solution called urine. Urea is made by mammalian liver cells from surplus amino acids. Some plants lose their leaves in autumn. Some of their waste by-products are lost at the same time. The process by which living things get rid of their biochemical wastes is called **excretion**.

5 All living things excrete.

3 Why do mammals have to excrete urea?

▲ **Fig 5**

▲ **Fig 6**

▲ **Fig 4**

Figs 5 and 6 show animals feeding. Fig 5 shows a carnivore and Fig 6 shows a herbivore. Green plants take in simple materials from their environment. They use light energy to make complex foods. The process is called **photosynthesis** (see Unit 30).

6 All living things feed and the process is called **nutrition**.

4 In what way do we indirectly rely on sunlight for our food?

▲ **Fig 7**

Individual plants and animals must eventually die. However, before they die, most will have been involved in the production of replacements or offspring. Fig 7 shows a plant called *Kalanchoe*. This plant produces large numbers of plantlets. The horse in Fig 8 has produced only one 'replacement'. All plant and animal species must produce replacements. If they do not, their species will become extinct. Replacements are provided by the process of **reproduction**.

7 All living things reproduce.

▲ **Fig 8**

Words you should know

**excretion   nutrition   offspring
photosynthesis   reproduction
respiration   sensitivity**

5 Many sexually reproducing organisms produce more than two offspring (replacements). Why do you think this is necessary?

5 Organ systems

In this unit you should learn the answers to these questions:
- What are cells, tissues and organ systems?
- What are the seven main organ systems in the body?
- What are the main parts of the male and female reproductive system?

Cells

The human body is a multicellular organism. It is made up of many different **cells**.

Do you know how many cells there are in your body? Imagine every person in Great Britain each won 2 million pounds in the National Lottery. The number of pounds needed in prize money is the same as the number of cells in your body.

100 000 000 000 000

The cells are not all the same. They have different jobs to do. They have structures to make them good for the job they do.

A collection of cells of the same type doing a job is called a **tissue.** A group of tissues is called an **organ.** Groups of organs working together to carry out a job are called an **organ system.**

All of the work of the body is shared out amongst the different organ systems.

Fig 1 shows a human male with some of the organs labelled with letters A-G.

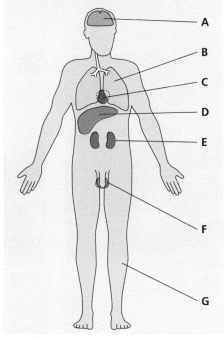

▲ **Fig 1** Organs in a human male

1 Identify each of the organs in Fig 1. Choose your answers from this list.
   brain   heart   kidney   liver
   lung   skin   testes

Organ systems

There are seven main organ systems in the human body. These are:

1 the **reproductive** system;

2 the **digestive** system (Units 11–12);

3 the **circulatory** system (Units 13–14);

4 the **respiratory** system (Units 15–16);

5 the **nervous** system (Unit 19);

6 the **excretory** system (Unit 26); and

7 the **endocrine** system (Unit 22).

2 Which of the organ systems transfers blood around the body?

3 Which organ system transfers messages quickly around the body?

4 Which of the organ systems controls the loss of wastes from the body?

5 Which organ system produces chemicals called hormones?

The reproductive system

Fig 2 shows diagrams of the male and female reproductive system. Fig 2a is the male reproductive system. Fig 2b is the female reproductive system.

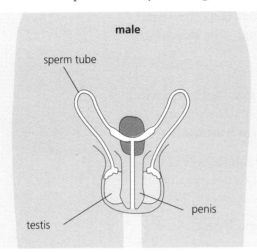
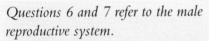

▲ **Fig 2a** *Male reproductive system (front view)*

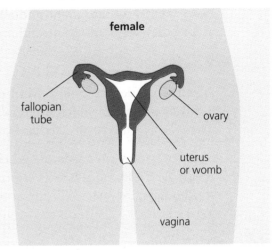

▲ **Fig 2b** *Female reproductive system (front view)*

Questions 6 and 7 refer to the male reproductive system.

6 Which organ produces sperm?

7 Through which organ does sperm leave the male to enter the female?

Questions 8–10 refer to the female reproductive system.

8 In which organ is the egg made?

9 Where does the egg come in contact with the sperm?

10 Through which organ is the baby born?

11 Fig 3 shows a side view of the male reproductive system. Copy this diagram and label the organs marked **A–C**.

12 Fig 4 shows a side view of the female reproductive system. Copy this diagram and label the organs **D–F**.

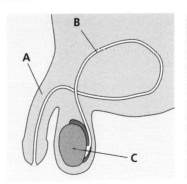

▲ **Fig 3** *Male reproductive system (side view)*

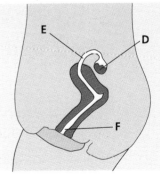

▲ **Fig 4** *Female reproductive system (side view)*

Words you should know

cell circulatory digestive endocrine excretory fallopian tube nervous organ organ system ovary penis reproductive respiratory sperm tube testes tissue uterus vagina

6 Plant and animal cells

In this unit you should learn the answers to these questions:
- ■ What is the basic unit of life?
- ■ What are the names of different parts of a cell?
- ■ In what ways are plant and animal cells the same?
- ■ In what ways are plant and animal cells different?

Cells

A **cell** is a basic unit of life. Most of a cell is **cytoplasm**. There is a **nucleus** which holds genetic information. The whole cell is held together by a **membrane.**

Some organisms are made of one cell. *Amoeba* (Fig 1) is a single-celled organism. It is found in ditches and small ponds.

Other organisms are made of many cells. These are multicellular organisms. In these organisms different cells have different jobs.

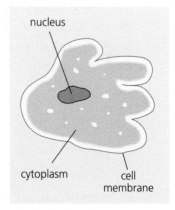

▲ *Fig 1* Amoeba

1 What is the name of the basic unit of life?

2 What is in the nucleus of the cell?

3 What holds a cell together?

4 Fig 2 shows two things *Amoeba* does. What are the amoebae doing in each case? ▶ *Fig 2*

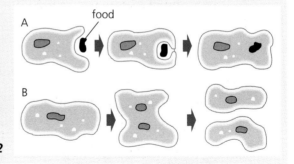

Plant and animal cells

Fig 3a shows a typical animal cell. Fig 3b shows a plant cell.

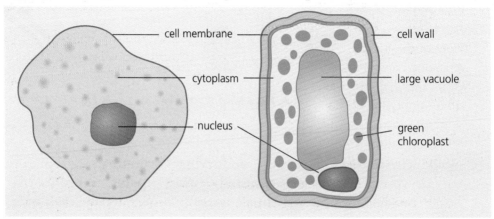

▲ *Fig 3a* A typical animal cell　　　▲ *Fig 3b* A typical plant cell

5 Write down three things which are in both plant and animal cells.

6 Write down three things that are in a plant cell and not in an animal cell.

7 Which part of a plant cell contains chlorophyll?

The nucleus of the cell is large enough to be seen with an ordinary **light microscope**. Some cell parts are too small to be seen with this microscope. An **electron microscope** is more powerful. It magnifies things more. Fig 4 shows a plant cell seen using an electron microscope.

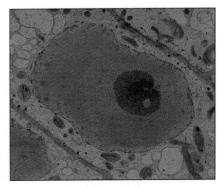

▶ *Fig 4 A plant cell seen through an electron microscope*

How are plant cells and animal cells the same?

Plant and animal cells are the same in a number of ways. Both plant and animal cells

- have a cell membrane around the outside
- have a jelly like substance called cytoplasm
- have a nucleus
- have organelles in the cytoplasm.

How are plant cells and animal cells different?

The table shows some of the differences between plant and animal cells.

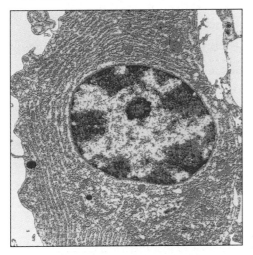

plant cell	animal cell
cell walls made of **cellulose**	no cell wall
large vacuole	no vacuole or many very small vacuoles
nucleus at edge of cell	nucleus anywhere in the cell
contains chloroplasts	no chloroplasts

8 Fig 5 shows another cell. Write down the parts you can see. Is it a plant cell or an animal cell?

◀ *Fig 5 Photograph of cell magnified*

Words you should know

cell   cell wall   chloroplast   cytoplasm
electron microscope   light microscope   nucleus   vacuole

7 Chromosomes and mitosis

In this unit you will learn the answers to these questions:
- Where are chromosomes found?
- What are genes and what do they do?
- What is mitosis?
- Where does it take place?

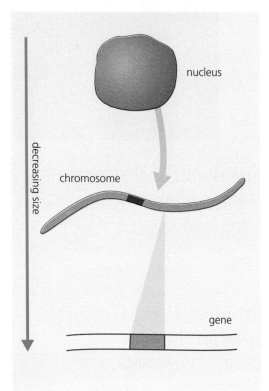

▲ **Fig 1**

Every nucleus in every human cell has 46 or 23 pairs of chromosomes. (Sex cells or gametes are different. See Unit 8) Other organisms have a different number of chromosomes. The chromosome number is a characteristic of a species.

The nucleus is the largest structure of a cell. Cells can divide to make new cells. When cell division is about to start small structures can be seen in the nucleus. They are called **chromosomes** (see Fig 1).

Chromosomes are made of protein and **deoxyribonucleic acid** (**DNA**). Normally they are long and very thin. When cell division starts they get shorter and fatter and can be seen. After division they become long and thin again.

Chromosomes have special parts called **genes**. Genes contain genetic information. An exact copy of each chromosome has to be made before a cell can divide. Each new cell must have the full set of chromosomes. In this way genetic information is passed on and characteristics can be inherited.

1 What are chromosomes made of?

We all start life as a single cell called a **zygote**. When we are adult we will have about 10^{14} cells. The original cell must have divided many times to make so many cells. This process of cell division is called mitosis.

2 Chromosomes are sometimes compared to 'strings of beads'. What do you think the 'beads' are supposed to represent?

Mechanism of mitosis

Mitosis involves a series of processes. These include:

1 **Replication** – making an exact copy of the DNA of each chromosome. Each chromosome becomes a pair of **chromatids**.

2 **Division** – the cell divides to make 2 new daughter cells. Each daughter cell has a full set of chromosomes. Daughter cells are identical to each other and to the parent cell.

3 What does 'replication' mean?

4 What structures become the new chromosomes in the daughter cell

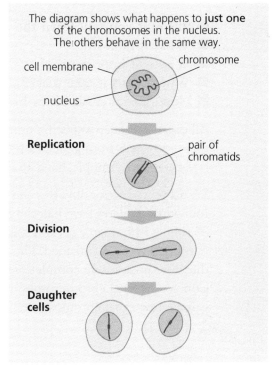

The diagram shows what happens to **just one** of the chromosomes in the nucleus. The others behave in the same way.

cell membrane

chromosome

nucleus

Replication

pair of chromatids

Division

Daughter cells

▲ **Fig 2** Mitosis in an animal cell

Importance of mitosis

Mitosis produces exact copies of cells. It is important in:

1 growth; **2** repair; and **3** asexual reproduction.

Growth. When growth of a tissue becomes necessary, the cells present in the tissue divide. The cells formed are genetically the same since they will have the same job to do. Mitosis gives exact copies.

Repair. When a tissue is damaged it is important that it is repaired. It is important also that damaged cells are replaced by cells of the same type.

Some animals and most plants can *reproduce asexually* (without sex). They do not need a partner. Gardeners can break off pieces of a plant or it can occur naturally (see Unit 38). The pieces grow into whole plants which are genetically identical to the parent.

5 Why is mitosis important for growth?

6 Why are asexually produced plants exactly like their parents?

Words you should know

chromosome   chromatid   mitosis   replication   zygote

8 Meiosis

In this unit you will learn the answers to these questions:
- ■ What is meiosis?
- ■ Why is it important?
- ■ Where does it take place?
- ■ How does meiosis differ from mitosis?

All organisms keep a specific number of chromosomes in the nuclei of their body cells from generation to generation. The nuclei of human body cells, for example, have 46 chromosomes present as 23 pairs.

Sexual reproduction involves the fusion of nuclei at **fertilisation**. Individual gametes have half the body cell chromosome number, e.g. 23 singles in human eggs and sperms, if the characteristic chromosome number is to be maintained. The **zygote** formed at fertilisation will therefore possess one complete set of chromosomes from the male gamete (paternal chromosomes) and one complete set from the female gamete (maternal chromosomes) (Fig 1).

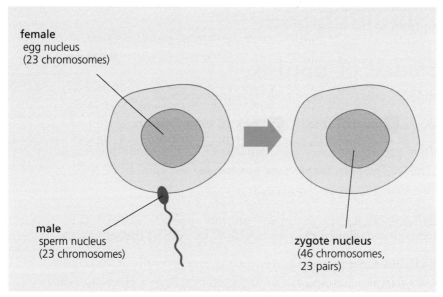

female
egg nucleus
(23 chromosomes)

male
sperm nucleus
(23 chromosomes)

zygote nucleus
(46 chromosomes,
23 pairs)

▲ **Fig 1** Fusion of human male and female gametes

1 What is a zygote?

2 Why does a zygote have twice as many chromosomes as the egg from which it was formed?

3 Where would you expect to find meiosis taking place in humans?

Fig 2 summarises the process of **meiosis** in an animal cell.

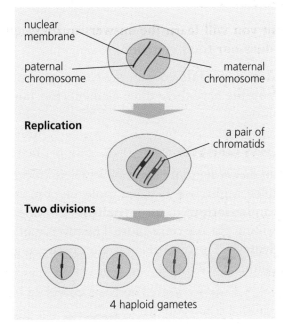

▶ *Fig 2 Meiosis in an animal cell*

The importance of meiosis

1 Reduces chromosome number in gametes. This avoids constant doubling-up of chromosome number at each new generation.

2 Pieces of chromosomes can be exchanged between the paternal and maternal chromosomes of the same pair. The material exchanged will be responsible for the same general genetic characteristics but the *details will differ*. This leads to a new combination of characteristics.

3 Gives opportunities for **variation** (difference) to occur.

The table compares meiosis and mitosis (see Unit 7).

Feature	Meiosis	Mitosis
Where it occurs	sex organs	body cells
Why it occurs	to make gametes for reproduction	for growth, repair and asexual reproduction
Number of divisions	2	1
Number of cells produced	4	2
Number of chromosomes in the nucleus of cells produced	half the number in body cells (n)	same number as in body cells (2n)
Type of cells produced	genetically different	genetically identical

Words you should know
fertilisation   meiosis   variation   zygote

9 Nutrients – the chemistry of food

In this unit you will learn the answer to this question:
- What does our food contain?

Carbohydrates and **fats** contain the elements carbon, hydrogen and oxygen. **Proteins** have these three elements too, but also contain the element nitrogen.

Carbohydrates

The human diet commonly contains a variety of carbohydrates. One of the simplest is **glucose**. Glucose molecules can combine together in pairs (**condensation**) to form **maltose**. Enzymes can reverse this change, forming glucose once more. The reversal of condensation is called **hydrolysis**. The reversible reaction between glucose and maltose is summarised in Fig 1.

glucose + glucose ⇌ combining together (condensation) / breaking down (hydrolysis) ⇌ maltose + water

▲ **Fig 1** Maltose formation / breakdown

This adding together of similar molecules is called **polymerisation**. If many units are added, a large chain can be produced. These are called **polymers**. One example of a glucose polymer is **starch**. Fig 2 shows the polymerisation of glucose to form starch. Sugars are soluble in water. Starch is insoluble in water.

glucose + glucose + ... + glucose ⇌ many glucose molecules / combining together / breaking down ⇌ starch + water

▲ **Fig 2** Starch formation / breakdown

Fats

Fat molecules are formed by two types of molecules combining together. These are **glycerol** and **fatty acids**. Once more this reaction can be reversed. Fig 3 summarises these changes. Fat is a very high energy food material.

glycerol + fatty acids ⇌ combining together / breaking down ⇌ fat + water

▲ **Fig 3** Fat formation / breakdown

Proteins

Proteins are polymers too. **Amino acids** (monomers) combine to form large chains called **proteins**. When protein chains are broken up amino acids are re-formed (Fig 4).

amino acid + amino acid + ... + amino acid ⇄ (combining together / breaking down) protein + water

▲ **Fig 4** Protein formation / breakdown

Vitamins

Vitamins are a group of complicated compounds. They have vital jobs to do in the body. You are likely to have heard of some of them, e.g. vitamin C.

Minerals

Humans need a large variety of mineral ions. Calcium in the form of calcium ions (Ca^{2+}) and iron as ions (Fe^{2+}) are examples of essential minerals. Essential minerals are needed in very small quantities.

Dietary fibre

This is the material which humans cannot digest, mainly made up of cellulose, plant cell walls. It is often referred to as **roughage**.

The table shows common sources for some of the food materials mentioned in this unit.

Food material	Source (examples)
starch	potatoes, rice, wheat flour
fat / oil	milk, butter, fish oils, plant oils
protein	lean meat, cheese, peas
vitamin C	citrus fruits
vitamin B complex	liver
vitamin A	vegetables, fruit, liver
vitamin D	liver, dairy products
calcium	dairy products, green vegetables
iron	liver, green vegetables
dietary fibre	plant matter, wholemeal flour

Words you should know

**carbohydrate   fat   hydrolysis
polymerisation   protein   vitamins**

1 Name the three elements found in all carbohydrates, fats and proteins.

2 Name an additional element found in all proteins.

3 How is starch formed?

4 Name the two types of compound involved in the formation of a fat.

5 Name the monomers involved in protein synthesis.

6 Name two mineral nutrients.

7 Name a single food source containing vitamins B, A and D.

8 Name a single food source containing both calcium and iron.

9 Name a good source for dietary fibre.

11 The human digestive system

In this unit you will learn the answers to these questions:
- ■ What happens to food in our gut?
- ■ How is the gut designed to deal with our food?

Our digestive system breaks down the complex food we eat into simple substances that the body can use.

Five important processes occur:

1 **Ingestion** – food is put in the mouth.

2 **Digestion** (both mechanical and chemical) – large, complex insoluble food chemicals are converted into simpler, soluble molecules.

3 **Absorption** – the useful products of digestion pass from our gut into the blood stream.

4 **Assimilation** – body cells use the food products that have been delivered by the blood.

5 **Egestion** – undigested, unusable food materials leave the body as faeces.

The gut is a single, continuous muscular tube. It is several metres long from mouth to anus. Different parts do different jobs.

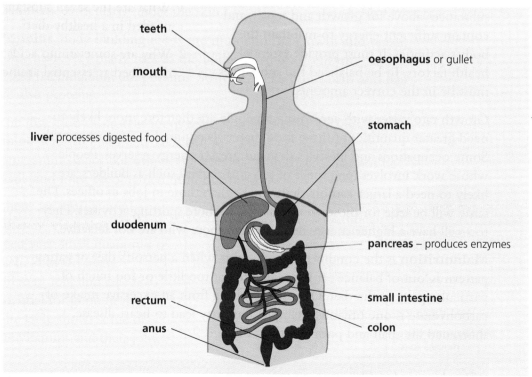

▲ **Fig 1** The human gut and associated organs

In the mouth the food is broken down by chewing and mixed with **enzymes** in saliva. These enzymes start to break down carbohydrates into simpler sugars. After swallowing, the food is moved along the gut by muscle action. The first part of this journey, from the mouth to the stomach, passes along the oesophagus.

Muscles of the gut contract and relax in a special way to squeeze the food along. Food is moved by **peristalsis** (See Fig 2).

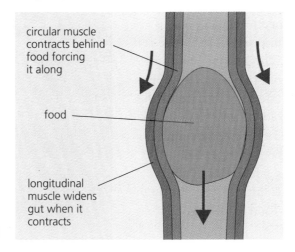

circular muscle contracts behind food forcing it along

food

longitudinal muscle widens gut when it contracts

▶ *Fig 2* *Peristalsis*

The main jobs of the parts of the digestive system are:

Body part	Main job
Mouth	Food chewed into small pieces for swallowing. Saliva softens food. Some amylase action.
Stomach	Food is stored for a few hours. Movements mix food with stomach (gastric) juices. Hydrochloric acid kills most bacteria and makes ideal conditions for proteases to work.
Small intestine	Alkaline juices neutralise stomach acids and make ideal conditions for amylases, lipases and proteases to complete chemical breakdown. Absorption also occurs here (see Unit 12).
Large intestine	Water (from digestive juices and food) is reabsorbed into the blood, especially in the colon. Unusable material becomes faeces which are stored in the rectum before egestion from the anus.

1 Write an account of the process of digestion.

Words you should know
absorption   digestion   egestion   enzymes   ingestion

12 Absorption and assimilation

In this unit you will learn the answer to this question:
■ What happens to food after it has been digested?

Absorption

The region of the small intestine where absorption takes place is very long in proportion to the rest of the gut. The average length of the small intestine of an adult man is seven metres. The surface of the **ileum** is folded, with each square millimetre of surface carrying a large number of finger-like projections called **villi**. These project into the gut space through which the food is passing.

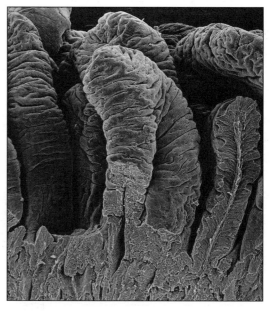

▶ **Fig 1** Photomicrograph of a section through the small intestine, showing folding and villi

The fact that the ileum is long and narrow means that the food is more likely to be brought close to the absorbing surface for a longer time. The folded internal surface increases the surface area for contact. It also provides a greater surface to carry villi, which in turn carry microvilli. These features provide a **very large surface area**, making the ileum an efficient organ for absorption.

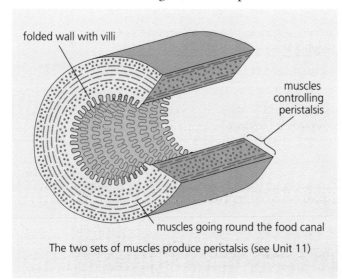

folded wall with villi

muscles controlling peristalsis

muscles going round the food canal

The two sets of muscles produce peristalsis (see Unit 11)

◀ **Fig 2** A cross section of the ileum

Fig 3 shows the structure of a single villus. The wall is very thin and is permeable to the products of digestion. Branches of the artery which goes to the small intestine form **capillaries** which deliver blood to each villus. Blood drains away from the villus to join blood from other villi before it leaves the small intestine.

Sugars, amino acids, fatty acids and glycerol diffuse across the thin membranes of the villus surface cells. They enter the blood and are carried away.

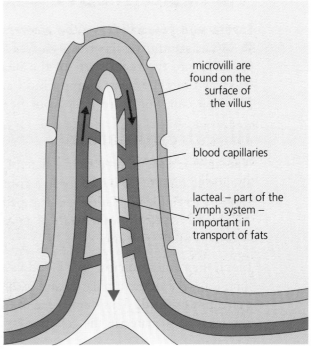

microvilli are found on the surface of the villus

blood capillaries

lacteal – part of the lymph system – important in transport of fats

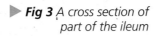

▶ **Fig 3** *A cross section of part of the ileum*

Assimilation

Food absorbed from the small intestine is transported to the liver. Some travels in the hepatic portal vein and some in the lymph. The liver controls what happens to the absorbed food.

1 The body needs glucose. It is used in respiration to produce energy. A constant amount of glucose circulates in the blood. The liver converts excess glucose to insoluble glycogen. An adult can store about 100 g of glycogen in the liver, and some can be stored in the muscles. Stored glycogen can be changed back to glucose when this is needed (see Unit 23).

2 Excess carbohydrates are converted to fat. Some fat is stored in the liver and some under the skin.

3 Amino acids cannot be stored. They are used to make proteins and are used for growth, repair and other healthy functions. Any left over are got rid of (see Unit 26).

1 List four features of the ileum which increase the efficiency of absorption.

Words you should know

absorption   assimilation   ileum   villus (plural **villi**)

13 The heart and circulation

In this unit you will learn the answers to these questions:
- What are the vessels through which the blood flows?
- What are the main parts of the heart?
- How does the heart pump blood around the body?
- What can you do to keep your heart healthy?

Blood circulation

The heart is a pump used to circulate blood around the body. It takes about one minute for blood to do a complete circuit of the body. Blood, carrying raw materials, is pumped to each organ in the body. The blood travels from the heart in an **artery.** The blood in the arteries is under pressure.

Blood then enters microscopic blood vessels called **capillaries.** Here a fluid leaks out of the capillaries and bathes the tissues. This fluid is called **tissue fluid.** This fluid contains the materials the cells need. It also takes away materials the cells need to get rid of.

Blood returns to the heart at a lower pressure through a **vein.** The veins contain **valves** to prevent blood flowing back to the tissues it has left.

> **1** Which blood vessels take blood from the heart?
>
> **2** Which blood vessels return blood to the heart?

Structure of the heart

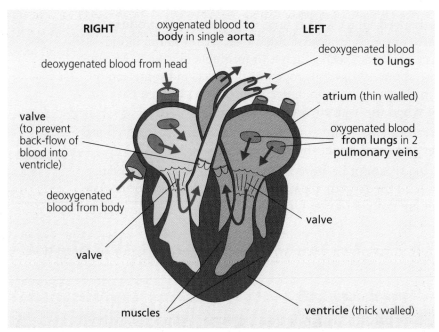

RIGHT

oxygenated blood **to body** in single **aorta**

LEFT

deoxygenated blood from head

deoxygenated blood **to lungs**

atrium (thin walled)

valve (to prevent back-flow of blood into ventricle)

oxygenated blood **from lungs** in 2 **pulmonary veins**

deoxygenated blood from body

valve

valve

muscles

ventricle (thick walled)

▲ **Fig 1** *Section diagram of the heart of a mammal*

How the heart pumps the blood

Fig 2 shows the stages involved in the pumping of the blood by the heart (the same happens, at the same time, on the other side of the heart). The stages are numbered 1–5.

Stage 1. The heart valves shut. The ventricles are full of blood. This is the first part of the heartbeat.

Stage 2. The ventricles squeeze and push the blood away from the heart.

Stage 3. The valves shut to prevent blood flowing back into the heart. The second part of the heartbeat is the sound of the valves closing.

Stage 4. The atrium fills with blood.

Stage 5. The heart muscle squeezes the blood into the ventricles.

The process then continues many times each minute – adult average 72 beats per minute.

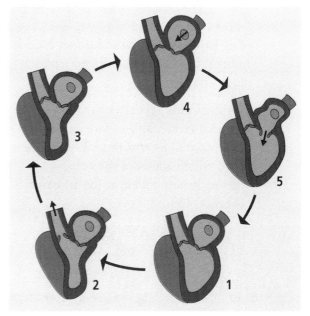

▲ *Fig 2*

The effects of exercise, diet, smoking and stress on the circulatory system

The heart is a muscular organ. Like other muscles it will increase in size as a result of exercise. It then becomes a more efficient pump. An athelete's heart beats much less than 72 times a minute, but it still pumps the same volume of blood as an average person.

The heart muscle is supplied by two coronary arteries. Blood delivers oxygen and glucose, which are essential for muscular contraction. Blockage of these vessels can starve the heart muscle of oxygen and glucose. This leads to coronary heart disease and possible death.

Three risk factors known to be associated with heart disease are:

1 diet; **2** raised blood pressure; and **3** smoking.

A diet involving high levels of **saturated fats** (typically animal fats) and **cholesterol** is particularly likely to increase the risk of heart disease. **High blood pressure** makes the heart work harder. It is common in middle-aged and older people and may be made worse by smoking, drinking too much alcohol, lack of exercise and too much stress.

Words you should know
artery atrium capillary valve vein ventricle

3 What causes coronary heart disease?

14 Blood

In this unit you will learn the answers to these questions:
- What is blood?
- What are the jobs of the different blood cells?

Fig 1a shows whole human blood. Fig 1b shows the same human blood after it has been centrifuged (spun at high speeds).

Centrifuging separates the heavier parts of blood, at the bottom of the tube, from a lighter fluid. The heavier part, which includes the cells, is normally suspended in the **plasma**, (straw coloured fluid).

▲ **Fig 1a** Whole blood

▲ **Fig 1b** Whole blood after centrifugation

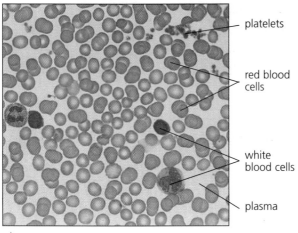

platelets

red blood cells

white blood cells

plasma

▲ **Fig 2** A colour micrograph of a blood smear

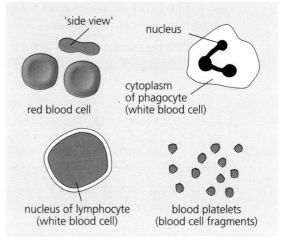

'side view'

nucleus

red blood cell

cytoplasm of phagocyte (white blood cell)

nucleus of lymphocyte (white blood cell)

blood platelets (blood cell fragments)

▲ **Fig 3** Blood cells and platelets

1 What are the names of the three types of blood cell visible in the blood smear?

2 Give four ways, other than colour, in which the white cells and the red cells differ.

Plasma

Materials are taken around the body in the blood. Most materials are transported in solution. The plasma acts as both the solvent and the transport medium.

Plasma delivers glucose to the cells from the liver. All living cells need glucose for respiration to produce energy. Plasma collects the waste product, carbon dioxide, and takes it to the lungs for excretion. Urea is another poisonous waste. It is made in the liver cells. Blood takes urea to the kidneys and it leaves the body in the urine. The table gives examples of materials transported in the plasma.

Transported in plasma	From	To
carbon dioxide	all cells	lungs
urea	liver	kidneys
products of digestion	small intestine (ileum)	all tissues
hormones	endocrine glands	target cells

Red blood cells

As shown in Fig 2 there are more red blood cells than white blood cells in healthy blood. There are about 5.5 million red blood cells in each cubic centimetre of blood. For every white blood cell there are about 500 red blood cells. Red blood cells contain a red iron pigment called haemoglobin. Blood can become oxygenated. Haemoglobin can pick up and release oxygen easily because it only forms a temporary combination with it. When surrounded by a lot of oxygen, **haemoglobin** becomes oxyhaemoglobin. When oxygen levels are low oxyhaemoglobin gives up its oxygen (as shown below). Blood is then de-oxygenated.

high oxygen availability

oxygen + haemoglobin ⇌ oxyhaemoglobin

low oxygen availability

3 Suggest one area in the body where there is likely to be a lot of 'free' oxygen around.

4 Explain where there is likely to be a high constant demand for oxygen in the body.

White blood cells

There are two main types of white blood cells. They do different jobs.
Phagocytes take in bacteria and cell debris ('rubbish').
Lymphocytes make antibodies.

Both play an important part in dealing with disease organisms (pathogens) which enter the bloodstream (see Unit 28).

Blood platelets

Blood **platelets** are important in blood clotting. When cells are damaged they release a chemical which starts a chain of chemical reactions. Finally a blood clot is formed.

Words you should know

blood cells   haemoglobin   lymphocytes   phagocytes   plasma   platelets

15 Breathing

In this unit you will learn the answers to these questions:
- What's inside the chest?
- How do we get air in and out of our lungs?
- In what way is the air breathed out different from the air breathed in?

Structure of the thorax

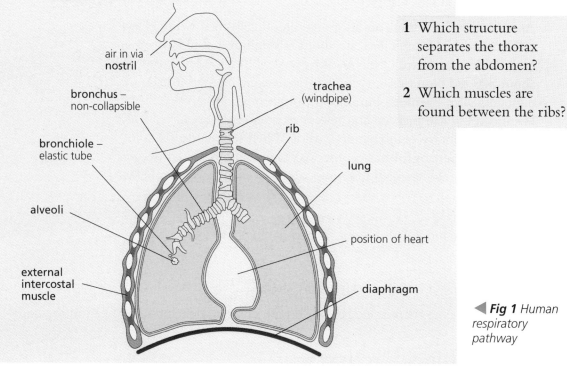

1 Which structure separates the thorax from the abdomen?

2 Which muscles are found between the ribs?

◀ **Fig 1** Human respiratory pathway

The mechanism of breathing

The thorax, or chest cavity, surrounds the lungs and is air-tight. When we breathe in (inhale), two parts of the body move. The intercostal muscles move the ribs up and out. The thorax is now larger from back to front. At the same time the diaphragm (a muscular sheet) contracts and flattens. This makes the thorax larger from top to bottom. Increased space within the chest cavity causes air pressure around the lungs to become lower. High pressure air that surrounds us rushes in and fills (inflates) the lungs.

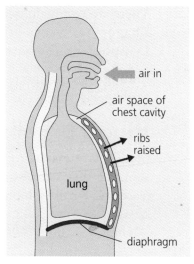

▲ **Fig 2** Inhalation

30

When we breathe out (exhale) the intercostal muscles move the ribs down and in. The thorax is now smaller from front to back. At the same time the diaphragm relaxes and becomes dome shaped. The thorax is now smaller from top to bottom. Decreasing the space around the lungs increases the pressure so air is forced out of the lungs. The lungs deflate.

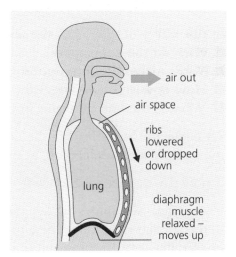

▶ **Fig 3** *Exhalation*

Composition of inhaled and exhaled air

The air that we breathe out is different from the air that surrounds us (see the table). The oxygen we need for respiration is removed from the air by the lungs, so there is less oxygen in the air that we breathe out.

Carbon dioxide is a poisonous waste product of respiration. We excrete it from our lungs. We breathe out more carbon dioxide than we breathe in.

	Inhaled	Exhaled	Approx. change
oxygen	21%	17%	20% decrease
carbon dioxide	0.04%	4%	100-fold increase
nitrogen	79%	79%	nil

The amount of water vapour in the air varies each day. The atmosphere may be dry or damp. Water is a waste product of respiration and so there is more in exhaled than in inhaled air.

The body does not use nitrogen so the amount does not change.

3 Which gas is used by the body?

4 What is the change in composition for oxygen and carbon dioxide during breathing?

5 Suggest a way not shown in the table in which air breathed out is likely to differ from inhaled air.

Words you should know

**bronchiole   bronchus   diaphragm   exhalation
inhalation   intercostal muscles   lung**

16 Gas exchange and lung structure

In this unit you will learn the answers to these questions:
- How do the lungs work?
- What makes the lungs good at their job?
- How does smoking affect the way the lungs work?
- What is the link between smoking and lung cancer?

Air enters the body through the nose or mouth. It travels to the microscopic **air sacs**, **alveoli**, in the lungs. It follows this pathway:

nose → trachea → bronchus → bronchioles → alveoli

The trachea (windpipe) divides into two **bronchi** which deliver air to the left and right lung. These tubes branch repeatedly and get smaller. The smallest tubes end in the microscopic alveoli.

Adaptations to give efficient gas exchange

The branching of the tiny tubes and the large number of alveoli provide a large surface area. If all of these were opened out in an adult it is estimated that the surface area would be approximately equal to a tennis court.

Cells lining the air passages and the air sacs produce mucus which keeps the surfaces moist. Oxygen is taken up by the blood, and carbon dioxide is released. The gases move by diffusion.

Every air sac has a rich supply of blood capillaries. The capillaries provide a constant supply of blood needing oxygen. This helps diffusion to occur quickly.

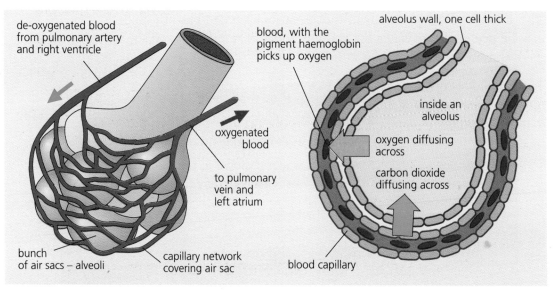

de-oxygenated blood from pulmonary artery and right ventricle

oxygenated blood

to pulmonary vein and left atrium

bunch of air sacs – alveoli

capillary network covering air sac

blood, with the pigment haemoglobin picks up oxygen

alveolus wall, one cell thick

inside an alveolus

oxygen diffusing across

carbon dioxide diffusing across

blood capillary

▲ **Fig 1a** *The blood supply to air sacs*

▲ **Fig 1b** *Detailed section of one air sac*

The air sacs allow efficient diffusion because they:

- have a very large surface area,
- have a rich supply of blood capillaries,
- are very thin,
- are moist.

The air that we breathe in through our nose is 'cleaned'. Mucus made by the cells of the nose traps dust, bacteria and fungal spores. Cells that line the air passages have microscopic hairs called cilia. Cilia help to move mucus to the back of the throat. Mucus is swallowed and stomach acid kills the bacteria and fungi. Mucus and cilia are also found in the other air passages. They help to clean the air before it reaches the lungs. Fewer bacteria and other disease causing organisms can enter, so damage is prevented.

Effects of smoking on the gas exchange system

Smoke contains harmful chemicals like tar, carbon monoxide and the drug nicotine. Tar stops cilia from working. Bacteria and particles are not removed from the air, which means that diseases like bronchitis may develop. Walls of the alveoli are damaged. The surface area for gas exchange is reduced and is therefore less efficient.

Carbon monoxide combines with haemoglobin to form carboxy haemoglobin, which does not break down. As a result as much as 15% of haemoglobin may be unavailable for oxygen transport in a smoker.

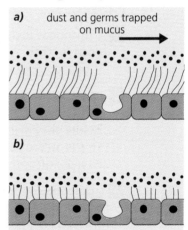

a) dust and germs trapped on mucus

b)

▲ **Fig 2a** Normal healthy ciliated cells
b Ciliated cells of a smoker

Smoking and lung cancer

Cancers arise when the normal pattern of cell division is upset. Cells sometimes divide and increase in number in an uncontrolled way. This leads to the formation of masses of cells, called **tumours**. Tumours which continue to divide and spread are said to be **malignant**. There is a lot of evidence to suggest that tobacco smoke causes tumours. The cells lining the air passages are most at risk of tumour development.

1 List four features of lung tissue which enable gas exchange to be efficient.

2 What does mucus do in the breathing system?

3 What are cilia?

4 Name two harmful chemicals in tobacco smoke.

Words you should know

air sacs   alveoli   bronchioles   bronchus (pl bronchi)   cilia   mucus   trachea

17 Aerobic respiration

In this unit you will learn the answers to these questions:
- Why do we need energy?
- How do we get energy from food?
- What is 'aerobic' respiration?

Living things need a supply of energy to get things done. Energy is obtained from food materials. The release of energy from food is called **respiration**. It goes on in every living cell.

Energy released from food is used in many ways. Three examples are listed below.

1. Movement involves **muscular contraction**. A lot of energy is needed (Figs 1, 2 and 3).

2. Most muscles have to be stimulated by **nerve impulses** before they will contract. Active nerve cells need energy to transmit impulses.

3. Some energy from food is released as **heat**. This may be used to keep a constant body temperature.

4. Plants use energy to absorb some ions from the soil.

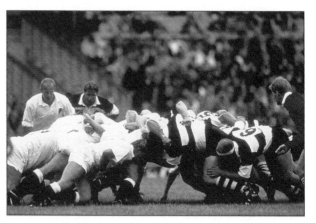

▲ **Fig 1** *Sporting activity requires much energy*

▲ **Fig 2** *Cheetahs can reach speeds of 70 mph over short distances*

▲ **Fig 3** *Terns regularly fly 22 000 miles each year when migrating*

Some organisms need a constant supply of oxygen for respiration. They respire aerobically – a process which requires oxygen. **Aerobic respiration** can be compared to the process of burning. Both processes need a fuel and a supply of oxygen. Burning and respiration both produce wastes. The waste products of respiration are **carbon dioxide** and **water**. These wastes are also produced by burning, but burning often produces additional material, seen as smoke. The energy released by burning is released as heat and light. Respiration releases some energy as heat, but some is locked into chemical compounds.

The table compares aerobic respiration and burning a carbon compound.

Aerobic respiration	Burning fuels
uses food containing carbon	uses fuel containing carbon
uses oxygen	uses oxygen
produces carbon dioxide and water as wastes	produces carbon dioxide, smoke and water as wastes
releases energy; some as heat, some locked up	releases energy; most as heat, some as light

Aerobic respiration can be summarised by the following word equation.

sugar + oxygen ➡ carbon dioxide + water + energy

▶ **Fig 4** Aerobic fitness improves the supply of oxygen and sugars to respiring cells

1 How do you think 'aerobics' makes someone fitter?

2 Why is 'aerobics' such an appropriate name for the type of exercise shown in Fig 4?

Words you should know   **aerobic respiration**

18 Anaerobic respiration

In this unit you will learn the answers to these questions:
- What is anaerobic respiration?
- How can energy be released without oxygen?
- What has respiration got to do with beer and bread?

▲ **Fig 1** *Exercise can lead to anaerobic respiration*

Some organisms can survive for a long time without a supply of oxygen. They obtain their energy by **anaerobic respiration**.

Human muscle tissue relies on anaerobic respiration when the blood supply can no longer deliver enough oxygen to keep aerobic respiration going. This can only be a temporary option for humans, for example, during exercise.

When oxygen is absent, the reactions in respiration form different products, with the release of only a small quantity of energy. The type of cell respiring determines which products are formed. Cells in plant tissues have enzymes which convert sugar to **ethanol** in the absence of oxygen. Animal cells, for example, muscle cells, produce **lactic acid** instead.

Muscle cells

Muscle cells are our only cells that can respire anaerobically. It can happen when the breathing system and the blood supply can not deliver oxygen fast enough to very active muscles (see fig 1). Anaerobic respiration can be summarised by this word equation:

glucose ➡ lactic acid + a little energy.

This is only a temporary form of respiration because lactic acid is poisonous. If levels of lactic acid increase, painful muscle cramp occurs. Then vigorous exercise has to stop. Fast breathing and fast heart beats continue until enough oxygen has been delivered to break down the lactic acid.

Yeast cells and fermentation

Anaerobic respiration in yeast cells can be summarised by the following word equation.

glucose ➡ ethanol + carbon dioxide + a little energy

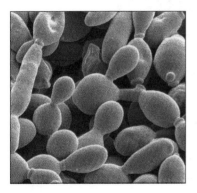

▲ **Fig 2** *Budding yeast cells*

Yeast can be used to make beer. Yeast converts the sugars in barley to alcohol and carbon dioxide in a process called fermentation. Different types of beers are produced by using different types of yeast, and different fermentation times. Various additives are also used to give a beer a distinctive flavour.

Wine makers make use of the natural yeasts which are found on the skins of grapes. Different types of grapes grow in different areas of the world. The wine is produced by fermenting the crushed grapes. Each grape growing region produces wine with a different distinctive flavour.

▲ **Fig 3** *A variety of beers and wines*

Baking

The baking industry takes advantage of the carbon dioxide produced in anaerobic respiration. The gas given off by respiring yeast cells gets trapped in the warm dough. Pockets of gas cause the dough to rise. The resulting bread has a much lighter texture. Unleavened bread is made without yeast added. The alcohol, made by the yeast, is destroyed during the baking process.

▲ **Fig 4** *Freshly baked loaves*

1 What are the products of anaerobic respiration in muscle cells?

2 What causes dough to rise during bread making?

Words you should know
anaerobic respiration   ethanol   lactic acid

19 Senses

In this unit you will learn the answers to these questions:

■ What changes are there in our environment?
■ How do we recognise change?
■ How do nerves work?

The environment in which we live is always changing. For instance as night becomes day there is more light and warmth. The changing factors are called **stimuli**. Some changes may be of advantage to us and others a disadvantage. Animals must be aware of changes if they are to live successfully.

We have **sense organs**, or **receptors**, which are sensitive to stimuli (as shown in the table).

Sense organs / receptors	Stimuli	Sense
eye	light	sight
ear	sound	hearing
	gravity	balance
nose	chemicals	smell
tongue	chemicals	taste
skin	pressure, heat, texture	touch

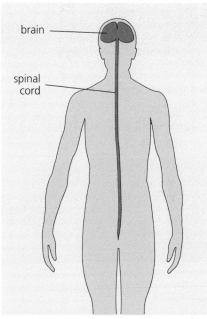

▲ Fig 2 *The central nervous system (CNS) of humans*

All receptors convert the energy they receive as a stimulus into a **nerve impulse**. For example, the energy received by light-sensitive cells of the eye causes nerve impulses in the optic nerve.

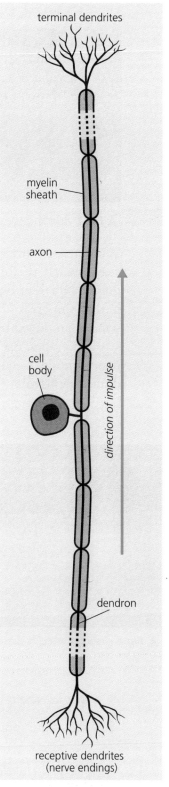

▲ Fig 1 *A sensory neurone*

There are different **neurones** (nerve cells) in our body. Fig 1 shows a **sensory neurone**. It carries impulses from receptors to the central nervous system (brain and spinal cord). **Motor neurones** take impulses from the **central nervous system** to the muscles and glands.

Neurones always have a cell body with a nucleus. Often they have a long fibre (axon) so that impulses can be carried a long distance e.g. the motor neurone from the base of the spine to the big toe is about 1 metre in length. To prevent the loss of an impulse neurones are insulated with a fatty (**myelin**) sheath.

Fig 3 shows runners at the start of a race. They are all waiting for the sound of the starter's gun. The sound of the gun is a stimulus. The ear (the receptor) detects sound waves when the ear drum vibrates. Sensory neurones carry impulses to the brain. The brain coordinates the information. Motor neurones from the brain carry impulses to the body muscles (**effectors**) and the runner moves out of the starting blocks (the **response** to the stimulus.)

▲ *Fig 3*

A typical nervous response may be summarised as follows:

stimulus ➡ receptor ➡ sensory neurones ➡ CNS (coordinator) ➡ motor neurones ➡ effector ➡ response

1 What are the jobs of the
a) sensory neurone?
b) motor neurone?
c) central nervous system?

Words you should know
**central nervous system   effector   myelin sheath   neurone
receptor   response   sense organ   stimuli**

20 The eye

In this unit you will learn the answers to these questions:

- Where does the light go after it enters the eye?
- The lens of a camera moves in and out. Why do our lenses not do the same?
- How do our eyes cope with bright and dim light?

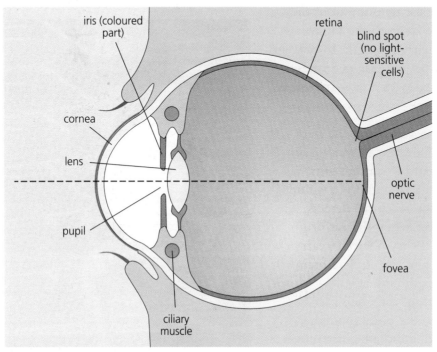

▲ **Fig 1** *Section through a human eye*

When we look at a person's face we only see a small part of their eyes. Most of the eyeball is hidden within the skull. The bone of the skull makes a protective **pocket**. The eyelids protect the front of the eye. Tears keep the surface of the eye clean.

Light enters the eye. First the **cornea** bends the light rays. Most of the focusing takes place here. Then light passes through the **lens**. An image of what we see is focused on the light sensitive cells of the **retina**. The most sensitive area is the **fovea**. The receptor cells of the retina change light energy into nerve impulses. Neurones in the **optic nerve** take the nerve impulses to the brain.

Light intensity, or brightness, varies. We can see in different light conditions because our eyes adjust automatically (Fig 3a and 3b). This is a reflex reaction (see Unit 21). The **iris** is made of special muscles. It may be coloured with brown or blue pigments. The **pupil**, which is a gap in the iris, looks black and lets light pass through.

The muscular iris controls the size of the pupil. In bright light the iris makes the pupil smaller. Less light enters the eye. The sensitive retina is not damaged. In dim light the iris makes the pupil larger. More light can enter the eye so that a good image can be made.

We can see near and far objects clearly. Our lens can focus a clear image of the object on the retina by changing shape. The lens is flexible. Ciliary muscles control its shape. When these muscles contract the lens is fatter. A fat lens bends light more so that near objects are focused clearly. To focus distant objects clearly the ciliary muscles relax, making the lens thinner. As we look at different objects the shape of the lens is changed to adjust the focus. This process is called **accommodation**.

1 In which tissue is light converted into nerve impulses?

2 What is the most sensitive region of the retina called?

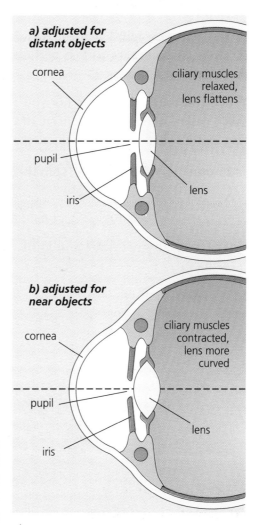

▲ **Fig 2** *Accommodation*

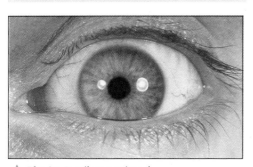

▲ **Fig 3a** *Pupil constricted*

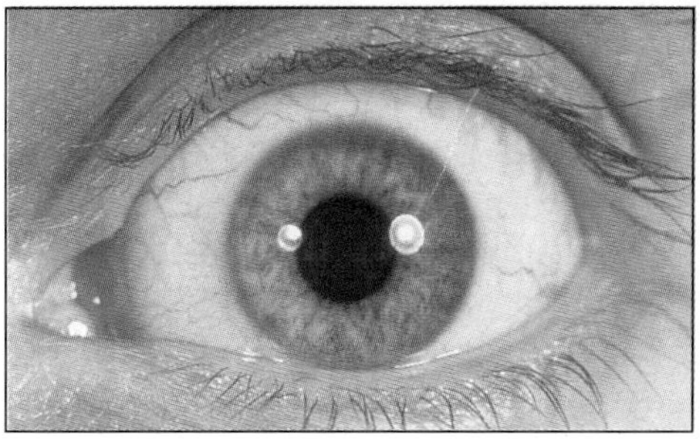

▲ **Fig 3b** *Pupil dilated*

Words you should know

**accommodation   blind spot   ciliary muscle   cornea   fovea
iris   lens   optic nerve   pupil   retina**

21 Reflex action

In this unit you will learn the answers to these questions:
- How do you react so fast without thinking?
- What is a reflex arc?

When you touch something hot you remove your hand very quickly. This is called **reflex action**. The pathway in the nervous system which allows this fast response is called a **reflex arc**. The pathway could be shown as:

The nerve pathway is shown in Fig 1.

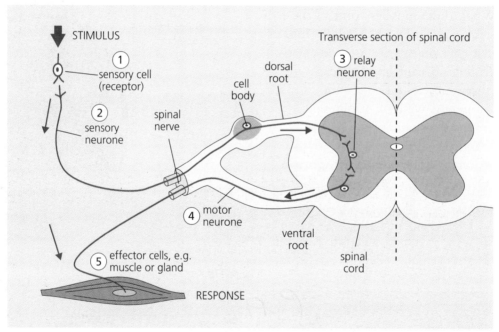

▲ *Fig 1 A reflex arc*

Heat stimulates **pain receptors** in the skin. Nerve impulses pass along the neurones in a **sensory nerve**. The sensory nerve enters the **spinal cord**. In the grey matter of the spinal cord are **relay neurones**. They receive sensory information and then pass information to the **motor neurones**. The nervous impulses pass along a motor neurone to muscles in the hand. The muscles are stimulated to contract and the hand is moved away from the hot object.

The time taken from **stimulus** to **response** is very fast, about a thousandth of a second. Speed prevents damage to the body. Reflex actions are fast because the brain, and thinking, are not involved. They are **automatic responses**.

Different relay neurones can also send sensory information to the brain. The brain is aware of the reflex response made. In some reflex arcs the effector is a gland.

We sneeze in an uncontrolled, explosive, way when pepper or pollen enters our nose (Fig 2). Not all reflexes are obvious. The response of the iris muscle (Fig 3) to light is a reflex action (see Unit 20).

The table summarises some human reflexes.

Reflex	Stimulus	Value
blinking	foreign particle on cornea	protects the eye
iris	change in light intensity	protects retina
sneezing	foreign particles in nose	protects the lungs
coughing	irritants in throat	protects the lungs
knee-jerk	tendons below knee cap stretched	maintains posture (balance)
withdrawal	pain	withdraws limb from danger

▲ *Fig 2* Sneezing

Fig 4 shows a doctor carrying out one of the routine tests which follow the birth of a baby.

▲ *Fig 3* Doctor checking the iris reflex

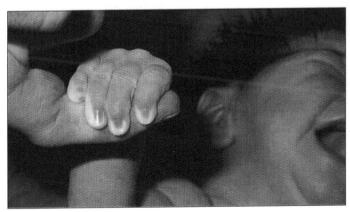

▲ *Fig 4* Checking the grip of a newborn baby

The baby is born with some reflexes, it has not learnt them.

1 a) Why is it an advantage that reflex arcs are fast?
b) Why are they faster than other nerve pathways?

2 What do
a) sensory neurones and
b) intermediate neurones do in a reflex arc?

Words you should know

motor neurones   pain receptor   reflex action   reflex arc
relay neurones   sensory nerve   spinal cord

22 Hormonal control

In this unit you will learn the answers to these questions:
- **What are chemical messages?**
- **How do cells 'know' who the message is for?**
- **What are the differences between hormonal and nervous control?**

Units 19, 20 and 21 have introduced the way in which the nervous system is involved in getting things in the human body to work together. There are some processes which are coordinated in a different way. These are processes which involve **hormones**.

> **Hormones are chemicals produced by specialised glands in the body.**

There are two types of glands in the human body (see Fig 1).

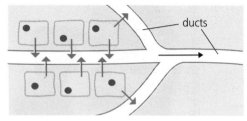

▲ **Fig 1a** *Cells in a ducted gland*

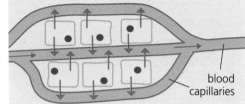

▲ **Fig 1b** *Cells in a ductless gland*

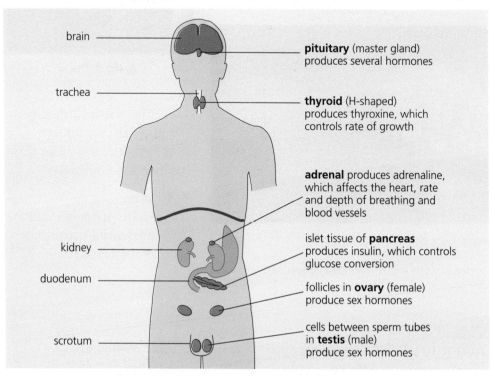

brain

trachea

kidney

duodenum

scrotum

pituitary (master gland) produces several hormones

thyroid (H-shaped) produces thyroxine, which controls rate of growth

adrenal produces adrenaline, which affects the heart, rate and depth of breathing and blood vessels

islet tissue of **pancreas** produces insulin, which controls glucose conversion

follicles in **ovary** (female) produce sex hormones

cells between sperm tubes in **testis** (male) produce sex hormones

▲ **Fig 2** *The endocrine system in humans*

The cells of tear glands produce fluids and the fluids collect in tubes called ducts. The ducts deliver the fluid directly to the exact place where it is needed to do its work at the eye surface. These glands are called ducted or **exocrine glands**. Some are listed in the table.

Gland	Ducted to
tear	eye
salivary	mouth
pancreas	duodenum
sweat	skin surface

Hormones are produced by glands without ducts. These are the ductless or endocrine glands. Their cells produce hormones which are secreted into the blood supply. Fig 2 shows the endocrine glands in the body. Hormones often affect parts of the body some distance away from where they were made.

Hormones are chemical messengers that cause changes in the body. The endocrine glands have well developed blood supplies with large numbers of blood capillaries. Hormones enter the plasma and are carried round the body in the blood. Some hormones, like adrenaline, affect many parts of the body. Other hormones are more specific and only affect certain cells. These are the **target cells**. The surface of their cell membranes can chemically recognise their specific hormone and interact with it. Other cells are not affected.

The table summarises the differences between hormonal and nervous coordinaton.

Feature	Hormonal	Nervous
message	chemical	electrical
source	hormone gland	receptor
aimed at	target cells	effector
carried by	bloodstream	neurone
speed	slow	very fast
duration	long lasting	brief
precision	general effect	very specific

1 What is a hormone?

2 What is a 'target cell'?

Words you should know
endocrine gland   exocrine gland   hormone   target cell

23 Insulin and sex hormones

In this unit you will learn the answers to these questions:
- ■ What does insulin do?
- ■ What do the sex hormones do?

Insulin, glucagon and the control of blood glucose levels

Glucose absorbed from the gut in the small intestine enters the bloodstream. The concentration of glucose in the bloodstream will therefore *increase* some time after a meal. Living cells use blood glucose as a raw material for respiration and other processes. These processes will *decrease* the concentration of blood glucose. Cells will only work properly if the glucose concentration is kept around a particular level.

The **liver** plays a role in the regulation of blood glucose concentration. Liver cells absorb glucose from the blood and convert it to **glycogen**, for storage in the liver. Glycogen can be broken down later to re-form glucose, which can be returned to the bloodstream.

When blood glucose concentration rises above normal (about 0.1%), a particular group of cells in the **pancreas** register the increase, and secrete the hormone **insulin** (see Unit 22). Insulin causes liver cells to convert soluble glucose to insoluble glycogen. Blood glucose concentration falls. If blood glucose concentration falls below the normal level, this too is registered by the cells of the pancreas and insulin secretion is reduced. When blood glucose concentration falls below 0.1% different cells in the pancreas produce a second hormone, called **glucagon,** which encourages liver cells to convert glycogen to glucose. This action restores the blood glucose concentration to its normal level.

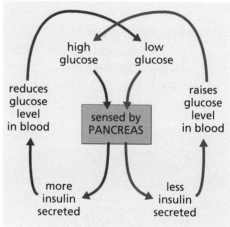

▲ **Fig 1** How feedback controls blood glucose level

1 What parts do the liver and pancreas play in controlling blood glucose level?

Sex hormones

Testosterone is one of a group of **male sex hormones**. Testosterone is produced by cells in the **testes**. This hormone controls the development of the male sex organs and later, at puberty, the **male secondary sexual characteristics**, e.g. production of sperm.

The **female sex hormones** are the **oestrogens** and **progesterone**. The **ovaries** secrete oestrogens. Oestrogens control the development of the **female secondary sexual characteristics**, e.g. production of eggs.

Each month in sexually mature females, an **egg follicle** starts to develop in an ovary. The follicle produces the egg and secretes **oestrogen**. This affects the lining of the uterus. It becomes thicker and spongy, and numerous blood vessels grow into it. Once the egg is released from the follicle at **ovulation** the follicle becomes the **corpus luteum**. Oestrogen production then stops and the corpus luteum secretes a second hormone, **progesterone** for a short time.

If an embryo buries itself in the lining of the uterus a **placenta** forms. Production of progesterone is then taken over by the placenta. Continued production of progesterone has two effects. Firstly, the lining of the uterus is not shed and, secondly, no further ovulation takes place.

If the egg released is not fertilised then blood progesterone level drops and the lining of the uterus breaks down. The tissues are lost, via the vagina, over a period of about five days with a considerable amount of blood. This is **menstruation**. The **menstrual cycle** (see Fig 2) usually takes about twenty-eight days but can vary considerably from one person to another.

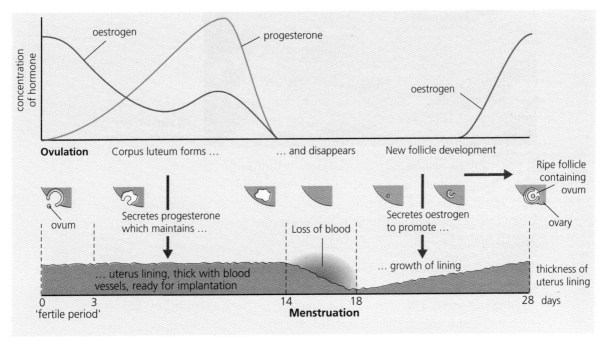

▲ **Fig 2** The main changes in the ovary, uterus and hormones which take place during the oestrus/menstrual cycle

Words you should know

insulin   menstrual cycle   menstruation   sex hormone

24 Medical uses of hormones

In this unit you will learn the answers to these questions:
- What happens when the message goes wrong?
- How can we change the message?
- Why do some people have to inject insulin?
- How can someone who cannot conceive be helped to have babies?

Hormonal treatment and diabetes

Some people have **diabetes**. Their condition can not be cured but it can be controlled. The problem is that their pancreas cells cannot make enough insulin.

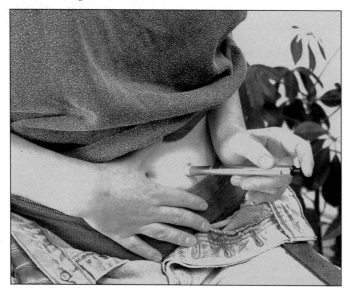

◀ **Fig 1** A diabetic injecting insulin

If not enough insulin is made the concentration of glucose in their blood will rise above the normal 0.1% level. The brain cells are very sensitive to blood glucose levels and high levels can damage body cells. If the glucose level is not corrected it can result in coma and death.

Diabetes can be inherited. Diabetics cannot control their blood sugar concentration. They need insulin to decrease blood glucose levels. Insulin is a protein so it would be digested if it was taken in by the mouth. Insulin injections are needed to control the problem.

Diabetes can also develop as a result of ageing. This form of diabetes can often be controlled by diet. Care is needed to balance the amount of carbohydrates eaten so that too much glucose is not produced by digestion.

Hormonal treatment and human fertility

The **contraceptive pill** is used to prevent pregnancy. It contains chemicals that are identical to the natural hormones, and which work in the same way. If taken correctly the progesterone in the pill will prevent ovulation. There is no egg to be fertilised. Sexual intercourse cannot result in pregnancy.

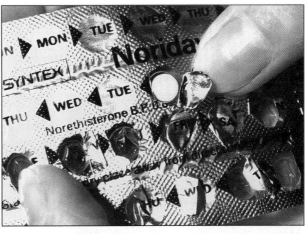

▲ **Fig 2** *A pack of contraceptive pills, showing the bubblepack day sequence*

Some people who wish to have children are not able to do so. There may be a problem of infertility. Sex hormones can help. If a woman is not producing enough eggs on a regular basis hormones can be used to increase her egg production. This increases the chance of fertilisation and pregnancy.

If a man does not produce enough sperm, or if few sperm reach the oviduct, fertilisation may not occur. This problem can be overcome by a process called **in vitro fertilisation** (IVF). The woman is given hormones to stimulate egg production. As a result many eggs may be released. These are collected from the ovary by a surgical operation. The eggs are placed in a sterile petri dish and sperm are added to them. If fertilisation occurs successfully several embryos may be formed. The woman is given hormones to prepare the uterus for pregnancy. The embryos are surgically placed in the uterus. Normal development will occur if the transplant is successful. Several embryos may be transplanted to make sure that at least one survives. This can lead to multiple (more than 1) births.

1 Why do some people have to inject insulin?

2 How does a contraceptive pill work?

3 Suggest two biological reasons why some couples who want to have children cannot.

4 What do the initials IVF stand for?

Words you should know

contraceptive pill   **diabetes**   **in vitro fertilisation**

25 Homeostasis

In this unit you will learn the answers to these questions:
- Why is it important for the surroundings of a cell to stay the same?
- How is a 'steady state' achieved by humans?

Living things have an **external environment**, their surroundings.
They also have an **internal environment** which surrounds their cells.

▲ **Fig 1a** External environment

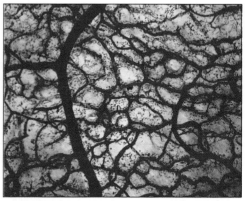

▲ **Fig 1b** Internal environment

All cells, within any tissue, are surrounded by tissue fluid. Tissue fluid leaks out from blood capillaries and is similar to plasma. It is important in the exchange of products between cells and blood (see Fig 2).

Cells need oxygen and foods, like glucose, which move by diffusion from the blood. Waste products like urea and carbon dioxide also move by diffusion. They are taken away by the blood for excretion. This delivery system also includes the distribution of heat, water and salts.

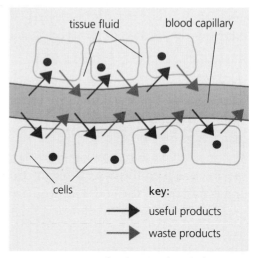

▲ **Fig 2** Exchange between cells and blood

To work efficiently the raw materials needed by a cell must be in the correct concentration at all times. A constant internal environment is needed. Complex animals like humans can control, or balance their internal environment by **homeostasis**.

> **Homeostasis is the maintenance of a steady state, providing a stable environment for cells.**

It is an advantage for animals to be able to keep a constant internal environment in spite of the charges in their external environment.

Ovens and central heating systems can be set at a constant temperature. The temperature is monitored by a sensor called a thermostat. A room thermostat set at 20°C will detect changes in the room temperature. If doors have been left open it will get cooler. The thermostat causes the heaters to be turned on. The room warms up. As soon as the temperature is above 20°C the thermostat causes the heater to be turned off (see Fig 3).

This system of control is called negative feedback. The thermostat detects the temperature change and sets off a series of events that return the temperature to normal.

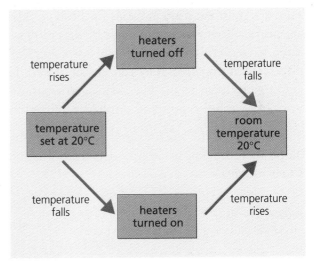

▶ **Fig 3** *Controlling the temperature*

Living organisms have negative feedback systems to keep their internal environment constant. The table shows a summary of some of these systems:

Homeostatic process controlling	Structures involved
body temperature	part of the brain and skin
water balance	part of the brain and kidney
breathing rate	part of the brain and muscles associated with breathing
blood glucose concentration	liver and pancreas

1 What is tissue fluid and why is it important?

2 Why do organisms need a constant internal environment?

Words you should know
**external environment   homeostasis   internal environment
negative feedback   sensor**

26 The kidney

In this unit you will learn the answers to these questions:
■ What jobs do kidneys do?
■ How do kidneys work as excretory organs?

Many chemical, or metabolic, reactions occur in living things. Metabolism includes chemical processes which build things up as well as those which break things down.

Some products of metabolic reactions are poisonous wastes. These substances must be excreted (got rid of) because they are harmful to us.

Humans must eat protein foods for body building and repair. Proteins are broken down to amino acids by digestion, a metabolic process. We often have more amino acids than we need. Amino acids contain poisonous nitrogen so they can not be stored. The excess amino acids are broken down in the liver. Nitrogen is removed and used to form urea. Urea is poisonous and must be removed from the body.

The **kidney** is the main excretory organ involved. It purifies the blood by removing waste products from it and it also controls our water balance.

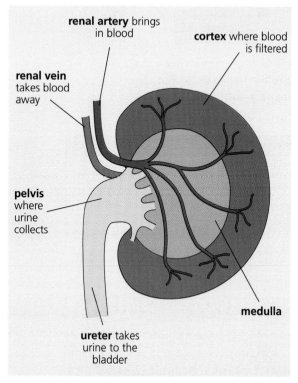

▲ **Fig 1** Section through a kidney

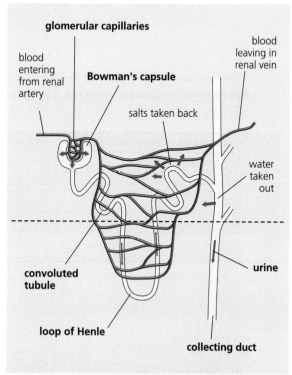

▲ **Fig 2** Diagram of a single kidney tubule (nephron)

Blood containing urea and other excretory products is delivered to each kidney in a renal artery. The artery branches many times and each kidney contains millions of blood capillaries. Each kidney also contains millions of microscopic structures called **nephrons**. These are the working units of the kidney. The main jobs of a nephron are:

1 Filtration

The special structure of the knot of capillaries (glomerular capillaries) causes high pressure. This forces all small molecules, useful and harmful, out of the blood into Bowman's capsule. The blood is filtered under high pressure (ultrafiltration). The liquid in the nephron is called the filtrate.

2 Reabsorption

In the first coiled (convoluted) part of the nephron the useful products, glucose, water and salts are reabsorbed from the filtrate into the blood. Energy is needed for this and it is called selective reabsorption. In the second coiled tubule final adjustments can be made to the filtrate and more reabsorption can occur.

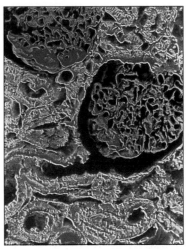

▲ **Fig 3** Photomicrograph of a Bowman's capsule

3 Urine formation

The liquid then left in the nephron contains the substances that the body does not need, like **urea**, excess salts and water. It is now called **urine**. Collecting ducts join together and urine leaves the kidney in a ureter. Urine is stored in the bladder ready for removal from the body.

Purified blood leaves the kidney in the renal vein and this is returned to the circulatory system.

We take in water in food and drinks. We lose water in sweat, tears, faeces, urine and in the air we breathe out. The body needs a balanced amount of water. A hormone controls the amount of water we lose in urine. It is part of our homeostatic system.

1 What is a nephron?   **2** What are the main jobs of the kidney?

Words you should know

kidney   nephron   urea   urine

27 Skin and homeostasis

In this unit you will learn the answers to these questions:
- Which structures in the skin are involved in temperature control?
- How does the skin help to keep our body temperature constant?

Our body temperature is about 37°C. There may be temperature changes in our internal and external environment. We may gain or lose heat in ways shown in the table. Our control systems keep our temperature constant at 37°C.

Heat gain	Heat loss
cell respiration	breathing out warmed air
muscle activity	lost with urine and faeces
eating hot food and drink	heat loss by conduction and radiation
Sun's heat absorbed	

Skin and temperature balance

Our main surface in contact with the external environment is our skin. Skin is important in heat exchange and is involved with temperature control.

The skin is involved in temperature control in three main ways. These are:

1 the ability to raise and lower hairs; **2** sweating; and

3 variable blood flow.

Hairs in the skin can be raised or lowered by **erector muscles** which are attached as shown in Fig 1. When we get cold the muscles contract and the hairs are raised. These hairs trap air forming a thick layer. The air is warmed up by conduction of heat from the skin. The air layer insulates us and reduces heat loss. Body temperature rises.

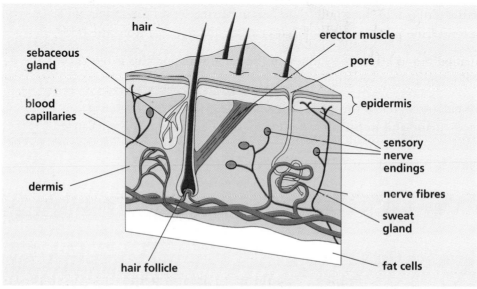

▲ **Fig 1** Diagram of a wedge of skin showing its internal structure

When our body temperature is steady, or we get warm, the hairs lie flat so that heat can be lost to the environment.

When our body temperature rises above 37°C our **sweat glands** secrete more sweat. The watery sweat is evaporated from the surface of the skin. The heat energy needed for evaporation comes from our body. This loss of body heat cools the skin and underlying tissues. When we are cold less sweat is secreted, there is less evaporation, and we lose less heat.

Muscles in the blood vessels control how much blood flows in our capillaries near the skin surface. If our body temperature rises above 37°C more blood flows near the surface due to **vasodilation**. The heat carried by the blood is easily lost to our surroundings and we are cooled.

If our body temperature falls muscles direct most blood through the shunt vessels. Less blood flows through the surface capillaries due to **vasoconstriction**. As a result less heat is lost. Body temperature will rise.

▲ **Fig 2** *Exercise raises body temperature causing sweating and reddening of the skin*

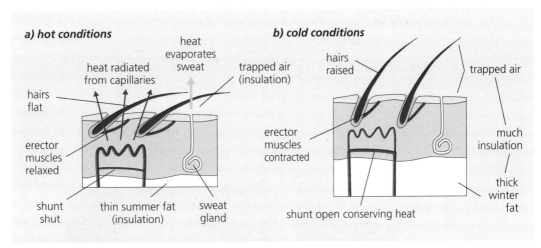

▲ **Fig 3** *The way the skin helps to maintain a constant body temperature*

1 List those structures in the skin which are involved in temperature control.

Words you should know

erector muscle   **sweat glands**   **vasoconstriction**   **vasodilation**

28 Defence mechanisms of the body

In this unit you will learn the answers to these questions:
- What part does the skin play in defence?
- What do tears and stomach acid have in common?
- How do white blood cells help to keep us healthy?

The outer **epidermis** (see Unit 27) of our skin is made of tough dead cells. This forms a protective barrier and covers most of our body. Bacteria and other disease causing organisms (pathogens) are kept out.

We may damage our skin, for instance with a cut. We bleed and the blood flow removes dirt and pathogens from the wound. Platelets in the blood quickly start the clotting process. The **clot** consists of a fine mesh of fibres (fibrin) which traps red blood cells. Clotting prevents the loss of blood. As the clot dries it forms a **scab**. The scab seals the wound and prevents entry of pathogens. It also protects the damaged area. When healing is complete, and new skin formed, the scab drops off.

Some parts of our body are not so well protected. For instance, our eye is not covered with tough dead cells. It is covered by a more delicate conjunctiva, which can be infected by bacteria causing 'redeye' or conjunctivitis. Tears normally wash away dust and pathogens. They also contain a substance which kills bacteria.

Bacteria and other pathogens can enter the body through the mouth and nose. They are trapped by the **mucus** in the air passages. They are killed by the hydrochloric acid in the stomach when the mucus is swallowed.

White blood cells are involved in protecting the body against infection. There are two types of white cells **phagocytes** and **lymphocytes**.

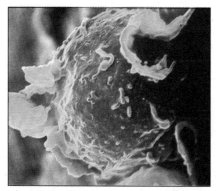

▲ *Fig 1a* Photomicrograph of a phagocyte

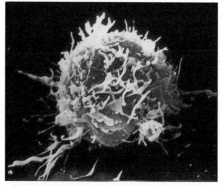

▲ *Fig 1b* Photomicrograph of a lymphocyte

Phagocytes protect the body by eating bacteria. The feeding process in phagocytes is described as **phagocytosis** (see Fig 2).

1 Phagocytes squeeze out of capillaries and feed on bacteria and cell 'rubbish' on the surface of cells.

2 A food vacuole is formed inside a phagocyte when its surface membrane comes into contact with bacteria.

3 The bacteria are taken into the food vacuole (engulfed).

4 The phagocyte secretes enzymes into the food vacuole.

5 The bacteria are killed and digested.

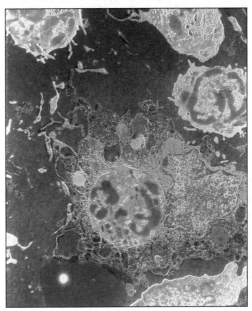

▲ **Fig 2** Phagocytosis – the phagocyte (green/blue) has engulfed a bacterium (shown in pink)

Lymphocytes recognise, in a chemical way, any foreign material that gets into our body. Pathogens contain substances called **antigens**. Lymphocytes react to these bacteria and viruses by producing molecules called **antibodies**.

Antibodies protect us from infection. They work in several ways.

■ Some kill bacteria by causing them to burst.

■ Some make bacterial membranes sticky so that they group (clump) together and it is easy for phagocytes to kill them.

■ Some produce antitoxins (chemicals) to neutralise the effect of the poisonous chemicals (toxins) which pathogens release into the plasma.

1 How does the skin protect us from infection?

2 Name two body secretions which are protective.

3 What is phagocytosis?

4 What are antibodies?

Words you should know

**antibodies   antigens   conjunctivitis   lymphocytes
phagocytes   phagocytosis   platelets   scab**

29 Solvents and drugs

In this unit you will learn the answers to these questions:
- What are drugs and solvents?
- How do they harm us?
- Drinking or driving?

What are drugs and organic solvents?

Some examples of drugs and organic solvents are listed in the table.

Drugs include a wide variety of substances. Doctors may give us drugs to make us better when we are ill. Some drugs are chemicals produced by living things. **Synthetic drugs** are chemicals made to copy the effects of natural drugs. Except for alcohol, caffeine and tobacco (nicotine) all the drugs in the list are illegal.

Drugs	Organic solvents, used in
alcohol	butane gas
caffeine	correcting fluid
cannabis	dry-cleaning fluid
cocaine	hairspray
ecstasy	oven-cleaners
heroin	paintspray
LSD	pain-relieving sprays
tobacco (nicotine)	polishes
valium	solvent-based glues

Organic solvents are chemicals made to dissolve substances which are not soluble in water.

Alcohol and tobacco are readily available drugs, but there are laws which restrict their sale. Anybody can buy drinks containing caffeine, i.e. tea, coffee, cola and cocoa. Many homes will have some alcohol around and many people smoke. Few people think of these three substances as drugs. Most houses will have products containing organic solvents. It is more likely that if abuse is going to occur, then it is legal drugs and solvents that are abused, and not substances such as cocaine and heroin.

What are the possible effects of drug and solvent abuse on the body?

All drugs affect the way the user feels and behaves. Drugs can affect humans and other animals. The effects may vary but the way that the brain and nerves work is always altered. There can also be physical effects caused by long-term substance abuse. Some effects are listed in the table.

Substance	Effect
alcohol	liver cells are poisoned and the liver does not work efficiently; brain damage
nicotine	destroys cells lining the air passages; bronchitis; increases risk of cancer (see Unit 16)
solvents	damage to brain, liver, kidneys and heart; some solvents have cancer-causing properties

Drinking or driving?

When a drink containing alcohol is swallowed the alcohol enters the bloodstream. It starts to go into the blood in the mouth and throat. A larger part enters the circulation from the stomach, and any which is left is absorbed in the small intestine. The amount of alcohol in the blood, the blood alcohol concentration (BAC), can be measured.

▲ *Fig 1* *Examples of drinks that each contain one unit of alcohol*

Different drinks have different amounts of alcohol in them. The effect they are likely to have on the body can be measured according to the number of units of alcohol they contain. One **unit of alcohol** will on average raise the BAC by **15 mg per 100 ml of blood.**

Alcohol is a **sedative** drug. It makes you feel sleepy, your reactions slow down and your ability to take decisions is not as good. There is an obvious danger if a person drinks and then drives. The **legal driving limit** in the UK is a BAC of **80 mg per 100 ml of blood**. Alcohol escapes from the blood passing through the lungs. A driver can be breath tested to see how much alcohol the exhaled air contains. This indicates whether the driver's BAC is likely to be 'over the limit' or not.

Drugs used wrongly are harmful and often **habit forming**. The body gets used to having a drug in the blood stream and the person has to keep taking it. If they stop they suffer from unpleasant withdrawal symptoms as the body reacts to the absence of the drug. A person in this state is **physically dependent** on the drug. Withdrawal symptoms are what happens, the way the body reacts, when the cells are not getting the drug any more.

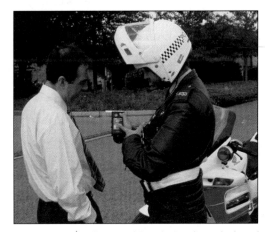

▲ *Fig 2* *A driver being breathalysed*

1 What is a drug?

2 How many units of alcohol are there in two pints of beer?

3 What does BAC stand for?

4 What is the legal BAC driving limit?

Words you should know
drug   sedative   solvent

30 Photosynthesis

In this unit you will learn the answers to these questions:
- What do plants need to make food?
- What makes leaves good at photosynthesis?

Photosynthesis

Green plants make their own food by a process known as **photosynthesis**.

Plants get carbon dioxide from their own respiring cells and also from the air, or water, around them. Water enters the roots of a land plant and some is transported to the leaves.

Most plants are green because they contain a coloured pigment called **chlorophyll**. Chlorophyll absorbs light energy for use in photosynthesis. Not all of the sun's energy is used for photosynthesis. The graph (Fig 1) shows that the best parts of the spectrum for photosynthesis are red and blue light. Green light is not used, it is reflected (which is why plants look green to us.) **Chloroplasts**, the site of photosynthesis, contain the chlorophyll.

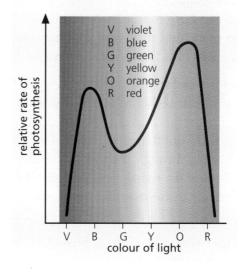

▲ **Fig 1** The effect of different coloured light on the rate of photosynthesis

In photosynthesis carbon dioxide and water join to produce carbohydrates like the sugar glucose. Soluble glucose molecules can join to make insoluble starch. This can be stored for later use. (Animals that eat plants take advantage of this). Oxygen is produced and plant cells can use it for respiration. So much is produced that it is a waste product for the plant and the excess is released into the atmosphere. This is vital for all living things.

The process of photosynthesis can be summarised in a word equation:

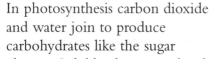

Photosynthesis is carried out by most plants in the leaves. All leaves have the same basic structure. This is shown in Fig 2.

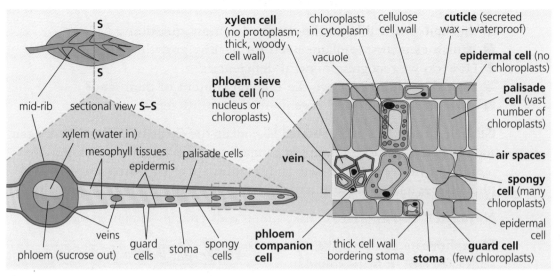

▲ **Fig 2** *Leaf structure*

The leaf as an organ for photosynthesis

The main features of a leaf are that it has:

- a large surface area to absorb light

- a large number of chloroplasts in the palisade mesophyll layer, which is nearest the light

- stomata (small pores) to let carbon dioxide in and oxygen out.

- spongy mesophyll cells, which are moist, with a large surface area for good gas exchange.

- a short diffusion pathway for gases because it is thin

- a good supply of veins for transport. Woody xylem tubes bring in water. Phloem takes away glucose to storage organs.

1 Name two materials used for photosynthesis.

2 What are the products of photosynthesis?

3 What traps light energy for photosynthesis?

4 Which two colours of light are best for photosynthesis?

5 Suggest three ways in which leaves are adapted for photosynthesis.

Words you should know

**chlorophyll   chloroplast   palisade cell   phloem
photosynthesis   stoma** (plural **stomata**)   **vein   xylem**

31 Plant mineral nutrition

In this unit you will learn the answers to these questions:
- **Which elements do plants need for healthy growth?**
- **How do we recognise mineral deficiencies?**
- **How do farmers improve the mineral content of their land?**
- **How are inorganic and organic fertilisers different?**

Carbohydrates, **fats** and **proteins** all contain the elements **carbon**, **hydrogen** and **oxygen**. These three groups of compounds, together with **water**, provide most of the matter in the nucleus and cytoplasm of a cell. **Nitrogen**, **phosphorus** and **potassium** are also **essential elements** for plant growth.

Nitrogen is used by plants to make amino acids, proteins and nucleic acids.

Phosphorus is used to make nucleic acids like DNA. It is also found in the molecule adenosine triphosphate (ATP).

Potassium plays an important role in the formation of cell membranes.

Sulphur is an important element in some amino acids and the proteins they form.

Nutrient	Deficiency symptoms
nitrogen	poor growth – little protoplasm made
sulphur	poor growth – little protoplasm made
calcium	faulty cell division
iron	pale leaves – lack chlorophyll
magnesium	pale leaves – lack chlorophyll
phosphorus	poor growth – lack of ATP for synthesis of protoplasm
potassium	poor growth – dehydration

Magnesium is essential for the manufacture of chlorophyll.

If plants do not get the minerals they need they develop deficiency symptoms as shown in the table. Plants require many other minerals for healthy growth. Only very small amounts of these trace elements are needed.

Farmers want a high yield from their crops so that they can make a good profit. The yield depends on the health of the environment and the health of the plants.

Magnesium is an example of a factor which limits photosynthesis. If a crop plant is grown in soil with a magnesium deficiency its yield will be reduced and the cash return on the crop unsatisfactory. This is summarised in the flow diagram in Fig 1.

Modern farming practice often involves **monoculture**. Here, one type of crop plant is grown, usually on a very large scale. All the plants are the same. All the plants will put the same demands on the environment. They will all want the

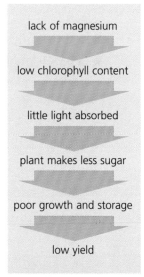

lack of magnesium

low chlorophyll content

little light absorbed

plant makes less sugar

poor growth and storage

low yield

▲ *Fig 1 Magnesium as a limiting factor in the yield of a crop plant*

same factors, the same resources. It is easy to see how a particular mineral nutrient could become scarce, particularly if the same crop is grown in consecutive years. One mineral nutrient could easily become a limiting factor. This can be avoided by crop rotation, the application of fertilisers or, preferably, both.

Fertilisers

There are two types of fertiliser. **Organic fertilisers** are those produced by animals and plants. These are composts and manures and are often called natural fertilisers.

▲ *Fig 2* East Anglian 'prairie' – wheat monoculture

Inorganic fertilisers are made by the chemical industry. Plastic fertiliser bags often have the initials NPK on them. This means that the fertiliser contains the elements nitrogen, phosphorus and potassium. These elements are present in natural fertilisers but not in such concentrated amounts. Small amounts of other mineral nutrients may also be present. The table below compares organic and inorganic fertilisers.

Using fertilisers will allow high yields to be achieved, provided that no other factor is limiting.

Artificial fertilisers do cause some problems. They can destroy the soil structure so that it becomes dust-like and can be blown away. Many artificial fertilizers dissolve quickly. They are released into the soil and soon taken up by plants. These nutrients are easily **leached** (washed out of the soil), and enter the drains, ditches, streams and rivers. This can cause problems of **eutrophication**. It upsets the balance of life in the water resulting in the death of plants and animals. Farmers may add more fertilisers to replace the nutrients lost and the problem is made worse. Artificial fertilisers need to be used with great care.

Feature	Organic (e.g. farmyard manure)	Inorganic (e.g. artificial fertilisers, NPK pellets)
cost	cheap	expensive
user friendliness	smelly, sticky, bulky	easier to handle, dry powder or pellets
nutrient release	slow	fast
effect on soil structure	good	poor
environmental risk	low	may lead to 'run off' – eutrophication

1 Name one plant use for each of N, P and K

2 What does the term 'monoculture' mean?

3 Suggest one way organic fertilisers are better than inorganic fertilisers.

4 What are the problems associated with artificial fertilisers?

Words you should know
essential elements   eutrophication   fertiliser   monoculture

32 Control of plant growth

In this unit you will learn the answers to these questions:
- What are plants sensitive to?
- What do plant hormones do?

The photograph in Fig 1 shows plants which had been left on a window sill for several days. The plants are responding to the **stimulus** of **light**. The shoots appear to 'bend' towards the window. They have not bent. They have grown into that position. The response is a **growth response** called a **tropism**. The light is stronger outside the window and the plant has grown into that position in response to it.

Germinating seeds always produce roots which grow away from the soil surface down into the soil. The developing shoot always grows towards the surface of the soil. This time the stimulus is **gravity**.

◀ **Fig 1** Plants 'grow' towards the light

Tropic responses are of benefit to a plant

Roots grow into a region where there is likely to be more water. They also become embedded in a better position, to anchor the plant.

A plant shoot system grows into a position where it will gain maximum light for photosynthesis. Plants which grow close together are in competition with each other for a variety of factors. An obvious one is light. A plant which is overshadowed by another will not photosynthesise well. It usually responds by growing out of the shaded area into a more brightly lit one. It will grow into a new position to do this. This is what makes it look as though the tissue which was already in place has simply bent. The old tissue however, has to stay where it was originally formed. It will be the new tissue, produced by growth, which creates the bend or curvature.

Plants produce chemicals that regulate growth and development. These substances behave in the way that the hormones found in mammals and other animals do. These are the **plant hormones** or **plant growth substances**.

One group of plant hormones is called **auxins**. Shoots which show the type of growth curvature described above have an uneven distribution of auxins. Auxins are produced in the shoot tip and in a plant evenly lit on all sides the auxin diffuses down the stem evenly. Uneven lighting changes the distribution of auxins in the shoot, with more being found on the shaded side. The growth substance promotes faster growth on the shaded side and as a result that side grows further. Growth curvature is the end result.

1 What is a tropism?

2 How does a plant benefit from growing towards the light?

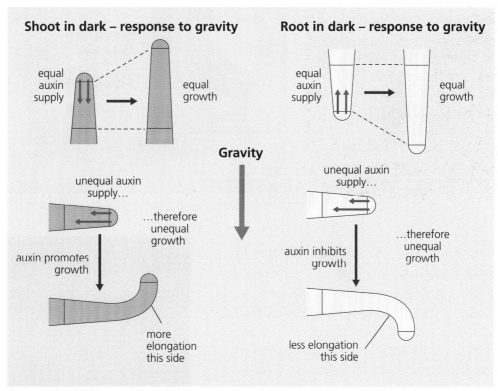

▲ *Fig 2* *How shoots and roots respond to gravity*

Words you should know

auxin   **tropism**

33 Uses of plant hormones

In this unit you will learn the answers to these questions:
- How does rooting powder work?
- What are selective weedkillers?
- How do we grow seedless fruits?

Rooting powders

Gardeners often want more plants. It is possible to take stem cuttings from certain types of plants. This is a form of asexual reproduction. It is done by cutting off small stems from big plants and letting each one develop into a new plant. To survive, the cuttings must produce roots quickly. This can be speeded up by using a plant hormone. The cut end of the stem is dipped into a commercially produced rooting powder which contains growth promoting chemicals (auxins). This encourages root tissue to develop. The cutting is placed in a pot of soil. As roots develop they anchor the plant in the soil and the plant soon becomes established.

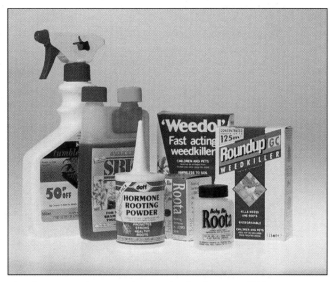

▲ **Fig 1** Rooting powders and selective weedkillers

Selective weedkillers

Herbicides are chemicals which kill plants. Some kill all the plants they come into contact with. Others, called **selective herbicides**, only kill some types of plants. Some of them are based on a naturally occurring plant growth substance such as an auxin (see Unit 32). A gardener may wish to improve the appearance of a lawn by killing the 'weeds'. A selective weed killer will destroy the weeds (unwanted plants) but not the grasses (see Fig 2).

▲ **Fig 2** Selective weedkiller used to kill broadleaved plants in a lawn

Seedless fruit

Sexual reproduction in plants usually involves **pollination** followed by **fertilisation** and the development of **seeds** and **fruits**. Growth substances are involved in this process. Pollen grains produce auxins.

If a flower is not pollinated it soon ages and falls off because it lacks the growth promoters supplied by pollen. Spraying with the correct concentration of auxin will therefore help to keep the flowers on the plant. This will increase the chance of successful fruiting and a bigger crop.

▲ **Fig 3** *Mechanical spraying of a fruit crop to set fruit*

An advantage of using auxin sprays in this way follows from the fact that no pollen is involved. Pollen delivers male gametes to the ovary to bring about fertilisation and the formation of seeds. If there are no pollen grains, fertilisation cannot take place. If fertilisation does not take place, no seeds will be formed. Fruits will develop, therefore, which are **seedless**. This practice is sometimes employed in grape and citrus crop production.

1 What do gardeners use rooting powder for?

2 What does a selective weedkiller do?

3 How are seedless grapes produced?

Words you should know
    herbicide   **rooting powder**   **selective weedkiller**

34 Transpiration

In this unit you will learn the answers to these questions:

■ How does water get into the roots of a plant?
■ How does water get up to the leaves?
■ What is transpiration?
■ How do plants maintain their water balance?

Roots are the organs which **anchor** plants and allow them to **absorb water** from the soil. Most of the water enters the root through specialised surface cells, called **root hair cells**. These provide a very large surface area for the uptake of water. The outer wall forms a hair like projection which pushes between soil particles. The wall is thin so water passes through it easily. Water enters root hair cells by osmosis, a special type of diffusion. Soil water is a dilute solution of salts.

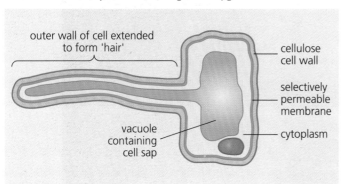

▲ **Fig 1** Root hair cell

Plant cells have a more concentrated solution of solutes. Water moves from the soil through the permeable membrane and enters the sap vacuole and the cytoplasm. Water is delivered to all parts of the plant in the xylem. Water evaporates from the leaf cells. It is lost through stomata (pores) to the air.

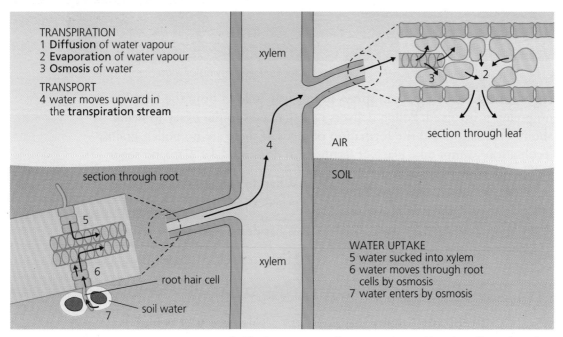

▲ **Fig 2** Water uptake, transport and loss in a flowering plant

Evaporation of water from the cells of the shoot system of a plant (the leaves in particular) to the atmosphere is called **transpiration**. The continuous flow of water through the xylem of the plant from root, to leaf, to air is called the **transpiration stream**.

Transpiration rate is affected by environmental conditions. The rate is speeded up if:

- air is dry not humid
- it is windy not still
- it is warm not cold
- it is light not dark.

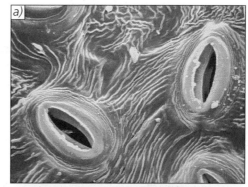

Guard cells surround the stoma. They are sensitive to light and cause the stoma to open more in bright light. Plants can lose more water than they can gain from soil, especially if the soil is dry. Then the stomata may close to reduce water loss and keep the plant in water balance.

Plants have adaptations to conserve (save) water. To reduce evaporation leaves may have:

- very waxy cuticles, e.g. holly
- small surface area (less stomata), e.g. pine needles and cacti
- stomata sunk in pits (protected from wind), e.g. pine needles

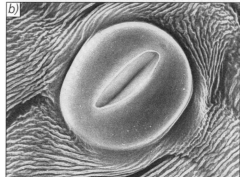

▲ **Fig 3** Photomicrographs of a) two open stomata and b) one closed stoma

- the ability to roll up (stomata protected), e.g. sand dune grass.

When the vacuole of plant cells are full of water they are turgid (rigid). This helps plant support. If too much water is lost the leaves wilt (droop). Water balance is very important for the healthy functioning of a plant, especially for photosynthesis.

1 In what ways are root hair cells specialised for water uptake?

2 What is transpiration?

3 Why does a plant wilt if it is not watered?

Words you should know

osmosis   transpiration   turgor   water balance   wilt

35 Variation

In this unit you will learn the answers to these questions:
■ How do living things differ?
■ What causes the variation?

Students in a teaching group at school may all be the same age, but, as individuals, they show different characteristics. They will differ in height, eye colour, skin colour, hair colour, blood group, and possibly gender, to mention but a few. An individual's characteristics illustrate what is described as **variation**.

There are two types of variation. These are **continuous** and **discontinuous** variation. The heights of a group of pupils in a class (all born in the same year) are recorded in the table. A histogram of the results is shown in Fig 1.

Height class/cm	121–125	126–130	131–135	136–140	141–145	146–150
Number of pupils	2	3	5	6	3	1

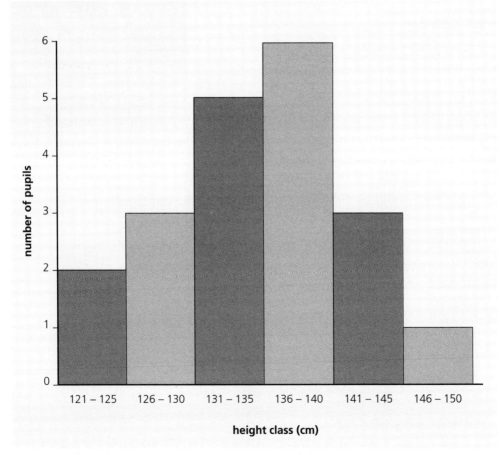

▲ *Fig 1 Histogram of heights in the teaching group*

As you might expect, there were one or two who were much taller than the others. Some were shorter, but the majority were around the 'average' for the class. The histogram in Fig 1 is based on a small number of students. If a much larger sample is taken then a curve similar to Fig 1 is produced, but which is much 'smoother'. This is described mathematically as a '**normal distribution**' curve. Body mass, index finger length and span are other examples which would produce data giving a normal distribution curve for a large group of individuals of the same age. Variation which produces a normal distribution within a population is called **continuous variation**. An individual will lie somewhere between the minimum and maximum on the scale for that characteristic.

Some characteristics fall into very distinct groups. Individuals are either male or female. Their blood group is either A, B, AB or O. There are no 'in-betweens'. Variation of this kind is called **discontinuous variation**.

All of the characteristics shown by an individual are the result of information inherited from their parents. Genetic material is passed on from generation to generation during reproduction. The potential to grow to a particular size, in terms of height and body mass, is already there at the start. It is determined by the genes present in the sperm and egg or, for an asexually produced organism, by the genetic material already present. Whether an individual reaches their potential growth rate and final size, for example, does depend on other things. The 'other things' will be factors in the environment. Continuous variation is a result of both genetic and environmental conditions. Data from twin studies, where identical twins have been brought up in two different situations, for example, in two different family groups, have shown this to be so.

On the other hand, the outcome of the genetic information any individual has concerning gender, blood group, eye colour and other examples of discontinuous variation is not influenced by the environment. Someone who is born blood group O will remain so whatever the environment. Discontinuous variation is the result of genetics alone.

1 What are the two types of variation shown by living things?
Give two examples for each.

Words you should know
continuous variation   **discontinuous variation**   **variation**

36 Reproduction and mutation

In this unit you will learn the answers to these questions:

■ What happens at fertilisation?
■ What makes us individuals?
■ How are twins formed?
■ How do mutants arise?
■ How is sex inherited?

Fertilisation

Fertilisation in humans usually occurs high in the oviduct. Sperms surround the egg as it travels down the oviduct towards the uterus. One of the sperms penetrates the egg membrane. Then changes take place in the membrane preventing other sperm getting in. The nucleus of the 'successful' sperm fuses with the egg nucleus. The **fertilised egg nucleus** becomes the **zygote**. The **embryo** develops from the zygote. It has genetic information from both gametes and so inherits characteristics from both parents.

Fertilisation is a random process. One human ejaculation (about $1.5\,cm^3$) contains about 100 million sperms. Each sperm will have its own unique combination of genes. Only one of these combinations will join the combination, also unique, of genes in the egg. This point explains, in part, how easy it is for different 'individuals' to arise in organisms that reproduce sexually.

Twins

Occasionally more than one egg is released in one month. If two eggs are fertilised, two zygotes result and twins may develop. Two, separate eggs are involved, each fertilised by a different and therefore genetically unique sperm. As a result each of the embryos will inherit a different combination of genes. These are **non-identical twins**.

Less often, an embryo may divide into two during its early stages. Each part then develops normally to produce two individuals. Both individuals will have arisen from the same fertilisation, one egg fusing with one sperm. The twins conceived in this way have identical genetics. They will be **identical twins**.

Mutation

Chromosomes are copied during meiosis. Occasionally the copying process goes wrong. Genetic information is written in chemical code in the chromosomes. The code may break and join up again the wrong way round. Bits of information may be lost or added. The message carried as a result may not necessarily be 'wrong', but it will certainly be different. Changed genes arising in this way will be formed randomly. They are called **mutant genes**, and the process is known as **gene mutation**.

Sometimes a whole chromosome may 'go missing' or 'turn up' during the formation of gametes. One example of this is responsible for **Down's syndrome**. Here the zygote receives an extra chromosome, usually from the egg. The individual therefore has a chromosome number of 47, not the usual 46. As a result, physical and mental development are not normal.

The rate at which mutations occur may be accelerated by specific environmental agents. These agents are called **mutagens**. Ionising radiation and particular chemicals are mutagens. Mutations may lead to abnormal cell growth, producing **tumours** or **cancers**. Mutagens of this kind are called **carcinogens**. Exposure to too much **sunlight** during sunbathing can lead to an increased risk of skin cancer. Over-exposure to **nuclear radiation** sources may induce tumour formation. Some of the chemical compounds in **tobacco smoke** are carcinogens.

1 What happens when an egg is fertilised?

2 How are non-identical twins formed?

3 What are mutations?

Inheritance of sex

The nuclei in the human testis and ovary have 23 pairs of chromosomes. One of the pairs is the **sex chromosomes**. A **female** has two sex chromosomes which look the same and are represented by the symbols **XX**. A **male** has two chromosomes, and one is shorter than the other. These are represented by the symbols **XY**. Fig 1 shows the way in which sex is inherited.

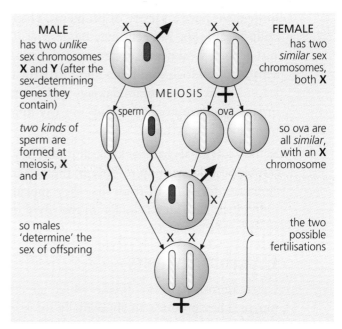

MALE has two *unlike* sex chromosomes **X** and **Y** (after the sex-determining genes they contain)

two kinds of sperm are formed at meiosis, **X** and **Y**

so males 'determine' the sex of offspring

FEMALE has two *similar* sex chromosomes, both **X**

so ova are all *similar*, with an **X** chromosome

the two possible fertilisations

MEIOSIS

sperm

ova

▶ *Fig 1* Sex determination

Words you should know

embryo   **fertilisation**   **mutagen**   **mutation**   **tumour**

37 Inheritance and disease

In this unit you will learn the answer to this question:
- ■ Why is it impossible to catch haemophilia?

Sickle-cell anaemia

In sickle-cell anaemia an abnormal form of haemoglobin is made which forms crystal-like structures in the red blood cells when oxygen concentrations are low. This changes the shape of the red blood cells.

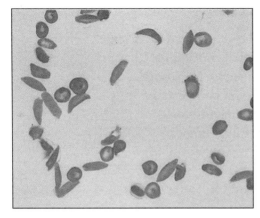

◀ **Fig 1** Photomicrograph of a blood smear of sickle-cell blood

Individuals have a variety of problems. They have **fewer red blood cells** because the red cells may be destroyed. This leads to **anaemia** and general weakness. Also, because their shape is changed, the red cells tend to block capillaries and **clotting** is common. This may lead to heart failure, brain damage and the failure of other vital organs. The symptoms show up in early infancy and the death rate in infancy is very high.

Some individuals have sickle-cell trait. They have some sickling of red blood cells with up to 50% of their haemoglobin in the abnormal form. Apart from that they appear normal. Such individuals have an advantage in that they have some resistance to the malarial parasite.

Cystic fibrosis

Cystic fibrosis (CF) is a disease which affects the cells which produce mucus. They produce an abnormally thick and sticky mucus. Organs which are particularly affected are the lungs, gut and pancreas. As a result this leads to a variety of distressing disorders.

The mucus blocks the air passages to the lungs. **Chronic lung congestion** occurs. This can be relieved temporarily by regular physiotherapy. Congestion of the lungs increases the risk of **respiratory infections**. These have to be combated by antibiotic treatment. The gut and the **pancreatic duct** can become blocked and foods normally digested by pancreatic enzymes remain undigested. Cystic fibrosis sufferers are often **diabetic** (see Unit 24).

Sadly there is no cure.

Duchenne muscular dystrophy

Duchenne muscular dystrophy is a disease which affects young boys. They have difficulty walking and in particular climbing stairs. The muscles gradually weaken and waste away. Sufferers are usually wheelchair-bound by the time they are about 10 years of age. **Muscle wastage** continues with consequent effect on vital systems. Breathing becomes increasingly difficult, ultimately impossible. Duchenne muscular dystrophy sufferers usually die from pneumonia. A life expectancy of 20 years is usually the maximum.

Haemophilia

Haemophilia is a disorder in which the individual lacks the blood clotting factor, **factor VIII**. This means that any **bleeding**, either internal or external, will continue unchecked. Consequently the sufferer can become **anaemic**. Bleeding also takes place into **joints,** leading to considerable pain.

Haemophilia can be treated successfully by regular injections of human factor VIII. At the moment, most of this is prepared from human blood donations. Sufferers feel safer, however, using genetically engineered factor VIII, thus avoiding possible HIV contamination.

1 Why do CF sufferers often have respiratory infections?

Words you should know
anaemia   clotting   congestion

38 Cloning and selective breeding

In this unit you will learn the answers to these questions:
- What is a clone?
- What do we mean by the term 'selective breeding'?

Asexual reproduction

Most flowering plants reproduce sexually. The following events occur:

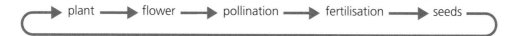

plant → flower → pollination → fertilisation → seeds

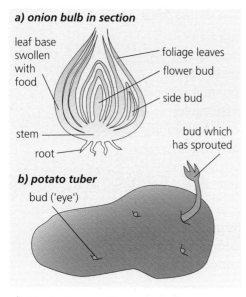

a) onion bulb in section

leaf base swollen with food
foliage leaves
flower bud
side bud
stem
root
bud which has sprouted

b) potato tuber

bud ('eye')

▲ **Fig 1** *Perennating organs also act as asexual reproductive organs*

In winter the cold kills many plants. Seeds and special organs survive to produce new generations. Some plants reproduce asexually. They may produce special structures which store food to survive the winter and which will make new plants in the spring. Food is stored in specialised structures (**perennating organs**) such as **bulbs** and stem **tubers**. These organs also allow the plants to reproduce.

Onion bulbs and potato tubers have **buds**. Buds are found between the swollen leaves of a bulb and on the surface of a potato. The potato buds are the 'eyes' of the potato. When more favourable conditions arrive, after the winter is over, stored food is used to promote the growth of one or more of the buds. New stems develop, and later roots, and a 'new plant' is produced from each of the buds involved. These will replace the original plant which has probably died back, before or during the winter. As a result, where one bulb or potato was planted one year, several may 'appear' in the next growing season. The plants will have reproduced themselves, but without producing any flowers. This is **asexual** or **vegetative reproduction**.

Some plants, like strawberry, produce **runners**. In this case food is sent to **lateral buds**. These grow to form side branches and form new plants when they contact the soil. This process is shown in Fig 2. When they are independent, the plantlets can be separated from the parent plant. This can occur naturally by decay or a gardener cutting through the runner.

▲ **Fig 2** *Runners from strawberry plants*

Cloning

Onion bulbs, potato stem tubers and strawberry runners are all parts of established plants. The cells which make up their structure will have been formed by mitotic divisions. It is important to remember that each time mitosis takes place, the genetic material present is copied (replicated) (see Unit 7). Therefore all the cells involved in any of these structures will have the same genetics as their 'parent' plant. The same will be true when a gardener takes leaf or stem cuttings from any other plant. It will have been **cloned**.

Selective breeding

Selective breeding is a slow process. Humans have used it for thousands of years. A farmer selects an animal or plant with the best characteristics and uses this organism for breeding. The best organisms from the next generation are selected and used for breeding. The process is repeated over many generations. Eventually plants or animals are produced with the required characteristics.

▲ *Fig 3 Different breeds of dog*

Cows, sheep, pigs, hens, wheat, oats, grapes and hops will all have been produced over many years of animal and plant breeding where specific features have been selected. The starting point will have been, and continues to be, wild (undomesticated) animals and plants. Some of the features which have been selected for are summarised in the table.

Organism	Feature selected
chickens	rapid weight gain
cattle	milk yield
wheat	fungus resistance
peas	height of plant
roses	scent and colour

Selective breeding has not been confined to the development of food animals and plants. Dog breeders, racehorse breeders and rose breeders will all have employed selective breeding to meet their own particular requirements (see Fig 3).

1 Why are cloned plants always the same?
2 Where did all our crop plants come from originally?

Words you should know

cloning   selective breeding

39 Evidence for evolution

In this unit you will learn the answer
to this question:
■ How did life on Earth begin?

Evolution

We know that plants and animals on the
Earth today are changing. Tropical rain forests
are destroyed. People fear that species like
tigers, pandas and black rhino may become
extinct. They also worry about reports of new
strains of bacteria which are resistant to
antibiotics, or wheat that has been made to be
resistant to fungi.

▲ **Fig 1** Dinosaurs

The Earth is changing now and probably has
changed in the past. **Evolution** is one widely
accepted theory to explain the changes.
Evolution means the slow changes to
organisms that take place over millions of
years. The earliest records of living cells are bacteria cells from
3000 million years ago. The theory suggests that today's plants and
animals had common ancestors, and have evolved or changed from
them. New organisms develop and others die and become extinct as
world conditions change. Part of the evidence for the theory comes
from fossils.

Fossil evidence

When a plant or animal dies its body, or parts of it, may be eaten.
Bacteria and fungi cause the rest to decay.

Sometimes animals and plants die in conditions where they are
not eaten, and decay is slowed down, or stopped altogether, with
perhaps only the softer tissues being
affected. As a result only the harder
parts, such as shells, teeth and bones,
have remained from the past as **fossils**
(see Fig 2). These are the fossils which
we can see in museums, quarries or
sea cliffs. They are the remains of plant
and animal bodies.

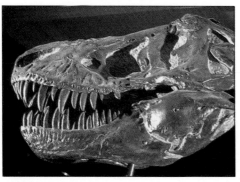

◄ **Fig 2** The fossil skull of a Tyrannosaurus rex

Fossils can be formed when organisms die in rivers, lakes or the sea. They sink to the bottom and get covered with mud and silt. If the sediments are deposited quickly other animals can not get at the dead bodies. Sediments keep out oxygen so that decay is slowed down or prevented. It is not a common event. It means that we are more likely to find fossils of some organisms than of others.

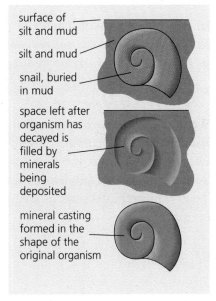

surface of silt and mud

silt and mud

snail, buried in mud

space left after organism has decayed is filled by minerals being deposited

mineral casting formed in the shape of the original organism

Fossils can be formed in different ways including:

1 casting;

2 impression; or

3 petrification (turn to rock)

▲ **Fig 3** *Fossilisation by casting*

Fig 3 shows the way in which an organism may be fossilised by forming a **cast**. Fossils of this type are found in sedimentary rocks. This type of rock shows layer upon layer of sand and silt deposits. Animals dying at the time when the layers were being formed could be trapped and casts formed later.

Marks such as dinosaur footprints or leaf prints in mud have also been preserved. Here the organism left an **impression** in the mud before it was preserved by the sediment laid down above it.

Sometimes water rich in mineral salts may get into the tissues of an organism before they decay. This eventually leads to the formation of rock, preserving the layout of the tissue. This process is called **petrification**. One example of this type of fossil is shown by the petrified forest in Arizona (see Fig 4). The petrified coniferous trees are estimated to be about 170 million years old.

▲ **Fig 4** *Arizona petrified forest*

1 What is our earliest record of living cells?

2 Why are fossils not a very reliable source of evidence about evolution?

Words you should know

evolution   **fossil**   **petrification**

40 Adaptation and competition

In this unit you will learn the answers to these questions:
- What is a 'predator–prey' relationship?
- Why are some plants avoided by grazing animals?

What makes a good predator?

A **predator** is a carnivorous animal. The animal or animals that it eats are its **prey**. Usually the predator is bigger than its prey. Sometimes, smaller predators hunt in groups. They can catch prey much larger than themselves.

Predators have well developed senses in order to locate their prey. It is important that the prey does not know the predator is there for as long as possible. One way this is achieved is by predators having good **camouflage**.

Large cats, like lions, use good hunting methods. They approach their prey from downwind, so that the prey cannot detect their scent. They also hunt as a pride (group). They work together but each lion has a different job to do.

▲ **Fig 1** A lion bringing down its prey

Predators move carefully and slowly to avoid detection. When they are close enough to the prey they attempt a 'kill'. A predator must be able to keep up a short burst of speed to succeed in capturing the prey.

The lion shown in Fig 1 is using its claws to grip its prey and weaken it by causing bleeding. The large canine teeth penetrate the prey's skin, causing damage to internal organs, more blood loss and at the same time enable the predator to 'hang on'. The prey may be killed rapidly or it may die from blood loss and exhaustion.

Predatory animals, as a group, have a wide variety of 'weapons' at their disposal. These include, webs, pitfall traps, poisons, and specialised beaks, claws and teeth.

◀ **Fig 2** An osprey with beak and talons showing

How are prey animals adapted to avoid capture?

It is important that the prey are well camouflaged and easily hidden. They need to be able to run very fast to avoid capture. Some may have horns, spines or spikes for defence.

The prey of carnivores often live in large groups because there is 'safety in numbers'. One individual may become aware of a predator and warn all the others (see Fig 3). If lots of prey run together they may avoid capture.

▲ **Fig 3** *The white tail of the rabbit running acts as a warning signal to other rabbits*

How to avoid being eaten when you can't run away

Unlike animals, plants cannot run away. Herbivorous animals only eat plants. One method of eating is called grazing. Grazers can eat plants at different heights. Some are selective grazers only eating a particular plant species or only eating plants at a certain stage of development. Many grazers are not selective and will eat any plant.

Some plants have adaptations so that they are not eaten. Plants that grow with their leaves close to the ground, as a rosette, make it difficult for the tongue and the teeth of the grazer to attack the plant. Taller plants may produce poisonous or nasty tasting chemicals so that they are not eaten. Spines, long hairs and stinging hairs also protect plants from grazers.

1 How are animals adapted to be predators?
2 How have plants adapted to avoid being eaten?

Words you should know

predator   prey

41 Environment

In this unit you will learn the answers to these questions:
- Who is to blame for acid rain?
- What is the greenhouse effect?
- What is wrong with global warming?

We are different from other animals because we have more control over our lives. We live safely in houses and are sheltered from the weather. We can use lighting and heating when it is needed. There are many forms of transport which help us to travel long distances easily. For most people food is easily available at all times of the year.

Humans have greater intelligence than other animals and can solve problems. We can adapt to changes in our world.

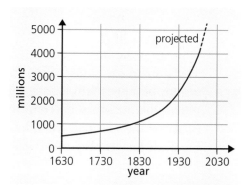

▲ **Fig 1** *The growth of the human population*

The main problem facing humans in the future is the rapid rate of population growth (see Fig 1). More people will need more resources and will cause more pollution. This has a great effect on the other plants and animals in our environment. Human activity causes many problems. Four important issues are the **greenhouse effect**, **acid rain** and the **destruction of the tropical rain forests and the ozone layer**.

We need energy to heat our homes, harvest our crops and for travelling by car. Each day, all around the world, huge amounts of energy are needed for transport, industry and agriculture. Most energy is provided by burning fossil fuels (coal, oil and natural gas). Many power stations also use these fuels to generate electricity. The waste gases of burning, carbon dioxide, sulphur dioxide and nitrogen oxides cause the **greenhouse effect** and acid rain.

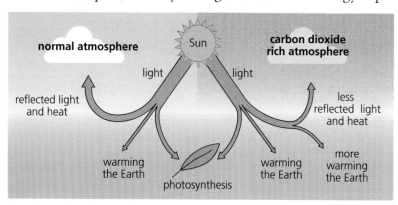

▲ **Fig 2** *The effects of increasing carbon dioxide in the atmosphere*

The extra heat trapped causes the greenhouse effect and results in **global warming**. Polar ice caps and glaciers steadily melt. The sea level rises. Large areas of land will be flooded unless the warming is stopped.

The concentration of carbon dioxide in the atmosphere has increased dramatically during the last century.

CFCs (Chloro fluoro carbons) used in aerosols and 'fridges, together with other pollutants, destroy the **ozone layer**. Ozone in the atmosphere filters out some of the ultra-violet light from the Sun. It acts as a type of heat shield. Damage to the ozone layer allows more ultra-violet light and heat to reach the Earth, which increases global warming. U.v. light also increases the risk of skin cancer.

▲ *Fig 3* *Generating electricity by burning fossil fuels*

Sulphur dioxide and nitrogen oxides react with water in the atmosphere and produce sulphuric and nitric acid. These acids reach the Earth in the rain. **Acid rain** affects the balance of metal ions in the soil. The concentration of aluminium increases. It is poisonous to plants. Concentrations of calcium, magnesium and potassium, (valuable plant nutrients) decrease. The acid rain enters lakes, streams, rivers and the sea. Most damage is done to plants, especially conifers (see Fig 4) in regions where the rain fell. Fresh water habitats are also affected and trout and salmon are very sensitive to the changes. Acid rain also damages buildings by erosion.

In many areas of the world, like South America, tropical rain forests have been destroyed. They have been cleared for farming, housing, industry and also for the sale of hardwood. It is happening on a huge scale.

▲ *Fig 4* *The effect of acid rain on a forest*

The main concerns are:

1. Loss of trees means less carbon dioxide is removed from the air – the greenhouse effect is increased.

2. Habitats are destroyed – plants and animals die.

3. Some species may become extinct – their genes are lost for ever.

4. New sources of food and drugs are lost as plants die.

1 Why is the burning of fossil fuels such an important environmental issue?

Words you should know

acid rain   **global warming**   **greenhouse effect**   **ozone layer**

42 Feeding relationships

In this unit you will learn the answers to these questions:

■ What are the feeding patterns in communities of plants and animals?

■ What happens to the energy taken into a community?

▲ **Fig 1** A small freshwater lake

The freshwater lake shown in Fig 1 is a **community**. It will have a number of populations of different species living in it. The **plants and animals** present will be **interacting** with each other and their **environment** to form an **ecosystem**. One important interaction in any ecosystem is the one based on feeding.

A feeding relationship involves the transfer of **energy** from one organism to another. Energy enters an ecosystem as **light**. Light energy is used by **plants** in photosynthesis to make **glucose**. Plants then use glucose to make other organic substances (see Units 30). Plants are the only organisms which can make their own food in this way. This means that all other organisms must be dependent on green plants for their food and therefore their energy. As a result, plants are called the **producer** organisms of an ecosystem.

All non-photosynthetic organisms are dependent on the products of photosynthesis for survival. This will mean that bacteria, fungi, animals and plants which cannot photosynthesise must get their food from the producers. Organisms which feed on others are called **consumers**.

There are basically three types of consumer. **Herbivores** are animals that feed on plants. **Carnivores** feed on other animals. **Omnivores** eat both plants and animals.

The sequence of organisms in a feeding relationship forms what is known as a **food chain**. Fig 2 shows a simple food chain which could be drawn up for the lake shown in Fig 1.

plankton (producer)

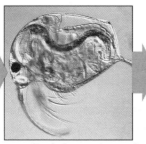
water flea (primary consumer)   stickleback (secondary consumer)

heron (tertiary consumer)

▲ **Fig 2** A food chain, based on the lake in Fig 1

Food webs arise when one producer or consumer can be eaten by more than one consumer. Food webs are interconnected food chains. Each **level of feeding** in a food chain is described as a **trophic level**.

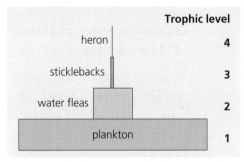

▲ **Fig 3** Pyramid of numbers for a freshwater food chain

It is possible to study the size of populations at each trophic level in a food chain. Data can be shown in a diagram called a **pyramid of numbers**. Fig 3 shows a pyramid of numbers for a freshwater food chain. Each trophic level is represented by a block which is scaled to represent the number of organisms at that trophic level.

Food chains often show this pyramid shape. There are usually more of the smaller producers than the herbivores. The carnivores are usually fewer in number, but larger in size, than the herbivores.

Sometimes it can be different if there is one large producer e.g. a single oak tree (see Fig 4).

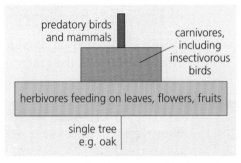

▲ **Fig 4** Pyramid of numbers for a food chain based on a tree

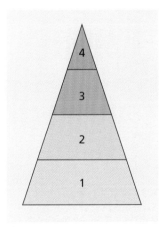

▲ **Fig 5** A pyramid of biomass

Feeding relationships can be shown more clearly if **biomass** is used instead of numbers. Biomass is the total dry mass (water is removed) of the organisms of a trophic level. It always results in a shape like Fig 5. There has to be a large biomass in level 1 to support its organisms in level 2, etc.

Energy is lost at each stage in a food chain or trophic level. Biomass is lost at each level because respiration uses up food reserves, and excretion and faeces also cause losses. Animals especially have less energy to pass on because movement increases the loss of energy in respiration and heat. Food chains can not be very long because of these losses.

1 What is the difference between a food chain and a food web?

2 When is a pyramid of numbers not shaped like a pyramid?

Words you should know

biomass	**carnivore**	**community**	**consumer**
ecosystem	**herbivore**	**omnivore**	**trophic level**

43 The carbon cycle

In this unit you will learn the answers to this question:
■ How is carbon recycled?

Carbon is one of the Earth's most important elements. Much of the planet's carbon is **fixed** into compounds in the bodies of plants and animals. Some of it is **free** in the air in **carbon dioxide** gas, and some dissolved in the sea and freshwater as hydrogen carbonate.

Plants and animals need a constant supply of carbon to make organic compounds such as carbohydrates, fats and proteins to stay alive.

How is carbon fixed?

Plants absorb carbon dioxide from the air and water around them. **Photosynthesis** fixes the carbon into glucose molecules (see Unit 30). Plants make other carbon compounds from this sugar. The bodies of plants, whole or in parts, are used by herbivores, and indirectly by carnivores, as **food**. The carbon which was fixed by photosynthesis is now part of an animal.

The waste materials which plants and animals produce contain carbon.

◀ **Fig 1** *Getting rid of waste carbon*

How is carbon released?

Plants and animals release carbon dioxide into the air when they respire (see Units 17 and 18).

When an organism, or part of an organism, dies it usually drops to the ground. Soil bacteria and fungi, the **decomposers**, use the compounds in these remains as their food. They carry out the process of decomposition.

Decomposers also release carbon dioxide into the air when they respire. The minerals in their food are released into the soil (see Unit 31). Some of the energy from decomposition is released into the surroundings. Rotting (decomposing) organic material, e.g. compost heaps, get warm.

In the past, large amounts of energy were trapped in fossil fuels such as coal, gas and oil. Today, the process still goes on, e.g. forming peat in bogs.

Burning fossil fuels releases carbon dioxide into the air. Burning wood, paper (made from plant cells) or fats and oils (from plants or animals) also releases the same gas.

The way in which carbon is fixed and released is one example of the recycling of an element. This cycle is described as the **carbon cycle**. Fig 2 is a summary of the recycling which takes place.

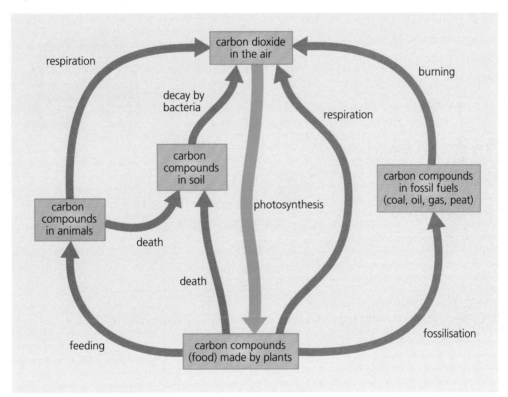

▲ **Fig 2** *The carbon cycle*

1 Which process(es) fix carbon dioxide?

2 Which process(es) release carbon dioxide?

Words you should know

carbon dioxide   decomposers

44 Materials

In this unit you will learn the answers to these questions:
- What are materials?
- What is a property?
- How can materials be grouped according to properties?

Raw materials

Fig 1 shows two houses – an old stone house and a modern brick house.

Raw materials are those which occur naturally. Manufactured materials are those made from raw materials.

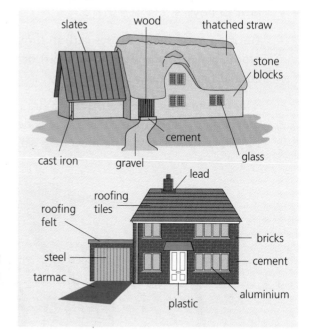

▶ **Fig 1** *The building materials used in two different houses*

Raw materials	Manufactured materials
thatched straw	cement
stone blocks	glass
wood	cast iron
slates	
gravel	

The table contains materials used to make the old stone house.

1 Which parts of the modern house are made of:
  a) raw materials
  b) materials manufactured from raw materials?

The best material for the job is used. It has special **properties** which make it better than other materials.

Properties of glass include:

- it is hard;
- it breaks easily (it is brittle);
- it has a high melting point;
- it does not react with chemicals.

Glass is used for windows because it lets light pass through it. Its special property is that it is transparent.

There are five major groups of materials. The properties of a material affect how good they are for a particular job. The cost of materials must be considered. Each group has different properties. These groups are:

   metals   plastics   ceramics (pottery)   glasses   fibres

This table summarises the main properties of these five materials.

Material group	Example of material	Typical properties of group	Raw material used
metals	iron, steel, lead, copper, brass	hard, strong, high density, good conductors of heat and electricity, malleable (can be beaten into thin sheets), ductile (can be drawn into fine wires), usually burn on heating, high melting points	metal ores in Earth's crust
plastics	poly(ethene), polystyrene, rubber	flexible, low density, easily moulded, poor conductors of heat and electricity, often transparent, melt and often burn on heating	crude oil, sap of rubber trees
ceramics (pottery)	china, concrete, bricks, tiles	hard, brittle, medium density, very high melting point, non-conductors of heat and electricity, very unreactive, do not burn	clay, sand and other minerals
glasses	Pyrex, lead crystal, soft soda glass	same properties as ceramics, often transparent	sand, limestone and other minerals
fibres	cotton, wool, paper, nylon, polyester	flexible, low density, may burn on heating, long stringy strands	natural fibres from plants and animals, crude oil

2 The table shows some of the properties of glass, copper, aluminium and stainless steel. Use the properties of materials from above to complete the table. (Copper, aluminium and stainless steel are metals.)

3 Why is glass unsuitable for making a saucepan?

4 The handle of a saucepan is usually made of plastic or wood. Suggest one property of the material used for the handle which is important.

Property	Glass	Copper	Aluminium	Stainless steel
good conductor of heat				
high density	✓	✓	✗	✓
high melting point				
shiny	✗	✓	✗	✓
reacts with an alkali	✗	✗	✓	✗

When choosing a material for a particular purpose it is important to make sure it has the best properties. Properties can be:

1 **Physical properties**, e.g. hardness, strength, melting point, conductivity of heat and electricity, density, transparency.

2 **Chemical properties**, e.g. does it burn, react with water, corrode, etc.

Words you should know

material   property   raw material

45 Solids, liquids and gases

In this unit you will learn the answers to these questions:
- What are states of matter?
- How are particles arranged in solids, liquids and gases?
- How do particles move in solids, liquids and gases?
- What is diffusion?

States of matter

All substances can exist in three states of matter:

solid   liquid   gas

The state depends on temperature and pressure.
Water, for example, can exist as:

- ice (solid) below 0°C;
- water (liquid) between 0°C and 100°C;
- steam (gas) above 100°C.

The properties of solids, liquids and gases are summarised in the table.

Property	Solid	Liquid	Gas
volume	definite	definite	fills the whole container
shape	definite	takes up the shape of the bottom of the container	takes up the shape of the whole container
density	high	medium	low
ease of flow	does not flow unless powdered	flows easily	flows easily
expansion on heating	low	medium	high
compression	very low	low	high
movement of particles	very slow	medium	very fast

1 In which state is water at
   a) 50°C
   b) −50°C ?

Changes of state

Water boils at 100°C and turns into a gas. When steam is cooled it condenses, forming liquid water. Water becomes ice at 0°C. When ice warms up it melts forming water.

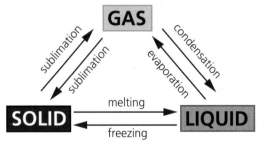

Steam, or water vapour, in the air can turn to solid ice without becoming water first. This is called **sublimation** and can happen in a freezer.

The changes of state of matter are summarised in Fig 1.

▲ **Fig 1** *Changes in the state of matter*

Substances are made up of particles

All solids, liquids and gases are made up of particles. Fig 2 shows simple representations of the arrangements of particles in solids, liquids and gases.

In a solid the particles are closely packed together. The arrangement of particles is usually regular. The particles are vibrating.

In a liquid the particles are not as closely packed as in a solid and the arrangement is not regular.

In a gas the particles are not regularly arranged. They are widely spaced and are moving in all directions. This movement is called **random movement**.

SOLID	LIQUID	GAS
Regular arrangement. Strong forces between particles. Particles only vibrate.	Irregular arrangement. Strong forces between particles. Particles move more than in solids.	Irregular arrangement. No forces (or only very weak forces) between particles. Rapid movement of particles but no pattern to the movement.

▲ *Fig 2 Arrangements of particles in solids, liquids and gases*

Diffusion

Particles of matter are always moving. They tend to move as shown in Fig 3.

▶ *Fig 3 Particles diffusing*

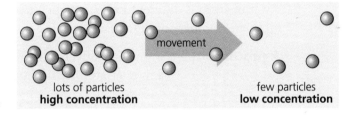

lots of particles
high concentration

movement

few particles
low concentration

This movement is called diffusion. Gases will not stay in an open container. The particles move rapidly in all directions. The smell of perfume quickly spreads through a room by diffusion. Diffusion can be shown using the coloured gas bromine (see Fig 4).

Diffusion does take place in liquids, but it is very slow. The particles in liquid cannot move as fast as gas particles. A purple crystal of potassium manganate(VII) will dissolve in water. If it is not stirred it will take hours for the colour to spread through the water.

Diffusion can occur in solids, but it is even slower because solid particles only vibrate.

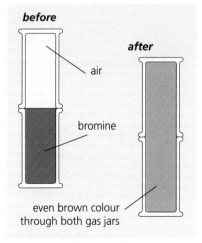

before

after

air

bromine

even brown colour through both gas jars

▲ *Fig 4 Diffusion of bromine in air*

Words you should know

diffusion   evaporation   freezing   gas   liquid melting   solid   sublimation

46 Structure of the atom

In this unit you will learn the answers to these questions:
- What are atoms made up from?
- What is the difference between atomic number and mass number?
- How many protons, neutrons and electrons are there in an atom?
- What are isotopes?

Atoms

Every substance is made up from very tiny particles called **atoms**.
Atoms are extremely small. A cube of iron (2 cm × 2 cm × 2 cm) contains about 600 000 000 000 000 000 000 000 atoms of iron.

We now know that atoms can be split up.

Protons, neutrons and electrons

All atoms are made up from three particles:

protons, neutrons and **electrons**

An iron atom is different from a copper atom because it contains different numbers of these particles.

A **proton** (p)   is a small, positively charged particle. Its mass is 1 a.m.u. (1 atomic mass unit).

An **electron** (e)   is much smaller than the other particles. Two thousand electrons have the same mass as one proton or neutron. The masses of electrons can be ignored. An electron has a single negative charge.

A **neutron** (n)   is a particle which has the same mass as a proton (1 a.m.u.) but has no charge — it is neutral.

All atoms are **neutral**, i.e. there is no overall positive or negative charge.

Atomic number (Z) and **mass number** (A) are two 'vital statistics' for any atom. The atomic number is the number of protons in an atom. It is also the number of electrons in an atom. The mass number is the total number of protons and neutrons in an atom.

A phosphorus atom has an atomic number of 15 and a mass number of 31. It can be represented as $^{31}_{15}P$. It contains 15 protons, 15 electrons and 16 neutrons. The number of neutrons is the difference between the mass number and the atomic number.

1 Atoms are neutral. What does this tell you about the numbers of protons and electrons in any atom?

2 Lithium has an atomic number of 3 and a mass number of 7. How many protons, electrons and neutrons are there in a lithium atom?

Arrangement of protons, neutrons and electrons

In any atom the protons and neutrons are tightly packed in the **nucleus** (Fig 1). The nucleus is positively charged.

The electrons move around the nucleus at high speeds in certain **shells** or **energy levels**. Each shell can only contain up to a fixed maximum number of electrons (Fig 2).

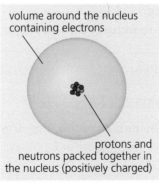

volume around the nucleus containing electrons

protons and neutrons packed together in the nucleus (positively charged)

▲ *Fig 1* *Arrangement of protons, neutrons and electrons in an atom*

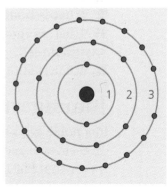

▲ *Fig 2* *Maximum number of electrons in shells 1, 2 and 3*

Fig 3 shows simple diagrams of some atoms.

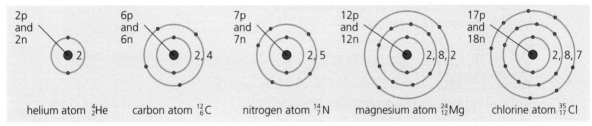

2p and 2n — helium atom ^4_2He — 2

6p and 6n — carbon atom $^{12}_6\text{C}$ — 2, 4

7p and 7n — nitrogen atom $^{14}_7\text{N}$ — 2, 5

12p and 12n — magnesium atom $^{24}_{12}\text{Mg}$ — 2, 8, 2

17p and 18n — chlorine atom $^{35}_{17}\text{Cl}$ — 2, 8, 7

▲ *Fig 3* *Simple diagrams of some atoms*

Isotopes

Atoms of the same element containing different numbers of neutrons but, of course, the same number of protons and electrons are called **isotopes**. For example, there are three isotopes of hydrogen (Fig 4):

■ normal hydrogen atom, ^1_1H (1 proton, 1 electron, 0 neutrons);
■ heavy hydrogen atom (deuterium), ^2_1H (1 proton, 1 electron, 1 neutron);
■ radioactive hydrogen atom (tritium), ^3_1H (1 proton, 1 electron, 2 neutrons).

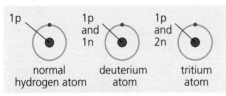

1p — normal hydrogen atom

1p and 1n — deuterium atom

1p and 2n — tritium atom

▲ *Fig 4* *The three isotopes of hydrogen*

All three atoms are hydrogen atoms because they contain one proton and one electron. The three isotopes of hydrogen have the same chemical properties but slightly different physical properties.

Words you should know

atom   atomic number   electron   energy level   isotope
mass number   neutron   nucleus   proton

47 Bonding

In this unit you will learn the answers to these questions:
- What is bonding?
- What are giant structures and molecular structures?
- What is allotropy?

Joining atoms together

In a noble gas, like helium or argon, the atoms are on their own and are not joined in any way. This is shown in Fig 1.

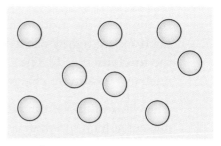

▲ **Fig 1** *The atoms in helium gas*

In elements and compounds, atoms are usually joined together in some way. The joining of atoms together is called **bonding**. The forces which hold the atoms together are called **chemical bonds**.

There are different types of chemical bond. The ionic bond is explained in Unit 48.

Molecular structures

Atoms, in elements and compounds, can join together in small groups, called **molecules.** For example, oxygen gas is made up of oxygen molecules. Each molecule is made up of a pair of oxygen atoms. Sulphur is made up of molecules of eight sulphur atoms, in a ring. Carbon dioxide is made up of molecules. Each molecule is made up from one carbon atom and two oxygen atoms.

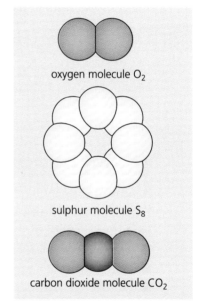

oxygen molecule O_2

sulphur molecule S_8

carbon dioxide molecule CO_2

▲ **Fig 2**

1 How many sulphur atoms are there in a sulphur molecule?

Giant structures

In some cases, atoms all join together to give one very large arrangement of atoms. This is called a **giant structure.** Fig 3 shows a giant structure of silicon and oxygen atoms in the compound silicon(IV) oxide. All of the atoms are bonded together. The structure continues in all directions. Silicon(IV) oxide is a giant structure of **atoms.** It is also possible to have a giant structure of **ions**, e.g. sodium chloride.

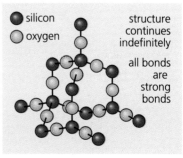

silicon
oxygen
structure continues indefinitely
all bonds are strong bonds

▲ **Fig 3** *Silicon(IV) oxide*

Giant structure or a molecular structure?

The table gives some information about two solids. One is silicon(IV) oxide and the other is iodine.

substance	melting point /°C	boiling point /°C	structure
silicon(IV) oxide	1610	2230	**giant structure**
iodine	114	183	**molecular**

A substance with a **molecular structure** is either a gas, a low boiling point liquid or a low melting point solid at room temperature. A substance with a giant structure is a solid at room temperature and has a high melting point.

Forms of carbon

Diamond and **graphite** are two forms of carbon with different properties and different structures. Different forms of the same element, in the same physical state, are called **allotropes**. Fig 4 shows the arrangement of atoms in diamond and graphite.

Diamonds were formed in the Earth when high pressures acted on carbon as the Earth cooled. The arrangement of carbon atoms is tetrahedral. Each carbon atom is attached to four other carbon atoms. All of the bonds are strong so it is difficult to break up the structure.

Graphite has a layer structure. The bonds within each layer are very strong. The forces between the layers are very weak. Graphite is soft because the layers slide easily over each other. Graphite, unlike diamond, is a good conductor of electricity as electrons move easily through the structure.

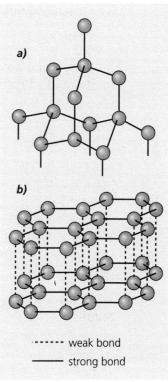

a)

b)

- - - - - weak bond
——— strong bond

▲ **Fig 4** *Arrangement of atoms in a) diamond and b) graphite*

A chance discovery in 1985 led to the identification of a new allotropes of carbon called **fullerenes**. Two fullerenes, C_{60} and C_{70}, can be prepared by electrically evaporating carbon electrodes in helium gas at low pressure. Fig 5 shows C_{60}.

2 Why is it important to evaporate carbon in helium rather than air?

3 What does the fullerene molecule remind you of?

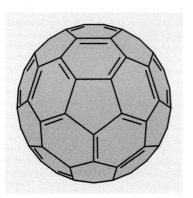

▲ **Fig 5** *Fullerene with 60 carbon atoms*

Words you should know

**allotrope   chemical bond   fullerene
giant structure   molecular structure**

48 Ionic bonding

In this unit you will learn the answers to these questions:
■ What is ionic bonding?
■ What properties will ionic compounds have?

Ionic bonding is one way of joining atoms together. It usually involves the combining of a metal atom with a non-metal atom.

A common example of ionic bonding is sodium chloride. The arrangements of electrons in sodium and chlorine atoms are:

Na 2, 8, 1   Cl   2, 8, 7

To understand how sodium and chlorine atoms bond, you must first understand a little about **noble gases** (see Unit 69). Noble gases have very stable electron arrangements, and atoms of other elements gain and lose electrons in order to achieve similar electron arrangements. (The noble gases are helium, neon, argon, krypton, xenon and radon.)

A sodium atom has one more electron than the noble gas neon. A chlorine atom has one less electron than the noble gas argon.

The sodium atom loses one electron and forms a sodium **ion**, Na^+, with an electron arrangement of 2, 8. The chlorine atom gains one electron and forms a chloride ion, Cl^-, with an electron arrangement of 2,8,8.

$$Na \atop atom \quad \rightarrow \quad Na^+ \atop ion \;+\; e^-$$

$$Cl \atop atom \;+\; e^- \quad \rightarrow \quad Cl^- \atop ion$$

The sodium and chloride ions are held together by strong electrostatic forces. This can be summarised by Fig 1.

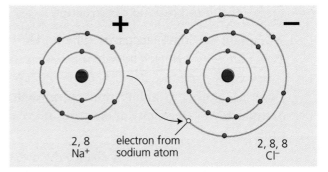

2, 8   electron from   2, 8, 8
Na^+ sodium atom Cl^-

▲ **Fig 1** Electron arrangements of Na^+ and Cl^-

The metal magnesium and the non-metal oxygen form magnesium oxide by ionic bonding in the same way. The electron arrangements of magnesium and oxygen are:

Mg 2, 8, 2   O   2, 6

Each magnesium atom loses two electrons and each oxygen atom gains two electrons.

$$Mg \rightarrow Mg^{2+} + 2e^-$$
$$O + 2e^- \rightarrow O^{2-}$$

Both magnesium ions and oxide ions have the same electron arrangement as neon, i.e. 2, 8 (with full outer electron shells). Again, strong electrostatic forces hold the ions together.

Properties of ionic compounds

Compounds containing ionic bonds usually have high melting and boiling points. At room temperature they are usually crystalline solids. The ions are held together in a **lattice**. Fig 2 shows a sodium chloride lattice. This is a cubic arrangement of sodium and chloride ions. Each sodium ion in the lattice is surrounded by six chloride ions. Each chloride ion in the structure is surrounded by six sodium ions. As a result of this structure sodium chloride:

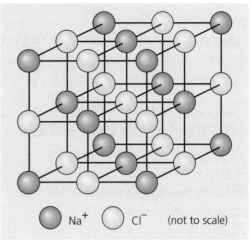

Na$^+$ Cl$^-$ (not to scale)

▲ **Fig 2** *Sodium chloride lattice*

■ forms a crystal (a crystalline solid) at room temperatures
■ has a high melting point
■ has a high boiling point
■ will dissolve in water
■ will not usually dissolve in organic solvents like hexane
■ will not conduct electricity when solid
■ will conduct electricity when molten or dissolved in water

1 Draw a diagram like Fig 1 to show the electron arangements of Mg^{2+} and O^{2-}.

2 In ionic bonding what force holds the ions together?

3 Why is the melting point of magnesium oxide much greater than the melting point of sodium chloride?

4 Three substances labelled A, B and C have melting points as follows:
A 90°C   B 595°C   C 120°C
Which compound is most likely to contain ionic bonding?

Words you should know

       ion   **ionic bonding**   **lattice**

49 Elements, mixtures & compounds

In this unit you will learn the answers to these questions:
- **What are elements?**
- **What are the differences between mixtures and compounds?**

Elements

Pure substances which cannot be split up into simpler substances are called **elements**. There are over 100 known elements, with 92 occurring naturally. Each element can be represented by a **symbol**, e.g. O for oxygen, Ca for calcium, Fe for iron, Mg for magnesium.

Most of the elements are metals. There are 22 non-metallic elements.

Elements are made of **atoms**. All atoms of the same element contain the same number of protons. A lump of sulphur is made up from sulphur atoms and a lump of carbon is made up from carbon atoms. Fig 1 shows a simple representation of atoms in sulphur and in carbon.

Key carbon ◯ sulphur

1 Use the Periodic Table on page 135 to identify the elements represented by the following symbols.

H; S; Na; Cl; P; K; Sb; Mn; Pb; Au; Ag; Hg.

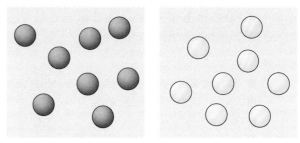

▲ **Fig 1** *Atoms in the elements carbon and sulphur*

Mixtures

Many substances exist as **mixtures** of other pure substances.

1 Air is a mixture of gases.

2 Universal Indicator is a mixture of simple indicators.

3 Sea water is a mixture of substances dissolved in water.

4 Crude oil is a mixture of hydrocarbons.

Fig 2 shows atoms in two mixtures of carbon and sulphur.

You will notice that the atoms of carbon and sulphur are not joined and the proportions of the two elements in the two mixtures are different.

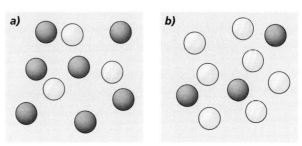

▲ **Fig 2** *Mixtures of carbon and sulphur atoms*

2 Which mixture *a)* or *b)* contains more carbon?

The properties of a mixture are always the same as the properties of the substances they contain. Sea water tastes salty because of the salt it contains.

A pure substance has a definite melting point. An impure substance (i.e. a mixture of substances) melts at a lower temperature and over a range of temperature. Butter is a mixture and it melts in a frying pan over a range of temperature.

Compounds

Compounds are pure substances made from two or more elements joined together.

Joining elements together involves a **chemical reaction** called **synthesis**, e.g. heating a mixture of iron and sulphur forms a compound called iron sulphide. Fig 3 shows the change which occurs when iron sulphide is formed.

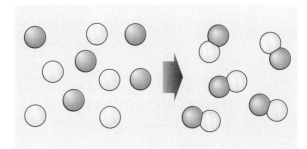

▲ **Fig 3** The synthesis of iron sulphide

The composition of a compound is fixed. For example, iron sulphide contains 7 parts of iron and 4 parts of sulphur by mass. One iron atom is combined with one sulphur atom. The **formula** of iron sulphide is written as FeS.

The table compares the properties of a mixture and a compound.

3 Hydrogen and oxygen combine together to form water, H_2O. In both hydrogen gas and oxygen gas the atoms are in pairs, i.e. H_2 and O_2.

Draw diagrams to show particles in
a) hydrogen gas; **b)** oxygen gas; **c)** a mixture of hydrogen and oxygen; **d)** steam.

	Mixture	Compound
Proportions of the elements	can be altered	must be fixed
Separation of the elements	easy	very difficult
Properties of the elements	stay the same as the elements present	new properties different from the elements present
Energy changes when made	no change	usually energy evolved (given off) or taken in

Words you should know

compound   element   formula   mixture   synthesis

50 Separating mixtures – 1

In this unit you should learn the answers to these questions:
- What is the chemical name for salt?
- What is rock salt?
- How is salt mined from the Earth?
- How is salt purified?

Rock salt

Salt is a chemical with many uses. It has been used for centuries to keep food from going bad. Its chemical name is **sodium chloride**. It can be made by burning a reactive metal in a reactive gas.

1 Name the reactive metal and the reactive gas that react to form salt.

Salt is found in the Earth in the rock called **rock salt**. Rock salt is crystals of salt mixed with materials that do not dissolve in water. Sandstone is such a material.

You will know that sea water tastes salty.

The rock salt deposits are what remains of large inland seas. The water has evaporated and left salt deposits underground.

Salt mining

Salt can be mined underground where the salt is close to the surface. This rock salt is crushed and put onto the roads in winter.

2 Why is crushed rock salt put onto the roads in winter?

Salt can also be mined by **solution mining**. This is shown in the diagram in Fig 1. A hole is drilled down to the rock salt. Cold water is pumped down the hole. The salt **dissolves**. The salt **solution** is pumped back to the surface. The salt solution is called **brine**.

3 Why can salt be mined in this way but coal cannot?

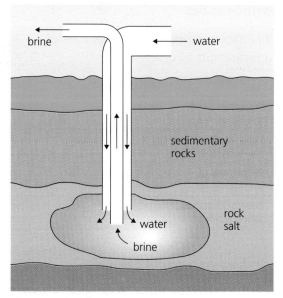

▲ **Fig 1** Solution mining

Making pure salt

Pure salt costs at least seven times as much as **impure** salt. How are pure salt and impure salt different? The extra cost is the cost of purifying the salt by removing **impurities**.

Pure salt can be made from rock salt in four steps. These are shown in Fig 2.

4 Choose the best word for each of the steps in Fig 2 from this list

dissolving   evaporating
filtering   grinding

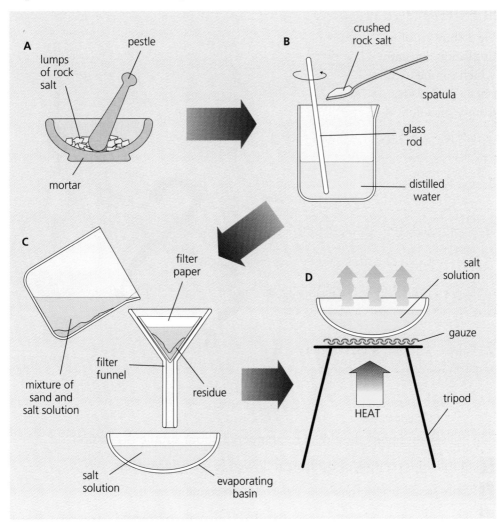

▲ **Fig 2** Purification of rock salt

Words you should know

**brine   dissolve   evaporate   filter   grind   impure   impurity
pure   rock salt   sodium chloride   solution mining**

51 Separating mixtures – 2

In this unit you will learn the answers to these questions:
- What is distillation?
- What are miscible and immiscible liquids?
- How would you separate immiscible liquids?

Separating a liquid from a solid

Water can be obtained from a solution of a solid in water
by **distillation**.

Fig 1 shows a simple
distillation apparatus
which can be used to
obtain pure water
from a salt solution.

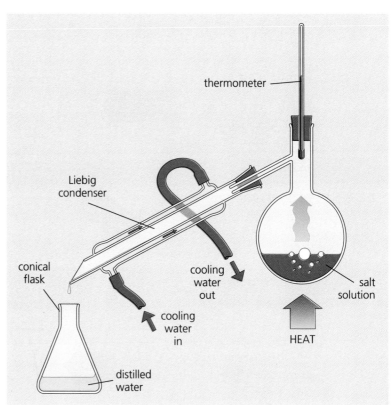

▶ *Fig 1 Distillation apparatus*

The following points should be remembered about simple distillation.

1. Distillation consists of **boiling** followed by **condensation**.

2. Only steam leaves the flask. The solid salt remains in the flask.

3. The bulb of the thermometer should be alongside the exit
to the condenser. The maximum temperature on the
thermometer during the experiment should be 100°C – the
boiling point of water.

4. The condenser is used for the efficient condensation of the steam.
The cooling water should enter at the bottom of the condenser
and leave at the top. The condenser must slope downward.

Separating mixtures of liquids

When two liquids are poured into the same container they may:

1 not mix but form two separate layers,

2 mix completely and form a single layer.

When the two liquids form separate layers they are said to be **immiscible** and when they mix completely and form a single layer they are said to be **miscible**.

An example of two immiscible liquids is glycerol and water. The table gives the densities of these two immiscible liquids.

Liquid	Density in g/cm³
water	1.00
glycerol	1.26

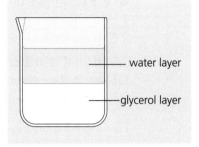

▲ *Fig 2 Glycerol and water*

Fig 2 shows the two liquids, glycerol and water, in a beaker. There are two layers with glycerol, the denser liquid, forming the lower layer. Immiscible liquids are best separated with a separating funnel (see Fig 3).

Miscible liquids can be separated by **fractional distillation** (see Unit 52).

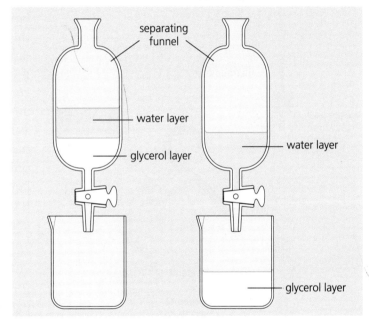

▶ *Fig 3 Separating liquids with a separating funnel*

1 Put the six statements below into the correct order so that they describe the method used to separate glycerol and water.

    A Put a second beaker under the separating funnel.

    B Put the mixture of water and glycerol into a separating funnel.

    C Leave the liquids to settle out into two layers.

    D Open the tap and allow the water to run into a beaker.

    E Remove the stopper from the separating funnel.

    F Open the tap and allow the glycerol to run into a beaker.

Words you should know

boiling   condensation   distillation   immiscible   miscible

52 Separating mixtures – 3

In this unit you will learn the answers to these questions:
- What is fractional distillation?
- What do petrol and whisky have in common?

Fractional distillation

Fractional distillation can be used to separate two or more liquids that have *different boiling points*. For example, hexane (boiling point 69°C) and methylbenzene (boiling point 111°C) can be separated by fractional distillation.

The apparatus in Fig 1 can be used for fractional distillation. The mixture to be separated is placed in the flask. The flask is then slowly heated with receiver 1 in place. The hexane, with the lower boiling point, starts to boil first and the vapour passes up the fractional distillation column. Any methylbenzene that vaporises condenses in the column and the liquid drops back into the flask. While the temperature on the thermometer remains below 69°C only the hexane distils over. The liquid collected in the first receiver is called the **first fraction**. It consists almost entirely of hexane.

When the temperature reaches 70°C, receiver 2 is put in place. It is removed when the temperature rises to 110°C. The second fraction (liquid boiling between 70°C and 111°C) is collected. Receiver 3 is then put in place and a third fraction (liquid boiling above 111°C) is collected. This consists largely of methylbenzene.

Fractional distillation is used in the refining of crude oil (Unit 57).

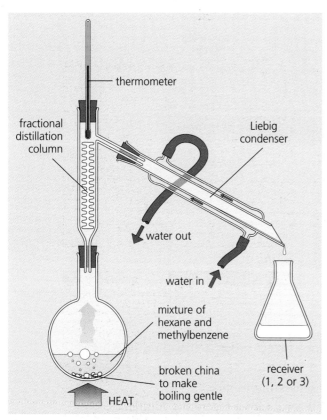

- thermometer
- fractional distillation column
- Liebig condenser
- water out
- water in
- mixture of hexane and methylbenzene
- broken china to make boiling gentle
- receiver (1, 2 or 3)
- HEAT

▲ *Fig 1* Fractional distillation

1 What is fractional distillation?

Whisky production

Whisky is a spirit produced by the fractional distillation of a mixture of ethanol (boiling point 78°C) and water (boiling point 100°C).

These are the main stages of production:

Malting Barley seeds are soaked in water and kept warm. They germinate and their starch is changed to sugar (malt). These seeds are dried in a peat fired oven. This gives whisky its flavour and stops seed growth. The barley (malt) is crushed into a powder.

Mashing Warm water is added to the powder. A sugary solution called 'wort' is produced.

Fermentation Yeast is added to the wort, and the sugar is changed to ethanol (an alcohol).

Distillation The mixture of ethanol and water is distilled twice in copper distillation vessels called stills. The stills are usually heated by steam-filled pipes.

Maturation The concentrated ethanol solution is stored in oak casks and absorbs colouring and flavour. Years later whisky is formed in the casks.

Mashing

Fermentation

2 During the fermentation froth is seen. What is produced to cause this froth?

Maturation

Words you should know

fermentation   fraction   fractional distillation

53 Separating mixtures – 4

In this unit you will learn the answers to these questions:
- What is chromatography?
- How can chromatography be used to identify substances present in a mixture?

Chromatography

Mixtures of substances dissolved in a solvent can be separated by chromatography.

Paper chromatography

Red ink contains dyes. They can be separated by **paper chromatography**. A spot of red ink is dropped onto the centre of the filter paper (Fig 1a), and left to dry. A teat pipette is used to add *one* water drop to the centre of the ink spot. If this is repeated slowly several times the ink blot gets larger. The different dyes in the ink spread out at different rates. Fig 1b shows the final result.

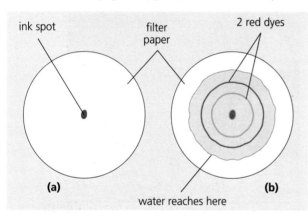

(a) **(b)**

◀ *Fig 1 Simple paper chromatography with red ink*

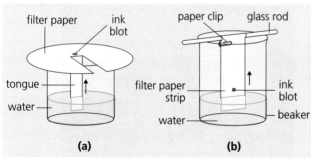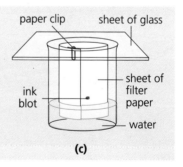

(a) **(b)** **(c)**

▲ *Fig 2 Three ways of carrying out paper chromatography*

Fig 2 shows three other ways of carrying out **paper chromatography**. In (a) the water rises up the tongue to the ink spot. The ink blot spreads out as before. In (b) and (c) the water rises upwards. The dyes separate to form spots of colour on the filter paper. This is called ascending paper chromatography. The strip of filter paper is called a **chromatogram**.

Identifying the dyes present in a sample

Fig 3 shows a chromatogram for a blue ink and also for three separate pure dyes – a pale blue dye, a dark blue dye and a purple dye. From these results we can conclude that:

1 the pale blue, dark blue and purple dyes are not split up as they each produce only a single spot on the chromatogram;

2 the blue ink is made up from a mixture of pale blue and purple dyes. The chromatogram for the blue ink shows two spots in the same positions on the chromatogram as the spots for pale blue and purple dyes.

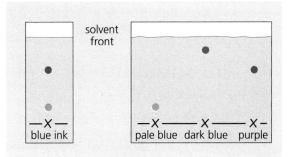

▲ **Fig 3** Paper chromatography of blue ink and three dyes

1 What colour dyes did the blue felt tip pen contain?

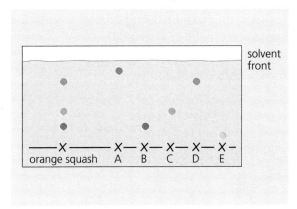

▲ **Fig 4** Chromatography of orange squash

2 Fig 4 shows a chromatogram of the colours present in orange squash and of five food dyes. Which dyes are present in the orange squash?

3 Ball point pen ink is insoluble in water, but it is soluble in ethanol. Draw and label a diagram like Fig 2b to show how you could investigate the dyes it contains.

Uses of paper chromatography

Paper chromatography is used to identify the colouring in coloured solutions, e.g. squashes, felt pens.

Words you should know

chromatogram   dyes   paper chromatography

54 Solubility

In this unit you will learn the answers to these questions:
- ■ What is solubility?
- ■ How does the solubility of a solute vary with temperature?
- ■ What is a solubility curve?

Water is a good **solvent** It dissolves a wide range of substances (called **solutes**). Some solutes dissolve more than others.

> **The solubility of a solute is the mass of the solute that dissolves in 100 g of solvent at a particular temperature.**

The solubility of sodium chloride

Fig 1 shows how to find the solubility of sodium chloride (salt) in water *at room temperature.*

A beaker is half filled with water at room temperature. Sodium chloride is added to the water in small portions. After each addition, the solution is stirred. Sodium chloride is added until no more sodium chloride will dissolve and some remains undissolved. This is called a **saturated solution**. A dry evaporating basin is weighed and some of the saturated solution, without sodium chloride crystals, is poured into the evaporating basin, which is then weighed again. The solution is carefully evaporated to dryness. After cooling the evaporating basin is weighed again.

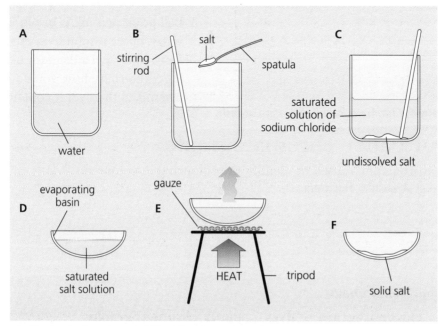

▲ **Fig 1** *Finding the solubility of sodium chloride in water*

Sample results:

1 Mass of evaporating basin   = 50.25 g
2 Mass of evaporating basin + sodium chloride solution = 118.25 g
3 Mass of evaporating basin + solid sodium chloride   = 68.25 g

From these results:

Mass of sodium chloride solution = 2 − 1 = 118.25 g − 50.25 g = 68.00 g

Mass of solid sodium chloride   = 3 − 1 = 68.25 g − 50.25 g = 18.00 g

Mass of water in solution   = 3 − 2 = 118.25 g − 68.25 g = 50.00 g

18.00 g of sodium chloride dissolved in 50.00 g of water at room temperature. 36.00 g (twice as much) sodium chloride would dissolve in 100.00 g (twice as much) water at the same temperature. This is the solubility of salt. It can be calculated as $^{18}/_{50} \times 100$ g of sodium chloride in 100 g of water.

Solubility curves

The experiment could be repeated at different temperatures. We could find out how the solubility of a solute changes with temperature. The results could be plotted on a graph as shown in Fig 2. The graph is called a **solubility curve**.

Fig 2 shows that the solubility of potassium chlorate increases as the temperature gets higher. This is true for most solutes in water.

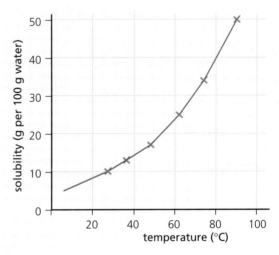

▲ **Fig 2** Solubility curve of potassium chlorate in water

1 What is the solubility of potassium chlorate in water at 20°C?

2 What is the solubility of potassium chlorate in water at 80°C?

3 What mass of potassium chlorate would dissolve in 50 g of water at 40°C?

Words you should know
saturated solution   solubility   solubility curve   solute   solvent

55 Change

In this unit you will learn the answers to these questions:
- ■ What are temporary (physical) and permanent (chemical) changes?
- ■ How does the mass change during a chemical reaction?
- ■ What are the three types of decomposition?

Physical and chemical change

Fig 1 shows two changes taking place. In *a)* a block of ice is melting to form a pool of water. This is a **temporary** or **physical** change. No chemical reaction has taken place. It is easy to reverse by putting the water back in the freezer. In *b)* wood is burning. This is a **permanent** or chemical change. There is an energy change with energy being lost to the surroundings. It is impossible to get the wood back from the ashes.

 a)

Block of ice melting

 **b)**

Wood burning

◀ **Fig 1**

Physical and chemical changes

Burning magnesium in oxygen is another permanent change. There is an increase in mass when magnesium burns.

0.24 g magnesium before burning

0.40 g residue after burning

However, this is not the whole story. The increase in mass is due to the oxygen which has combined with the magnesium. The sum of the mass of magnesium and the mass of oxygen is equal to the mass of magnesium oxide formed. This is true in all chemical reactions.

> **The sum of the masses of the reacting substances = the sum of the masses of the substances produced.**

Which of the following changes are physical (no chemical reaction taking place) or are chemical (chemical reaction taking place)?

1. A mixture of hydrogen and oxygen explodes.

2. Sugar is added to water and the mixture is stirred.

3. Water in a kettle is boiled and turned to steam.

4. A sparkler firework is lit.

5. A piece of iron rusts.

6. A sample of flour is sieved to remove lumps.

7. A cake mixture is cooked to produce a sponge cake.

8. Copy and complete the following:
   A physical or _____ change is one where _____ chemical _____ has taken place. A _____ change is one that cannot easily be _____.

Decomposition

Decomposition is the breaking down of a substance into simpler substances. There are three types of decomposition.

1. **Thermal decomposition.** A substance is split up by heating, e.g. mercury oxide is split up on heating into mercury and oxygen (Fig 2).

2. **Catalytic decomposition.** A substance is split up with the help of a catalyst, e.g. hydrogen peroxide is split into water and oxygen by manganese(IV) oxide.

3. **Electrolytic decomposition.** A substance, which is molten or dissolved in water, is split up by an electric current, e.g. molten lead bromide is split into lead and bromine (Fig 3).

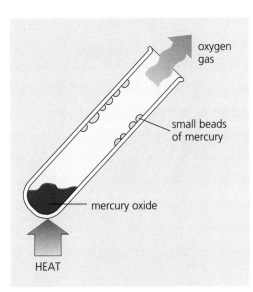

▲ **Fig 2** *Thermal decomposition: heating mercury oxide splits mercury oxide into mercury and oxygen*

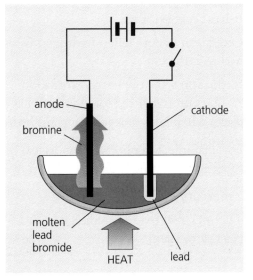

▲ **Fig 3** *Electrolysis: molten lead bromide is split up into lead and bromine by electrolysis*

9 Copy and complete the following:
The splitting of a substance into simpler products is called _____ . This can be carried out by heating , using a _____ or by electrolysis.

Words you should know

chemical change   decomposition   physical change

56 Oxidation and Reduction

In this unit you will learn the answers to these questions:
- What is meant by the words oxidation and reduction?
- What are redox reactions?

Oxidation and reduction

A substance which combines with oxygen is said to be **oxidised**. The process is called **oxidation**. Any burning or combustion process is oxidation.

When a piece of magnesium is burned in oxygen, white magnesium oxide is formed.

magnesium + oxygen ➡ magnesium oxide

Magnesium has gained oxygen.
It has been oxidised.

Oxidation occurs when hydrogen is lost in a reaction.

Reduction is the opposite of oxidation.
A substance is reduced (or reduction has taken place) when it loses oxygen or gains hydrogen.

For example, Joseph Priestley discovered oxygen by heating mercury oxide.

mercury oxide ➡ mercury + oxygen

The mercury oxide is reduced because it has lost oxygen.

▶ **Fig 1** Joseph Priestley

When chlorine reacts with hydrogen, hydrogen chloride is formed.

hydrogen + chlorine ➡ hydrogen chloride

The chlorine has gained hydrogen and has been reduced.

1 Name an element which may added when a substance is oxidised.

2 Name an element which may be removed when a substance is reduced.

3 Margarine is formed when fats and oils are reacted with hydrogen. Are the fats oxidised or reduced when they are made into margarine?

Redox reactions

Oxidation and reduction reactions occur together. When one substance loses oxygen, another gains it. A reaction where both oxidation and reduction occur is called a **redox reaction.**

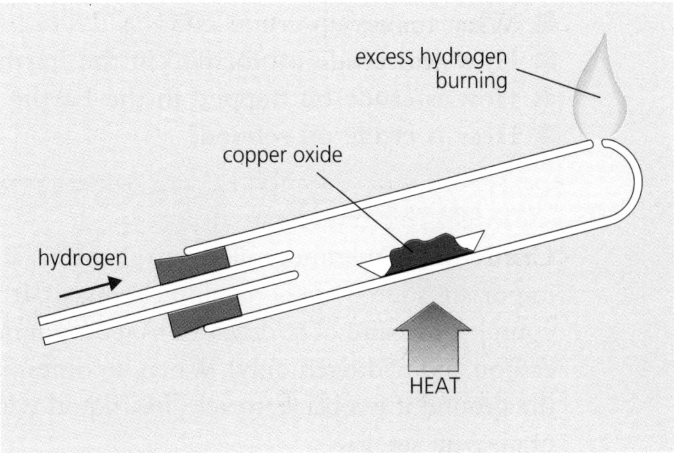

▲ **Fig 2** *Reducing copper oxide*

For example Fig 2 shows an experiment where copper oxide is turned to copper. The copper is heated in hydrogen gas.

The equation for the reaction is:

copper oxide + hydrogen ➡ copper + hydrogen oxide (water)

4 Which substance has been oxidised and which substance has been reduced?

The reduction of copper oxide does not take place on its own. Hydrogen must be there if reduction is to take place, Hydrogen is called the **reducing agent.** The change from hydrogen to hydrogen oxide uses oxygen from the copper oxide. Copper oxide is the **oxidising agent.** The overall reaction is called a **redox reaction**

Metal extraction reactions are redox reactions.

5 In Unit 61, the Thermit reaction is summarised by the equation

aluminium + iron(III) oxide ➡ aluminium oxide + iron

In this reaction, **a)** which substance is oxidised?
b) which substance is reduced?
c) which substance is the reducing agent?
d) which substance is the oxidising agent?

Words you should know

**oxidation   oxidising agent   redox reaction
reducing agent   reduction**

57 Crude oil and its refining

In this unit you will learn the answers to these questions:
- What makes up crude oil?
- How was crude oil formed in the Earth?
- How is crude oil trapped in the Earth?
- How is crude oil refined?

What is crude oil?

Crude oil (sometimes called petroleum) is an important source of energy and chemicals. It is a complex mixture of hydrocarbons (compounds of carbon and hydrogen only). When it comes out of the ground it is a black, treacle-like liquid with an unpleasant smell.

1 Which two elements are combined in the compounds which make up crude oil?

How crude oil was formed

Crude oil was formed in the Earth millions of years ago. A large area of the Earth was covered with sea and the sea contained tiny sea creatures called **plankton**.

When these creatures died they sank to the sea bed and were mixed with mud. Over millions of years this layer was compressed by the rocks above and partial decomposition of the remains produced crude oil and the natural gas found with it.

▲ *Fig 1* Marine plankton magnified

The layers of sedimentary rocks bent and deposits of crude oil became trapped between layers of **impermeable rocks**. The crude oil remained trapped until oil explorers drilled down to the deposits. Then the crude oil is forced to the surface under pressure with the natural gas. Fig 2 summarises the processes which produce crude oil.

Refining of crude oil

Crude oil is separated into useful fractions by **fractional distillation** (Unit 52). The fractional distillation separates the crude oil into different fractions. Each fraction has a range of boiling points and contains all of the carbon compounds boiling within the temperature range.

▶ *Fig 2* Processes which produce crude oil

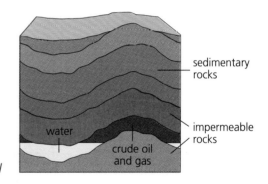

sedimentary rocks

impermeable rocks

water

crude oil and gas

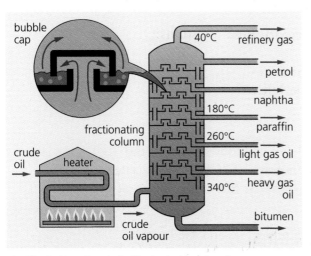

▲ Fig 3 *Fractional distillation of crude oil*

The crude oil is heated in a furnace and the vapour is passed into the bottom of the fractionating column (Fig 3). The hot vapours pass up the column. When each fraction reaches the tray where the temperature is just below its own boiling point it condenses and changes back into a liquid. In this way the different fractions are separated and drawn off separately.

The fractions which come off from the top of the column are called **light fractions**. They have low boiling points and are clear, light-coloured, runny liquids which burn readily. Those that condense near the bottom of the column are **heavy fractions**. They are darker in colour, viscous (thick and difficult to pour) and catch alight less easily.

2 How do we know that crude oil is a mixture of substances rather than one pure substance?

The table contains the properties and uses of the fractions produced by the fractional distillation of crude oil.

The fractions produced contain hydrocarbons called **alkanes**. Alkanes all fit a general formula C_nH_{2n+2}, e.g hexane is C_6H_{14}. The light fractions contain small alkane molecules and heavy fractions contain large alkane molecules.

3 Which fraction boils off first?

4 Write down four properties of the petrol fraction.

Fraction	Boiling point range/°C	Number of carbon atoms in molecules	Uses
refinery gas	up to 40	1 – 4	gases for gas cookers, liquified petroleum gas (LPG)
petrol	40 – 140	5 – 10	fuel for vehicles, chemicals
naphtha	140 – 180	8 – 12	raw material for chemicals and plastics
paraffin	180 – 250	10 – 16	aircraft fuel, heating and raw material for chemicals
light gas oil	250 – 300	14 – 20	fuel for trains and lorries, raw materials for chemicals, plastics
heavy gas oil	300 – 340	20 – 30	fuel for ships, factories, central heating
bitumen	above 340	more than 25	for roads and roofing

Words you should know

alkane   crude oil   fraction   impermeable rocks   plankton

115

58 Uses of Alkanes

In this unit you will learn the answers to these questions:
- What are alkanes?
- Why do alkanes make good fuels?
- What is produced when an alkane burns?

Alkanes

Fractional distillation of crude oil produces fractions with differing boiling points (Unit 52). Each fraction consists of hydrocarbons called **alkanes.** The table gives information about the first six members of the alkane family.

The light fractions contain small alkane molecules and the heavy fractions contain large alkane molecules.

Alkanes are called **saturated hydrocarbons** because all of the links between carbon atoms are single bonds.

Alkane	Formula	Structure	Melting point/°C	Boiling point/°C	State at room temperature and pressure
methane	CH_4		−182	−161	gas
ethane	C_2H_6		−183	−89	gas
propane	C_3H_8		−188	−42	gas
butane	C_4H_{10}		−138	0	gas
pentane	C_5H_{12}		−130	36	liquid
hexane	C_6H_{14}		−95	68	liquid

1 Write down the formula of the alkane containing seven carbon atoms.

2 Write down the names of the four alkanes which might be in the refinery gas which leaves the fractional distillation column.

Reactions of hydrocarbons

The hydrocarbons called alkanes are fairly unreactive. Petrol, for example, does not react with sulphuric acid (an acid), sodium hydroxide (an alkali), sodium (metal and strong reducing agent) or potassium manganate(VII) (strong oxidising agent). However, alkanes do burn well to produce energy. These are exothermic reactions. Most of the uses of alkanes rely on these reactions. Fig 1 shows a pie diagram which shows the uses of the alkanes made from crude oil.

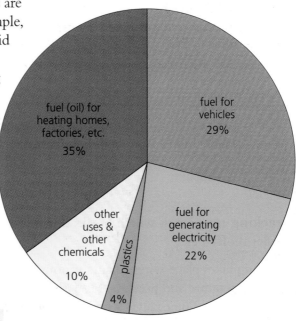

▲ **Fig 1** *A pie diagram showing the uses of crude oil*

3 What percentage of crude oil is used for fuel?

Burning or **combustion** of hydrocarbons, including alkanes, requires oxygen from the air. Providing there is a *plentiful* supply of oxygen, the products are water vapour and carbon dioxide.

If hydrocarbons, including alkanes, burn in a *limited* supply of oxygen, water vapour is still produced but the poisonous gas carbon monoxide, CO, can be produced.

4 Finish these word equations for the burning of methane:

plentiful supply of air   methane + oxygen ➡ _____ + _____
limited supply of air   methane + oxygen ➡ _____ + _____

Every year people die of carbon monoxide poisoning because gas fires and boilers are not properly adjusted. It is important that there is enough oxygen to completely burn the gas.

Words you should know
combustion   **fuel**   **saturated hydrocarbon**

59 Cracking hydrocarbons

In this unit you will learn the answers to these questions:
- What is cracking?
- What products are formed by cracking alkanes?
- How do you test for unsaturated compounds?
- What are alkenes?

Cracking alkanes

Alkanes are **saturated** hydrocarbons. They contain only single carbon–carbon and carbon–hydrogen bonds.

E.g. propane

Cracking is a process which breaks down long-chain alkanes into smaller molecules.

Cracking takes place when alkane vapour is passed over a catalyst at high temperature and pressure. Fig 1 shows how cracking is carried out in industry. The catalyst which is used becomes spent and has to be treated before reuse.

It is also possible to change the shape of hydrocarbon molecules by processes of **reforming**.

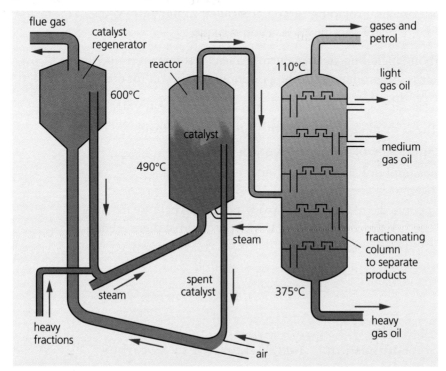

▲ **Fig 1** Industrial cracking process

Cracking liquid paraffin in the laboratory

Liquid paraffin is a mixture of alkanes with about 12 carbon atoms. If liquid paraffin vapour is passed over strongly heated broken china, the vapour is cracked to produce a colourless gas. This is insoluble in water and can be collected over water. The apparatus in Fig 2 can be used for cracking liquid paraffin vapour.

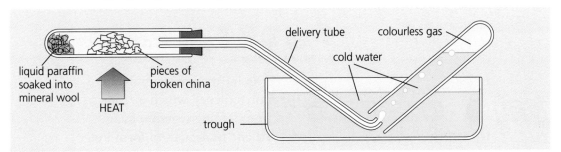

▲ **Fig 2** *Cracking liquid paraffin vapour*

The table summarises the properties of liquid paraffin and the gas which is produced by cracking liquid paraffin.

Property	Liquid paraffin	Gas produced by cracking liquid paraffin
colour	colourless	colourless
state	liquid	gas
smell	no smell	sweet smell
flammable	burns well after heating	burns well with a yellow flame
test with bromine	red colour remains	turns colourless

The colourless gas collected is an alkene called ethene.

The structure of ethene is

Alkenes can be distinguished from alkanes by the reaction with bromine. Bromine is red in colour. When it reacts with ethene it produces a colourless product called 1,2-dibromoethane. The solution is therefore decolorised.

Alkanes contain only single bonds and do not decolorise bromine.

1 An oily liquid collects on the surface of the water in the trough. What is this liquid and how is it formed?

2 During the experiment water from the trough sometimes enters the delivery tube. Why does this happen?

Words you should know

catalyst   cracking   reforming

60 Polymerisation

In this unit you will learn the answers to these questions:
■ What are polymers and how are they made?
■ What are polymers used for?

Materials we commonly call plastics are more correctly called **polymers**. They are made by a process of **polymerisation** by joining together small molecules called **monomers**. The process is summarised by:

monomer molecules   polymer

The most common polymer is poly(ethene), which is made from joining together many ethene molecules to form long poly(ethene) chains.

You will notice that the monomer molecules contain a carbon–carbon double bond but the polymer does **not** contain double bonds.

The conditions used to produce poly(ethene) can vary and the properties of the final polymer will depend upon the reaction conditions.

1 If ethene is heated at high temperatures and high pressures in the presence of a catalyst, **low density poly(ethene)** is produced.

2 If ethene is bubbled through an organic solvent containing complex catalysts, **high density poly(ethene)** is formed.

Both contain poly(ethene) chains.

1 In which form of poly(ethene) are the chains more closely packed together?

2 The average relative molecular mass of a poly(ethene) chain is 140 000.
The relative molecular mass of an ethene molecule is 28.
How many ethene molecules are there in an average poly(ethene) chain?

◀ **Fig 1** Many parts of a car are now made from polymers

3 Write down six items in a car made from polymers. For each item write down why a polymer is better than other available materials.

Polymers made from crude oil

The process of cracking (Unit 59) produces alkenes from long-chain alkanes. These alkenes can be used to make a wide range of polymers. The table gives information about some common polymers.

Polymer	Structure of polymer	Monomer	Uses of polymer
poly(styrene) or poly(phenylethene)	$\left[\begin{array}{c} C_6H_5 \quad H \\ -C-C- \\ H \quad H \end{array}\right]_n$	styrene or phenylethene $C_6H_5 \quad H \\ C=C \\ H \quad H$	flowerpots, yoghurt cartons, plastic model kits, ceiling tiles
poly(vinyl chloride) or PVC or poly(chloroethene)	$\left[\begin{array}{c} Cl \quad H \\ -C-C- \\ H \quad H \end{array}\right]_n$	vinyl chloride or chloroethene $Cl \quad H \\ C=C \\ H \quad H$	artificial leather for furniture, luggage cases, clothes
poly(tetrafluoro-ethene) or PTFE	$\left[\begin{array}{c} F \quad F \\ -C-C- \\ F \quad F \end{array}\right]_n$	tetrafluoroethene $F \quad F \\ C=C \\ F \quad F$	non-stick coatings in saucepans

4 Propene, C_3H_6, has of a structure of Draw the structure of part a poly(propene) chain.

Uses of polymers

Polymers have become increasingly useful in recent years for several reasons.

1 There is a wider range of different polymers around now and each polymer has its own properties.

2 Traditional materials such as wood and metals have become less available and more expensive.

3 Polymers have much lower densities than metals.

4 The reactivity of polymers is very low and so, unlike metals, there are no corrosion problems.

Words you should know

monomer **polymer** **polymerisation**

61 Reactivity series

In this unit you will learn the answers to these questions:
- How do different metals react with air, water and dilute hydrochloric acid?
- How can metals be arranged in order of reactivity using reactions with air, water and dilute acid?
- What are displacement reactions and when do they take place?

Reactions of metals

Metal	Reaction with air	Reaction with water	Reaction with dilute hydrochloric acid
potassium	burn in air or oxygen to form an oxide	reacts violently with cold water to produce hydrogen; hydrogen burns with a lilac flame	violent reaction to produce hydrogen (dangerous)
sodium		reacts quickly with cold water to produce hydrogen; hydrogen does not ignite	
calcium		reacts slowly with cold water to produce hydrogen	
magnesium		reacts very slowly with cold water; violent reaction with steam	react with acid to produce a metal chloride and hydrogen; react more slowly down list
zinc		reacts fairly quickly with steam	
iron		reacts only reversibly with steam	
lead	converted to the oxide by heating in air or oxygen but do not burn	no reaction with water	exceedingly slow reaction to produce hydrogen
copper			hydrogen not produced; no reaction with dilute hydrochloric acid
silver	not affected by air or oxygen		

There is a wide variety in the way metals react with air, water and dilute hydrochloric acid. The table compares the reactivity of some metals.

In the table the metals have been arranged in order of reactivity. The most reactive metals are at the top of the list and the least reactive metals at the bottom. This order of metals is called the **reactivity series**. Other metals can be included in the series, as shown here. This reactivity series can be used to explain many reactions which take place.

most reactive
potassium
sodium
calcium
magnesium
aluminium
zinc
iron
lead
copper
silver
gold
least reactive

Displacement reactions of metals

A **displacement reaction** is a reaction where one metal replaces another during a chemical reaction. For example, if an iron nail is put into blue copper(II) sulphate solution, a displacement reaction takes place.

iron + copper(II) sulphate ⟹ iron(II) sulphate + copper

The blue colour of copper(II) sulphate solution fades and a brown deposit of copper forms on the nail. The reaction takes place because iron is more reactive than copper. Iron is higher in the reactivity series than copper.

No reaction takes place when zinc is added to magnesium sulphate. Zinc is less reactive than magnesium (zinc is below magnesium in the reactivity series).

1 Write a word equation for the reaction which takes place when zinc is added to silver nitrate solution.

Displacement reactions can take place when a metal is added to an aqueous solution of a metal compound. They can also take place when a mixture of a powdered metal and a powdered metal oxide is heated.

One industrial application of a displacement reaction is the **Thermit reaction** used to weld lengths of railway track together (Fig 1). If a mixture of aluminium powder and iron(III) oxide is heated, a very violent reaction takes place. Aluminium, being more reactive than iron, replaces iron in iron(III) oxide.

▲ **Fig 1** A Thermit reaction used to weld rail tracks

2 Suggest a metal which could be used instead of aluminium for this reaction.

aluminium + iron(III) oxide ⟹ aluminium oxide + iron

Words you should know
displacement reaction   **reactivity series**   **Thermit reaction**

62 Extraction of metals – 1

In this unit you will learn the answers to these questions:
- How do metals exist in the Earth?
- How can aluminium be extracted from its ore?

The method of extraction of a metal depends on the position of the metal in the reactivity series. Metals at the top of the reactivity series form stable compounds and require electrolysis to extract them. Metals in the middle of the reactivity series are extracted by reduction, often with carbon. Metals at the bottom of the reactivity series are usually extracted by heating alone.

Metal ores

Few metals are found uncombined in the Earth. Most metals are usually present in the Earth as **ores**. An ore is a rock containing a mixture of substances including a compound of the metal that is to be extracted. The aluminium ore **bauxite**, for example, consists of about 40% aluminium oxide (a compound of aluminium and oxygen) with iron oxide, sand and titanium dioxide.

The table gives the names and chemical constituents of common ores.

Metal	Common ore	Chief chemical constituent of ore
potassium	carnallite	potassium magnesium chloride
sodium	rock salt	sodium chloride
calcium	limestone	calcium carbonate
magnesium	carnallite dolomite	potassium magnesium chloride magnesium calcium carbonate
aluminium	bauxite	aluminium oxide
zinc	zinc blende	zinc sulphide
iron	haematite	iron(III) oxide
lead	galena	lead sulphide
copper	copper pyrites	copper sulphide and iron sulphide
mercury	cinnabar	mercury sulphide

1 Is there any link between the position of a metal in the reactivity series and the type of compound present in the ore - chloride, carbonate, sulphide?

2 It has been estimated that one cubic mile of sea water contains £100 000 000 worth of gold. Why can't gold be extracted economically from sea water?

Extraction of aluminium

Although aluminium is present in small quantities in almost every handful of soil, it is extracted from bauxite.

Bauxite is found mainly in tropical and subtropical parts of the world – Australia, Guinea, Jamaica, Indonesia, India and Brazil.

3 Why is it not economic to use soil? The soil would not have to be transported.

4 How is the bauxite obtained from the ground?

Removing the ore in this way leaves ugly scars on the landscape (Fig 1).

Bauxite is purified at the mining site. During the purification, the ore is treated with strong alkali. The main impurity is red iron oxide. This forms a red mud which is pumped into huge ponds and left. These also spoil the landscape.

▲ **Fig 1** *Open cast mining of bauxite in Australia*

The extraction of aluminium is carried out by electrolysis of molten aluminium oxide dissolved in molten **cryolite**. Electrolysis takes place in carbon-lined steel tanks (pots). The carbon lining acts as a cathode and carbon anodes are used (Fig 2).

5 What are the advantages of purifying the bauxite and producing pure aluminium oxide at the mining site?

The products of electrolysis are aluminium (produced at the cathode) and oxygen (produced at the anode).

cathode   aluminium ions + electrons   ➡   aluminium atoms

anode   oxide ions   ➡   oxygen molecules + electrons

The aluminium collects at the bottom of the pot and can be removed. The carbon anodes burn in the oxygen produced and have to be replaced from time to time. The exhaust gases from the pots are bubbled through water to remove soluble gases.

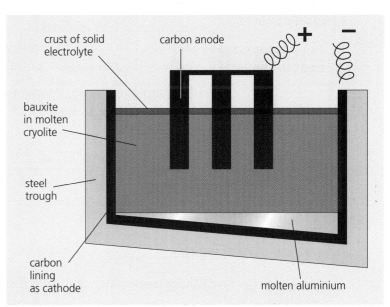

▶ **Fig 2**
Extraction of aluminium

crust of solid electrolyte

carbon anode

bauxite in molten cryolite

steel trough

carbon lining as cathode

molten aluminium

Words you should know

     anode   **bauxite**   **cathode**   **cryolite**   **ore**

63 Extraction of metals – 2

In this unit you will learn the answers to these questions:
- How is iron extracted from iron ore?
- How is steel produced from iron?
- How is copper purified by electrolysis?

Extraction of iron

An ore containing a large amount of iron (called a 'rich' ore) is **haematite**. This is often mixed with 'poorer' ores for extraction.

Iron is produced in a **blast furnace** (Fig 1). A furnace is about 70 metres high, made of steel and lined with fireproof bricks. The raw materials are **iron ore**, **coke** (carbon) and **limestone**. They are loaded from time to time through the top of the furnace.

Hot air is blown into the base of the furnace through a series of pipes called **tuyères**. Burning the coke produces sufficient heat to raise the temperature inside the furnace to 1900°C, sufficient to melt the contents of the furnace. Carbon monoxide is produced in the furnace. This acts as the reducing agent which reduces the iron oxide to iron.

The limestone (calcium carbonate) added to the furnace removes the impurities, especially the sand, forming **slag** – calcium silicate.

The hot waste gases escaping from the blast furnace contain carbon monoxide.

The main reactions in the blast furnace are:

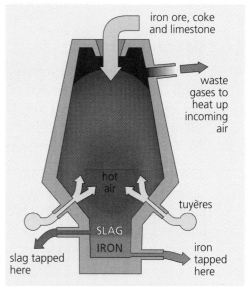

▲ *Fig 1* Extraction of iron in a blast furnace

1 What are the three solid materials added to the blast furnace?

2 What is the reducing agent in the furnace?

3 What can the waste gases be used for?

4 What are the two liquids tapped off the furnace?

carbon + oxygen ➡ carbon dioxide

calcium carbonate ➡ calcium oxide + carbon dioxide

carbon dioxide + carbon ➡ carbon monoxide

iron(III) oxide + carbon monoxide ➡ iron + carbon dioxide

calcium oxide + silicon dioxide ➡ calcium silicate

5 Give two reasons why limestone is added to the blast furnace.

The iron obtained is impure, containing carbon, phosphorus and silicon. Most of the iron produced is immediately turned into steel. The steel-making furnace (Fig 2) is tilted and loaded with 30% scrap iron and 70% molten iron from the blast furnace. A water-cooled lance is lowered into the upright furnace and pure oxygen is blown, under high pressure, onto the surface of the molten iron. The oxides of carbon and phosphorus escape as gases. Limestone is added to remove other impurities as slag. Finally, any additional substances are added for the grade of steel being produced.

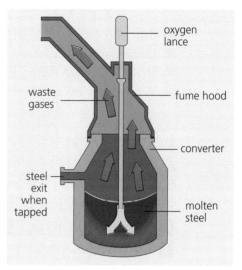

▲ **Fig 2** *Steel-making furnace*

Purification of copper by electrolysis

Copper is extracted by **reduction** from its ore. Very pure copper is required for many purposes, e.g. electrical wiring. Copper is purified by electrolysis (Fig 3) with the anode made of an impure copper plate and the cathode a pure copper plate. The electrolyte is copper(II) sulphate solution.

During the electrolysis the anode dissolves and pure copper is deposited on the cathode.

Anode copper atoms ➡ copper ions + electrons
Cathode copper ions + electrons ➡ copper atoms

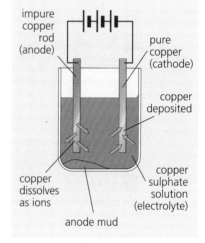

▲ **Fig 3** *Purification of copper by electrolysis*

The impurities that were in the impure plate collect at the bottom of the cell as 'anode mud'. This can be refined to produce precious metals such as silver, gold and platinum.

◀ **Fig 4** *Steel production: a worker taking the slag from a blast furnace*

Words you should know

anode   **blast furnace**   **cathode**   **haematite**   **reduction**   **slag**

64 Types of rock

In this unit you will learn the answers to these questions:
- What are sedimentary, igneous and metamorphic rocks?
- How are these different rock types formed?
- What tests do geologists use to identify minerals in rocks?

What is a rock?

A **rock** is a solid part of the Earth's crust. Some rocks are almost pure substances, but most rocks are made up of a mixture of chemicals called **minerals**. The properties of a rock will depend upon:

1 the type of minerals;   **2** the concentration of the minerals in the rock;
3 how the minerals are held together.

Identifying the minerals in rocks

A **geologist** can identify minerals in a rock by carrying out a series of tests. These include:

1 **Colour** There can be considerable variations in the colours of minerals.

2 **Streak test** The colour of the mineral in a powdered form is helpful in identification. The simplest way of doing this is a streak test where the mineral is scratched across an unglazed ceramic tile called a **streak plate**. Different materials produce different colours.

3 **Lustre** Look at the mineral – is it shiny, glassy, dull, etc.?

4 **Hardness** Hardness is measured on Moh's scale. This is a scale of hardness from 1 to 10 using certain standard materials.

5 **Density** The density can give a guide to identifying the minerals present. For example, galena (lead sulphide) has a very high density.

6 **Testing with acid** When dilute acid is added to a carbonate mineral, fizzing will be seen as carbon dioxide is produced.

7 **Crystal shape** This can also be useful in identifying minerals present in a rock.

Moh's scale	Mineral
1	talc
2	gypsum
3	calcite
4	fluorite
5	apatite
6	feldspar
7	quartz
8	topaz
9	corundum
10	diamond

Rocks can be divided into three groups according to the way they are formed. These three groups are **sedimentary rocks**, **igneous rocks** and **metamorphic rocks**.

Sedimentary rocks

A sedimentary rock is formed when a layer of mud, sand or other natural debris is compressed. This process is called **consolidation**. The sedimentary rocks are laid down in layers, called **beds**, and the joins between layers are called **bedding**

▲ **Fig 1** *A cliff of sedimentary rocks, showing the layered structure*

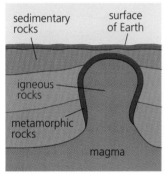

▲ **Fig 4** *An intrusion*

planes (Fig 1). New rocks are deposited on existing rocks and so the older the rocks are, the lower they are in the Earth's crust. After being deposited, these layers can tilt and twist. Examples of sedimentary rocks are shown in Fig 2.

Igneous rocks

Igneous rocks are hard rocks formed when the molten magma inside the Earth's crust crystallises. These rocks are composed of crystals of different minerals. The crystals are not packed together in any pattern. The sizes of the crystals are determined by the rate of cooling of the magma. If the crystallisation is slow, large crystals are formed, while rapid cooling produces small crystals. Examples of igneous rocks are shown in Fig 3. Magma from deep inside the Earth can push its way close to the surface. These 'upwellings' of magma are called **intrusions** (Fig 4). They cool to form igneous rocks.

Metamorphic rocks

Metamorphic rocks are also hard rocks formed when high temperatures and high pressures act on other rocks. For example, the action of high temperatures and high pressures on the sedimentary rock limestone produces marble. Around a magma intrusion, the high temperatures and high pressures cause rocks to change to metamorphic rocks.

1 Are these rocks sedimentary, metamorphic or igneous?
a) limestone **b)** granite
c) marble **d)** sandstone

2 Why are fossils not found in igneous rocks?

Fossils, the remains of plants and animals from millions of years ago (see Unit 39), are commonly found in sedimentary rocks and less commonly in metamorphic rocks. An example of a metamorphic rock is shown in Fig 5.

Words you should know
fossil igneous metamorphic mineral sedimentary rock

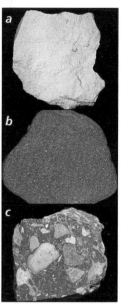

▲ **Fig 2** *Examples of sedimentary rocks*
a *limestone*
b *sandstone*
c *conglomerate*

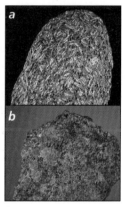

▲ **Fig 3** *Examples of igneous rocks*
a *granite* ***b*** *basalt*

▲ **Fig 5** *Example of metamorphic rock: marble*

65 Uses of rocks

In this unit you will learn the answers to these questions:
- What are natural rocks used for?
- What factory-made materials can be used as substitutes for rocks?

Stone for buildings

Fig 1 shows the two houses we used in Unit 44.

The old cottage is made of limestone blocks and part of the roof is made of slate. Limestone is a sedimentary rock and **slate** is a metamorphic rock produced by the action of high temperatures and high pressures on mud. These traditional materials have properties which make them suitable for use in house-building.

▲ *Fig 1* An old stone cottage and a modern brick house

> **1** Write down the properties of
>   **a)** limestone   **b)** slate
>   which make them suitable for house-building.

◀ *Fig 2* A slate mine in North Wales showing the slates in sheets

However, with the growth in the number of houses built in this century, these materials have become expensive and alternatives have been developed. The walls of a modern house are often made of bricks and the roof made of ceramic tiles. Both of these are made from clay and the clay is baked in an oven. The formation of bricks and tiles is like the formation of metamorphic rock. The change taking place is permanent and the resulting products are hard and brittle.

Using stone for statues

Igneous and metamorphic rocks are frequently used for statues. They are generally harder than sedimentary rocks.

Cement and concrete

Cement is a very useful material produced by heating limestone powder with clay. When water is added to cement, a chemical reaction takes place which causes the cement to harden.

Usually cement is mixed with water, sand and gravel to produce **concrete**. Concrete is a very useful building material. It is poured into moulds to produce concrete railway sleepers, beams, lamp-posts, etc. However, concrete is not a strong material unless it is reinforced. In Fig 3 it can be seen that a vertical force will cause the beam to bend and break. Reinforcing the concrete with steel rods transfers the forces sideways and makes the beam stronger.

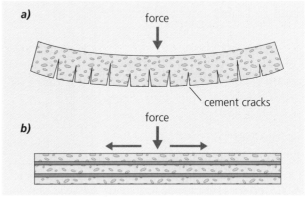

▲ **Fig 3 a)** The vertical force causes the concrete to break **b)** The reinforcing steel rods transfer the force sideways

Fig 4 shows the Library of Celsus in Ephesus, Turkey. In the rebuilding, missing parts of the structure were made using reinforced concrete mixed with chippings of marble. This gives it an appearance similar to the original marble.

2 Look for examples of rocks in use in your area.

◄ **Fig 4** The Library of Celsus in Ephesus, Turkey

Words you should know

cement   concrete   slate

66 The rock cycle

In this unit you will learn the answers to these questions:
- What is weathering or erosion of rocks?
- What is the rock cycle?

Breaking down of rocks

The rocks in the Earth's crust are constantly being broken down by **weathering** or **erosion**. These processes are caused by the action of wind and rain, water and ice.

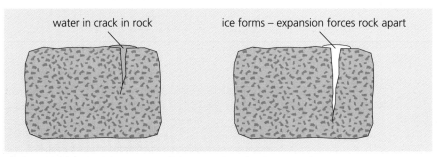

water in crack in rock

ice forms – expansion forces rock apart

▲ **Fig 1** *Repeated freezing and thawing breaks down rocks*

Rocks can be broken down by repeated freezing and thawing (Fig 1). When water freezes it expands considerably, forcing rocks apart. This process occurs over and over again, eventually breaking down the rock.

Rocks break down even in the absence of water. Rocks in a dry desert area can be broken down by the wind. The wind picks up sand particles and hurls them at exposed rocks. This natural 'sandblasting' produces more sand, which continues the process. The erosion of the Sphinx in Egypt by sand is a good example of this type of weathering (Fig 2).

▲ **Fig 2** *The Sphinx, Egypt, eroded by 'sandblasting'*

The rock fragments produced by these forms of weathering often get washed into rivers. As the fragments get carried along in rivers they become more rounded, losing sharp edges. As the speed of the river slows, the fragments drop and are deposited on the river bed. Heavy fragments drop first and fine fragments are carried further.

Conglomerate is a rock containing large fragments (see Unit 64). This will be deposited close to where the river enters the sea (Fig 3). Shale is made of very fine particles and is formed away from the entry of the river into the sea.

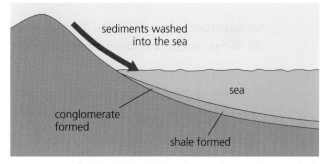

▲ **Fig 3** *Formation of conglomerate and shale*

The rock cycle

Rocks are being broken down and new rocks are being formed all the time. Molten rocks in the magma are crystallised to form igneous rocks. Weathering and erosion of rocks produces sediments which are deposited to produce sedimentary rocks. Metamorphic rocks can be produced from sedimentary rocks. Rocks returning to the magma complete the cycle. The rock cycle is summarised in Fig 4.

The rock cycle is driven by two energy processes. On the surface, processes are powered by the Sun's energy. Within the Earth, energy is provided by radioactive decay.

1 Name a sedimentary rock containing round pebbles.

2 Name a sedimentary rock made of very fine particles.

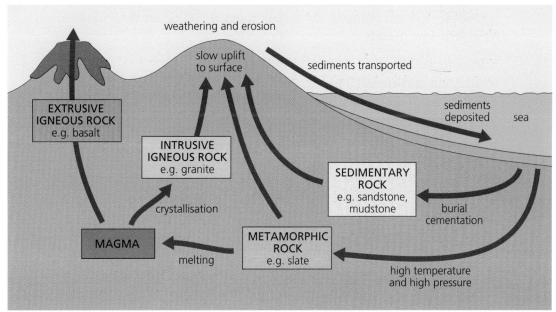

▲ **Fig 4** *The rock cycle*

Words you should know
    crystallisation   erosion   weathering

67 The Periodic Table

In this unit you will learn the answer to this question:
- ■ What is the Periodic Table?

About one hundred and fifty years ago chemists were discovering a large number of new elements. They were also able to determine atomic weights of the elements (now called atomic masses) accurately.

In 1869, the Russian chemist Dmitri Mendeléev produced a classification of the elements which has lasted in the form of the modern **Periodic Table** (page 135 opposite).

▲ **Fig 1** *Mendeléev (1834–1907)*

The modern Periodic Table is a way of classifying the elements. The elements are arranged in order of increasing **atomic number** to avoid any elements out of order when atomic masses are used. The Periodic Table can help you to make predictions about elements you have not yet met. Fig 2 shows the main parts of the Periodic Table. The **main block** of the Periodic Table consists of eight chemical families (i.e. groups I – VII and group 0). Between groups II and III are three rows of **transition metals**.

Elements are classified as metals and non-metals. The bold red line which goes down through the main block elements in steps separates metals on the left-hand side of it from non-metals on the right-hand side of it.

1 Are there more metals or more non-metals in the Periodic Table?

2 What change occurs across period 2 from lithium to neon?

3 What change occurs down group IV from carbon to lead?

4 Elements have been named after famous scientists or places. Write down three examples of each.

Words you should know

atomic number	**group**	**period**
Periodic Table	**transition metals**	

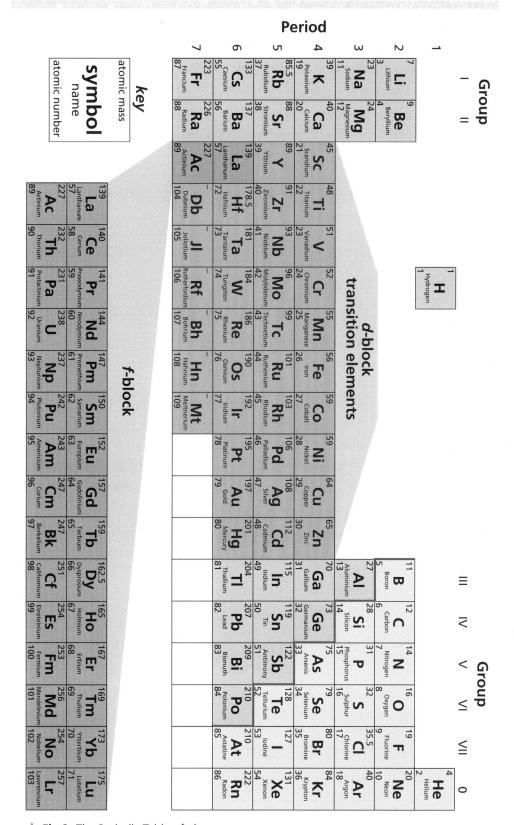

▲ **Fig 2** The Periodic Table of elements

68 The alkali metals

In this unit you will learn the answers to these questions:
- What are the alkali metals and where are they placed in the Periodic Table?
- How does the reactivity of alkali metals change down the group?

The elements in group I of the Periodic Table include lithium, sodium, potassium, rubidium and caesium. These form a family of elements called **alkali metals**. The table gives some information about these elements.

Element	Symbol	Atomic number	Melting point/°C	Boiling point/°C	Density/ g per cm³	Date of discovery
lithium	Li	3	181	1331	0.54	1817
sodium	Na	11	98	890	0.97	1807
potassium	K	19	63	766	0.86	1807
rubidium	Rb	37	39	701	1.53	1861
caesium	Cs	55	29	685	1.87	1861

There are similarities between the elements and certain trends down the group.

▲ **Fig 1** Sir Humphrey Davy (1778–1829): he discovered potassium and sodium by electrolysis

1 All of the elements are reactive metals. They are stored under paraffin oil to prevent reaction with air and water.

2 All of the elements are soft metals that can be easily cut with a knife. The softness increases down the group.

3 The melting points and boiling points decrease down the group.

4 The alkali metals are generally less strong than other metals but have better heat and electrical conductivities.

5 The densities generally increase down the group.

Because alkali metals form very stable compounds they were not discovered until the start of the 1800s. They were all discovered by the electrolysis of molten materials.

> **1** When an alkali metal is cut, a shiny surface is produced. This quickly turns dull. Suggest why this is so.

Reactions of alkali metals with oxygen (air)

All alkali metals burn in oxygen to form solid oxides. For example:

sodium + oxygen ➡ sodium oxide

The solid oxides are alkaline.

Reactions of alkali metals with cold water

All alkali metals react with cold water to form a soluble alkaline hydroxide and hydrogen gas. For example:

sodium + water ➡ sodium hydroxide + hydrogen

The table compares the reactions of some of the alkali metals with cold water.

Alkali metal	Reaction with cold water
lithium	Lithium floats on water, gently fizzing and producing a colourless gas. The gas burns with a squeaky pop (hydrogen). Remaining solution is alkaline.
sodium	Sodium floats on water, fizzing rapidly and producing a colourless gas. The gas burns with a squeaky pop (hydrogen). Remaining solution is alkaline.
potassium	Potassium floats on water, fizzing violently and producing a colourless gas. From time to time hydrogen ignites and burns with a lilac-pink flame. Remaining solution is alkaline.
rubidium	Rubidium sinks (denser than water). Very violent reaction over in a fraction of a second. Remaining solution is alkaline.

least reactive
Li
Na
K
Rb
most reactive

The metals become **more reactive** down the group.

Reactions of alkali metals with chlorine

All of the alkali metals burn in chlorine gas to form a salt. For example:

lithium + chlorine ➡ lithium chloride

sodium + chlorine ➡ sodium chloride

potassium + chlorine ➡ potassium chloride

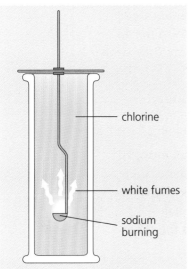

chlorine

white fumes

sodium burning

A small piece of alkali metal (sodium) is heated in the bowl of a combustion spoon until it starts to burn. The spoon is then lowered into a gas jar of chlorine (Fig 2). As the sodium continues to burn, it combines with the chlorine gas to produce white fumes of sodium chloride that settle as a solid on the cool sides of the gas jar.

◀ **Fig 2** *Apparatus to show the reaction of an alkali metal (sodium) with chlorine*

Uses of alkali metals

There are few uses of alkali metals. There are, however, many uses of alkali metal compounds. A small quantity of metallic sodium is used in sodium street lights, which have an orange colour. Sodium is used as a coolant in some nuclear power stations. It is a good conductor of heat and removes heat from the reactor.

Words you should know

alkali metal

69 Noble gases

In this unit you will learn the answer to this question:
■ What are noble gases and what are they used for?

The **noble gases** are a family of unreactive gases placed in group 0 of the Periodic Table.

These gases were not known in 1869 when Mendeléev devised the Periodic Table (Unit 67) and had to be added later. These gases occur in the atmosphere, sometimes, as in the case of argon, in fairly large amounts.

helium	He
neon	Ne
argon	Ar
krypton	Kr
xenon	Xe
radon	Rn

History of the discovery of the noble gases

▲ **Fig 1** Lord Rayleigh (1842–1919)

▲ **Fig 2** William Ramsay (1852–1916)

Have you ever found something you didn't expect?

Many of the great discoveries in Science have been made following chance experiments.

The discovery of the noble gases, at the end of the nineteenth Century, was the result of some careful experiments. The gases are all around us in the air but because of their almost total inactivity they were never noticed.

In 1894 Lord Rayleigh and William Ramsay discovered the noble gas called argon following some very careful experiments with air. They removed the oxygen, carbon dioxide and nitrogen from the air. They believed removing these three gases would leave no gas remaining. But there was and this is the gas argon. Careful fractional distillation of air led to the discovery of the other noble gases.

Reactions of noble gases

Until about forty years ago it was believed that noble gases did not react with other chemicals under any conditions. However, it is now possible to form a number of noble gas compounds. The first one, xenon tetrafluoride, XeF_4, was discovered by accident. A mixture of xenon and fluorine was passed through a heated nickel tube. When the resulting gases were cooled, white crystals of xenon tetrafluoride were formed.

1 Why is a compound between xenon and fluorine more likely than compounds between neon and fluorine or xenon and iodine?

xenon + fluorine ➡ xenon tetrafluoride

Uses of noble gases

Helium is used for filling weather balloons and airships. It is denser than hydrogen and therefore is not as good as hydrogen for lifting balloons. Its main advantage is that it is not flammable and can be used safely without fire risks.

Nitrogen dissolved in the blood under pressure can cause a severe condition called diver's bends when a diver comes back to the surface. To avoid this, nitrogen is not used in a diver's breathing apparatus. A diver's breathing apparatus contains a mixture of helium and oxygen.

▼ *Fig 3*
A helium-filled airship

Neon is used to fill light tubes for advertising signs. The tubes are filled with neon at low pressure and an electric spark is passed through the tube.

Argon and argon/nitrogen mixtures are used to fill electric light bulbs. The tungsten filament is heated by an electric current until it glows. Oxygen must not be inside the bulb or the filament will burn out.

Krypton and xenon are used in special bulbs for lighthouses and projectors.

Radon is a radioactive gas and is used in the treatment of cancers.

▲ *Fig 4* *Neon is used to fill the light tubes for advertising signs*

◀ *Fig 5* *Lighthouses use special bulbs which contain krypton and xenon*

2 Reactive metals like magnesium can be welded in an atmosphere of helium. Why is this better than welding in air?

Words you should know
noble gases

70 The halogens – 1

In this unit you will learn the answers to these questions:
- ■ What are the halogen elements and where can they be found in the Periodic Table?
- ■ How do the physical properties such as melting and boiling point change down group VII?
- ■ How does the reactivity of halogens decrease down group VII?

fluorine	F
chlorine	Cl
bromine	Br
iodine	I
astatine	At

The **halogens** are a family of reactive non-metallic elements placed in group VII of the Periodic Table.

The table contains information about some of the halogens.

Element	Atomic number	Melting point /°C	Boiling point /°C	Density at room temperature and atmospheric pressure/g per dm³	Appearance at room temperature and atmospheric pressure
fluorine F	9	−220	−188	1.58	colourless gas
chlorine Cl	17	−101	−34	2.99	greenish-yellow gas
bromine Br	35	−7	58	3.12	dark red liquid
iodine I	53	114	183	4.94	black shiny solid

Although the halogens show similarities to one another in physical and chemical properties, there is a gradual change down the group. All of the halogens have simple molecular structures with **diatomic** molecules, i.e. Cl_2, Br_2, I_2. The covalent bonds are strong but the bonds between separate molecules are weak. The molecules are therefore easily separated and so their boiling points are relatively low.

As we move down the group, the halogen molecules get heavier and larger. Therefore, from fluorine to iodine, they are gradually more difficult to melt and vaporise. This is shown by their increasing melting and boiling points.

Reactions of halogens with water

The table summarises the reactions of halogens with cold water.

Halogen	Reaction with cold water
fluorine	Violent reaction with cold water forming oxygen and hydrogen fluoride gases.
chlorine	Forms a mixture of hydrochloric acid and hypochlorous acid. The solution is strongly acidic and a strong bleach.
bromine	Forms a solution of hydrobromic acid and hypobromous acid. The solution is acidic and a bleach.
iodine	Only reacts slightly with water. Very slightly acidic and a mild bleach.

These reactions show a decrease in reactivity down the group.

Reactions of halogens with metals

The word 'halogen' means salt-producer. All halogens react with metals to produce salts. For example, sodium burns in chlorine to form sodium chloride (see Unit 68):

> sodium + chlorine ➡ sodium chloride

In similar reactions, fluorine forms fluorides, bromine forms bromides and iodine forms iodides. The table shows the reactivity of halogens with hot iron.

Halogen	Reaction with hot iron
chlorine	reacts rapidly to form iron(III) chloride iron + chlorine ➡ iron(III) chloride
bromine	reacts slowly iron + bromine ➡ iron(III) bromide
iodine	reacts very slowly iron + iodine ➡ iron(III) iodide

Reactions of halogens with hydrogen

The reactions of halogens with hydrogen clearly show the differences in reactivity of the halogens.

Mixtures of fluorine and hydrogen react explosively to produce hydrogen fluoride.

> hydrogen + fluorine ➡ hydrogen fluoride

Chlorine and hydrogen can be mixed together without reaction providing they are kept in the dark. In sunlight they react together explosively.

> hydrogen + chlorine ➡ hydrogen chloride

Mixtures of bromine and hydrogen react together on heating to produce hydrogen bromide.

> hydrogen + bromine ➡ hydrogen bromide

Iodine and hydrogen only react partially when they are heated.

> hydrogen + iodine ⇌ hydrogen iodide

From these reactions the order of reactivity can be established.

1 Which is the most reactive halogen?

2 What is a diatomic molecule?

most reactive
fluorine
chlorine
bromine
iodine
least reactive

Words you should know
halogens   diatomic

71 The halogens – 2

In this unit you will learn the answers to these questions:
- How can hydrochloric acid be produced from sodium chloride?
- What are the uses of fluorine, chlorine, bromine and iodine?

Hydrogen halides

In Unit 70, the reactions of the halogens with hydrogen were compared. When hydrogen reacts with chlorine, the compound called hydrogen chloride is formed.

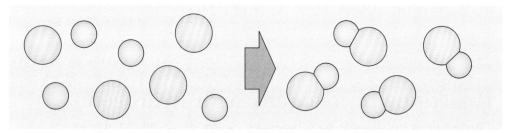

▲ **Fig 1** *Hydrogen and chlorine reacting*

Hydrogen chloride, HCl, is one of the **hydrogen halides** – compounds of hydrogen with a halogen element.

Hydrogen chloride can also be made from the reaction of concentrated sulphuric acid with salt (sodium chloride). Because hydrogen chloride could be made from salt, it was called 'salt gas'.

1 Write down the names and formulae of the other hydrogen halides.

The equation for the reaction is

$$\text{sodium chloride} + \text{conc. sulphuric acid} \rightarrow \text{sodium hydrogensulphate} + \text{hydrogen chloride}$$

This gas turns damp blue litmus paper red. The gas dissolves well in water to form a colourless solution.

This apparatus can be used to produce a solution of the gas in water.

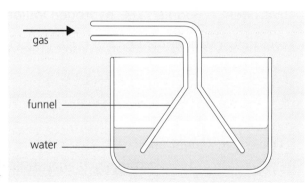

gas

funnel

water

▶ **Fig 2** *Hydrogen chloride gas dissolved in water*

The table shows the properties of the aqueous solution.

Test	Observations	Conclusions
Test pH with Universal Indicator	Red	pH 1
Add magnesium ribbon	Fizzes. Colourless gas burns with a squeaky pop	Gas is hydrogen
Add sodium carbonate	Fizzes. Colourless gas turns limewater milky	Gas is carbon dioxide
Test conductivity of solution	Solution conducts electricity	Solution contains ions
Test for chloride ions – acidify with dilute nitric acid and add silver nitrate solution	White precipitate	Chloride present

The results of these tests confirm that the aqueous solution produced is hydrochloric acid.

2 A solution of dry hydrogen chloride in dry methylbenzene turns Universal Indicator green and gives no gas with magnesium ribbon or sodium carbonate. Suggest a reason for these observations.

Testing for chlorides, bromides and iodides

A solution suspected of containing sodium chloride, sodium bromide or sodium iodide is acidified with dilute nitric acid, and silver nitrate solution is added. If a chloride is present a *white* **precipitate** of silver chloride is formed, e.g.

silver nitrate + sodium chloride ➡ silver chloride + sodium nitrate

If sodium bromide is present, a *cream* precipitate of silver bromide is formed. If silver iodide is present, a *yellow* precipitate of silver iodide is formed.

3 Write word equations for the tests for sodium bromide and sodium iodide.

Uses of halogens

- **Fluorine** is used in the form of fluorides in toothpastes and drinking water, as it hardens the enamel on teeth and reduces tooth decay. Fluorine is used to make PTFE (Unit 60) for non-stick coatings on saucepans.
- **Chlorine** is used in making household bleaches. It is used to kill bacteria and viruses in drinking water and swimming pools. Chlorine is also used to make PVC (Unit 60) which is used in furniture etc.
- **Bromine** is used in making fire-retardant materials, disinfectants and medicines.
- **Iodine** is used in medicines, disinfectants and photographic chemicals. Radioactive iodine is used as a medical tracer.

Words you should know

hydrogen halide   precipitate

72 Rates of chemical reactions – 1

In this unit you will learn the answers to these questions:
- What is meant by rate of reaction?
- What is the relationship between rate and time?
- How does decreasing particle size affect the rate of a reaction?

Chemical reactions can take place at different speeds. An explosion, such as the reaction of hydrogen and oxygen together to produce water vapour, is a very fast reaction – it is over in a tiny fraction of a second. The rusting of iron and the souring of milk are slow reactions.

A reaction which is over in a fraction of a second is a very fast reaction. We say it has a **high rate of reaction**. As the time taken for the reaction to be completed increases, the rate of reaction decreases. That is:

$$\text{rate of reaction} \propto \frac{1}{\text{time}}$$

Altering the rate of reaction

We know that changing the conditions can alter the time a reaction takes. Keeping milk cool in a refrigerator slows down the souring process. It is difficult to study very fast reactions or very slow reactions. It is better to study reactions which progress steadily and where changes in rate of reaction can be clearly seen. Then it is possible to identify factors which alter the rate of reaction and possibly try to explain why.

Effect of particle size on the rate of reaction

Calcium carbonate reacts with dilute hydrochloric acid as follows:

calcium carbonate + hydrochloric acid ➡ calcium chloride + water + carbon dioxide

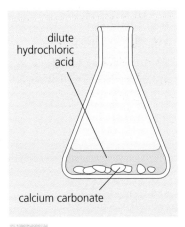
dilute hydrochloric acid

calcium carbonate

Fig 1 shows a flask containing calcium carbonate and dilute hydrochloric acid. The progress of the reaction can be followed in several ways, including:

1 measuring the volume of carbon dioxide produced at regular intervals;

2 measuring the total mass of the container, calcium carbonate and hydrochloric acid at intervals. Remember that the carbon dioxide escapes from the container during the reaction.

◀ **Fig 1** *Calcium carbonate and dilute hydrochloric acid*

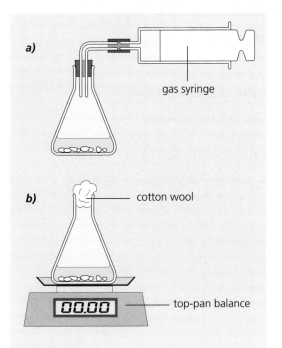

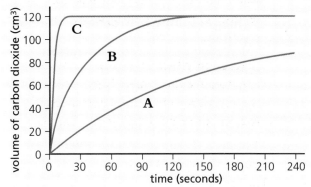

Fig 2a shows how the gas can be collected in a gas syringe and its volume measured at intervals. Fig 2b shows how the loss of mass can be measured using a top-pan balance.

1 What is the job of the cotton wool in Fig 2b?

▲ *Fig 2* Measuring **a)** the volume, **b)** the mass

▲ *Fig 3* Reactions of different samples of calcium carbonate with dilute hydrochloric acid

Fig 3 shows graphs which were obtained when three samples of calcium carbonate reacted with the same volume of dilute hydrochloric acid of the same **concentration** and the same temperature. All possible **variables** were kept constant apart from the **surface area**. The three samples of calcium carbonate used were:

A 1.00 g of large lumps of marble (calcium carbonate);
B 1.00 g of small lumps of marble (calcium carbonate);
C 1.00 g of powdered calcium carbonate.

Powdered calcium carbonate has a much larger surface area than the small lumps which, in turn, have a much larger surface area than the large lumps.

Although lumps of coal do not react with oxygen in the air without heating, mixtures of coal dust and air can be explosive.

2 What is the effect of increased surface area on the rate of reaction?

3 At the end of each experiment some calcium carbonate remains in the flask. What does this tell you about the contents of the flask at the end of the experiment?

4 Use Fig 3. After how many seconds is the reaction with small lumps complete?

Words you should know

rate of reaction   surface area

73 Rates of chemical reactions – 2

In this unit you will learn the answers to these questions:
- How is the rate of reaction affected by increasing the concentration of a reactant?
- How does increasing temperature affect the rate of reaction?

Effect of concentration

The equation showing the reaction of magnesium and hydrochloric acid is:

magnesium + hydrochloric acid ➡ magnesium chloride + hydrogen

Increasing the acid **concentration** would affect the rate of the reaction. We can easily make a qualitative prediction and describe the effect in words. We could test the prediction by doing a simple experiment. All the **variables**, apart from acid concentration, are kept constant. Fig 1 shows the results. The more concentrated acid produced more hydrogen bubbles i.e. it increases the rate of the reaction.

We could make a quantitative prediction about acid concentration. For example, doubling the concentration of the acid will double the rate of the reaction. We would investigate the prediction by doing another experiment. Our constant controlled variables are:

- equal mass of magnesium
- equal volume of acid (40 cm³)
- equal length of magnesium ribbon.

Different concentrations of hydrochloric acid are the tested variable.

The time taken for the magnesium to react and disappear was measured.

Increasing the concentration of hydrochloric acid speeds up the reaction, i.e. increases the rate of reaction.

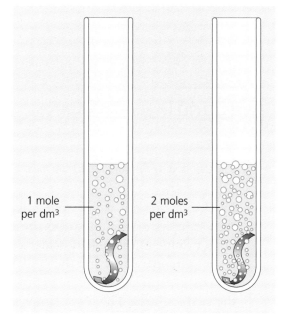

▲ **Fig 1** *Increasing the concentration of acid causes more hydrogen bubbles to be formed*

Experiment	Concentration of acid/mole per dm³	Time/ seconds
A	0.5	500
B	0.7	250
C	0.8	160
D	1.0	100
E	1.5	30

Effect of temperature

The effect of temperature on the rate of a reaction can be studied using the reaction between sodium thiosulphate solution and dilute hydrochloric acid.

1 Can you think of everyday examples where reactions are speeded up or slowed down by changing temperature?

$$\text{sodium thiosulphate} + \text{dilute hydrochloric acid} \rightarrow \text{sodium chloride} + \text{water} + \text{sulphur} + \text{sulphur dioxide}$$

When sodium thiosulphate solution and dilute hydrochloric acid are mixed, the solution goes cloudy. Eventually, it is not possible to see a cross through the beaker (Fig 2).

2 Why does the solution turn cloudy?

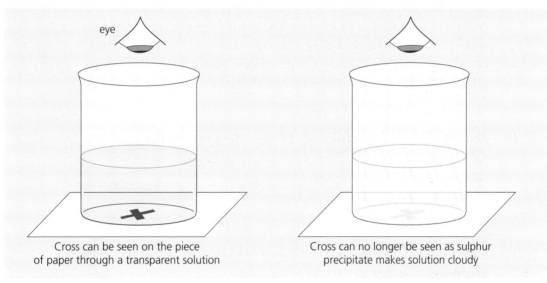

Cross can be seen on the piece of paper through a transparent solution

Cross can no longer be seen as sulphur precipitate makes solution cloudy

▲ **Fig 2** *Reaction between sodium thiosulphate solution and dilute hydrochloric acid causes the solution to become cloudy*

In an experiment to investigate the effect of temperature on the rate of reaction, the volumes and concentrations of the sodium thiosulphate solution and dilute hydrochloric acid are kept the same. Only the temperature is changed. The time is measured until the cross just disappears from view through the beaker.

Temperature/ °C	Time for the cross to disappear/ seconds
20	280
30	132
40	60
50	33
60	18

We can see from the results that the time taken for the cross to disappear decreases as the temperature of the solutions rises.

3 How does a) increasing acid concentration and b) increasing the temperature affect the rate of reactions?

Words you should know
concentration   variable

74 Rates of chemical reactions – 3

In this unit you will learn the answer to the question:
■ What is a catalyst?

Catalysts

If a jet of hydrogen gas is directed at a piece of platinum gauze, a reaction takes place between the hydrogen and oxygen from the air, forming water. The gauze glows hot and acts as a **catalyst**.

> **A catalyst is a substance which alters the rate of a chemical reaction without being used up. The mass of catalyst remains unchanged throughout the reaction.**

The filler used to repair holes and dents in car-bodywork comes in two tubes. One large tube contains the **resin**. The small tube contains the hardener or catalyst. The resin does not set hard until mixed with the hardener. When the two are mixed a fast reaction occurs and some heat energy is given out. The dent is filled. After 10 minutes the mixture has set so hard that it can be cut with a saw or filed into shape.

1 Why is it an advantage that the resin does not set until the hardener is added?

2 Why is it important that the resin does not set too quickly when the hardener is added?

Decomposition of hydrogen peroxide

Hydrogen peroxide decomposes very slowly at room temperature into water and oxygen.

hydrogen peroxide ➡ water + oxygen

A wide variety of substances will speed up the decomposition of hydrogen peroxide. One of these substances is manganese(IV) oxide. Fig 1 shows the volume of gas collected at intervals when:

1 no manganese(IV) oxide is added to the hydrogen peroxide;

2 one spatula measure of manganese(IV) oxide is added to hydrogen peroxide.

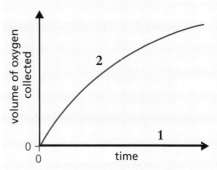

▲ *Fig 1 Volume of oxygen collected from hydrogen peroxide*

3 Draw a diagram of apparatus which could be used for this experiment.

4 In order to be sure that the difference in the volume of gas produced is due only to the manganese(IV) oxide, various factors have to be kept the same. List the factors which should be kept the same.

Examples of catalysis

There are many examples of catalysis in industry and everyday life.

1 In the Haber process (Unit 76), finely divided iron is used as a catalyst for the reaction of nitrogen and hydrogen at a temperature of about 450°C.

2 In the Contact process, vanadium(V) oxide pellets act as a catalyst for the reaction of sulphur dioxide and oxygen at a temperature of about 450°C.

3 In the manufacture of nitric acid, a platinum–rhodium gauze acts as a catalyst in the first stage when ammonia and oxygen react together to form nitrogen monoxide and steam.

4 In the manufacture of margarine, a nickel catalyst is used to aid the reaction of hydrogen with unsaturated oils to form margarine. The temperature is about 140°C.

5 Long-chain hydrocarbons are cracked when crude oil vapour is passed over a heated ceramic catalyst.

6 Catalytic converters are included in car exhaust systems to reduce emissions of carbon monoxide and oxides of nitrogen. The converter contains finely divided platinum.

7 The filler used to make minor body repairs to a car consists of a resin which is hardened by adding a catalyst. This sets in a few minutes to make a material which is so hard it can be sandpapered.

▲ **Fig 2** *A catalytic converter from a car*

Inhibitors

Sometimes it is necessary to slow down reactions by adding negative catalysts or **inhibitors**. For example, sulphur dioxide is added to lemon juice to stop it oxidising and going bad. Phosphoric acid is added to hydrogen peroxide to slow down its decomposition.

Words you should know

catalyst   inhibitor   resin

75 Enzymes

In this unit you will learn the answers to these questions:
- What are enzymes?
- Under what conditions do enzymes operate?
- What are enzymes used for?

Enzymes are proteins that control vital biological processes. They often act as biological catalysts. In the human body enzymes control the breakdown of food and reactions which make chemicals such as fats, carbohydrates, proteins and DNA. Enzymes are used today in a wide range of industrial processes. These include fermentation, baking, cheese making, tenderising meat and treating leather. The table summarises some of the enzymes used in industrial processes.

Enzyme	Examples of use
α-amylase	stain removal, paper manufacture, making syrups
lipases	speeding up the ripening of cheese
proteases	stain removal, making leather pliable, making biscuit flour
catalase	preservative in soft drinks, rubber manufacture
glucose oxidase	preservative in soft drinks, detecting diabetes
pectinase	clearing fruit juices

1 What is added to milk when cheese is made?

One of the most familiar household uses is in biological washing powders. Although the first biological washing powder was produced in 1913, only in the last twenty years have they been widely used.

Enzyme decomposition of hydrogen peroxide

Chemical catalysts work under a wide range of conditions. Fig 1 shows how enzymes are only effective in limited conditions. If a small piece of liver is added to hydrogen peroxide, a rapid evolution of oxygen is seen.

Catalase from the liver acts as a very effective catalyst and speeds up the decomposition of hydrogen peroxide.

hydrogen peroxide ➡ water + oxygen

One molecule of catalase will decompose 40 000 molecules of hydrogen peroxide each second.

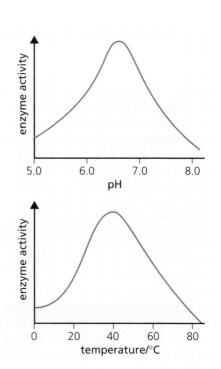

▶ **Fig 1** *Effectiveness of some enzymes under different conditions*

150

Hydrogen peroxide is harmful to us. The enzyme catalase in our blood breaks it down to the safe products, water and oxygen.

2 Using Fig 1:
   a Which two conditions have varied?
   b What are the conditions needed for the enzyme to be most effective.

Biological washing powders

Fig 2 shows a label from a biological washing powder.

3 Refer to the table (page 154). Which enzymes is the washing powder likely to contain?

4 Why should biological washing powders not be used with silk, wool and leather?

5 When soaking stains in biological washing powder, why is it better to use water at 40°C rather than hotter water?

6 Why should the powder be completely dissolved before the clothes are added?

7 Why should the clothes be thoroughly rinsed after washing?

8 What effect can biological washing powders have on the skin?

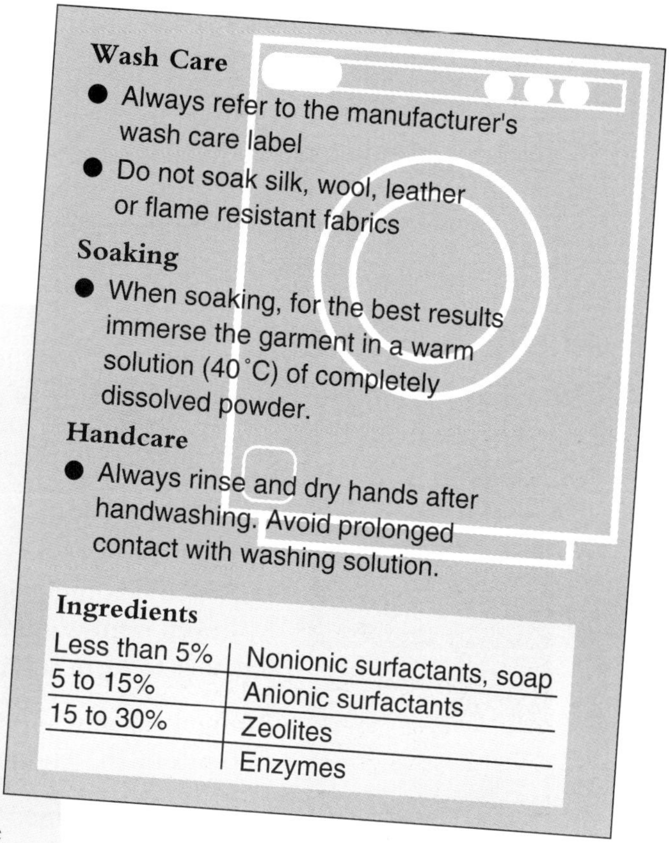

Wash Care
● Always refer to the manufacturer's wash care label
● Do not soak silk, wool, leather or flame resistant fabrics

Soaking
● When soaking, for the best results immerse the garment in a warm solution (40 °C) of completely dissolved powder.

Handcare
● Always rinse and dry hands after handwashing. Avoid prolonged contact with washing solution.

Ingredients	
Less than 5%	Nonionic surfactants, soap
5 to 15%	Anionic surfactants
15 to 30%	Zeolites
	Enzymes

▲ **Fig 2** Biological washing powder

Words you should know

enzyme

76 The Haber process

In this unit you will learn the answers to these questions:
- What is the Haber process?
- What is the major use of ammonia?

Why is nitrogen important?

Nitrogen is absorbed by plants through the roots as a solution of nitrates. The nitrogen is used to build up proteins in the plants. When plants grow they use up nitrogen. Land can become short of nitrogen, affecting the growth of crops.

To overcome this, farmers used to rely on animal manure and crop rotation. To add to these sources of nitrogen, guano, a natural fertiliser from Chile, was imported. This consisted of the droppings of seabirds. However, these supplies were used up a hundred years ago.

A new source of nitrogen compounds was therefore needed for agriculture, and also to meet the demands of the dyeing and explosives industries.

1 When a protein, e.g. milk powder, is mixed with calcium hydroxide (an alkali) and heated, a strong-smelling gas is produced which turns damp red litmus paper blue. This gas is **ammonia**, NH_3. What does this tell us about the composition of proteins?

The Haber process

▲ **Fig 1** *Fritz Haber (1868–1934)*

In 1904 the German chemist Fritz Haber suggested that nitrogen from the air and hydrogen from water could be combined together to form ammonia.

Ammonia is now produced in very large amounts by the **Haber process**.

Hydrogen is obtained from the cracking of methane or naphtha. Methane and steam are passed over a nickel catalyst at high temperatures and pressures.

methane + steam ➡ carbon monoxide + hydrogen

Carbon monoxide is removed from the gas. The hydrogen is then mixed with nitrogen from the air in the ratio of 3 parts of hydrogen to 1 part of nitrogen by volume.

The mixture of nitrogen and hydrogen is compressed and passed over a heated catalyst. The catalyst consists of finely divided iron. The catalyst is heated to about 450°C to start the reaction. Depending upon the conditions, part of the mixture of nitrogen and hydrogen is converted into ammonia. The equation is:

nitrogen + hydrogen $\rightleftharpoons$ ammonia

The mixture of gases, containing ammonia, is cooled and ammonia liquefies and can be separated. The unreacted nitrogen and hydrogen mixture is recycled. The process is summarised in Fig 2.

The $\rightleftharpoons$ sign in the equation shows that the reaction is reversible. A **reversible reaction** is a reaction which can go from left to right or right to left, depending on the conditions.

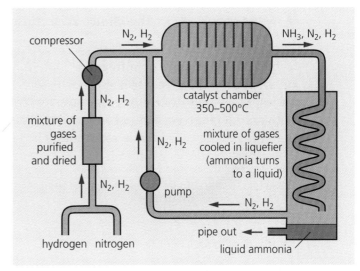

▲ **Fig 2** The Haber process

Use of ammonia

Fig 3 shows a graph of world population growth and world ammonia production from 1900 to 1980. There was a rapid growth in the mass of ammonia produced due to the development of the Haber process.

Fig 4 shows a pie diagram of the uses of ammonia.

2 What is most of the ammonia used for?

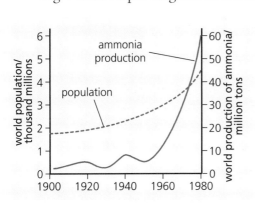

▲ **Fig 3** Ammonia production and the growth of population 1900 – 1980

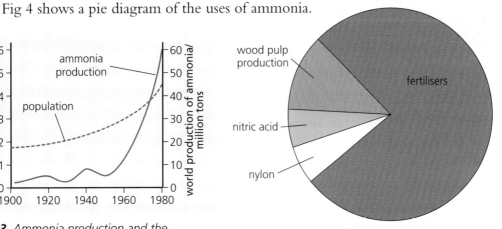

▲ **Fig 4** Uses of ammonia

Words you should know

ammonia   **Haber process**   **reversible reaction**

77 Fertilisers

In this unit you will learn the answers to these questions:
- Which elements are essential for plant growth?
- How is nitric acid manufactured from ammonia?
- How is ammonium nitrate manufactured?
- What factors affect the choice of fertiliser?

Essential elements for plant growth

For good plant growth, quantities of nitrogen, phosphorus and potassium are required. Other elements are required in smaller amounts. Elements such as boron and iron are required in very small amounts and are called **trace elements**. The table shows the importance of nitrogen, phosphorus and potassium.

Element	Importance of the element to a growing plant	Natural sources	Artificial fertilisers
nitrogen	necessary for the growth of stems and leaves	dried blood (14% N), hoof and horn (14% N)	sodium nitrate, calcium nitrate, ammonium sulphate, ammonium nitrate, urea
phosphorus	essential for root growth	slag, bone meal	ammonium phosphate, calcium superphosphate
potassium	for the production of flowers	wood ash	potassium sulphate

1 A fertiliser bag is labelled 'NPK 15:5:10'. What does this mean?

2 Which two substances in the 'Artificial fertilisers' column of the table could be mixed to produce a fertiliser which would provide nitrogen, phosphorus and potassium?

Industrial production of ammonium nitrate and ammonium sulphate

Ammonia is manufactured by the Haber process (Unit 76). Much of this ammonia is converted into nitric acid in a three-stage process.

Stage 1
A mixture of ammonia and air is passed over a heated platinum/rhodium alloy gauze catalyst.

ammonia + oxygen ➡ nitrogen monoxide + steam

▶ *Fig 1* Ammonia plant

Stage 2

The mixture of gases is allowed to cool.

nitrogen monoxide + oxygen ➡ nitrogen dioxide

Stage 3

The mixture of gases dissolves in water to produce nitric acid.

nitrogen dioxide + water + oxygen ➡ nitric acid

Manufacture of ammonium nitrate from ammonia and nitric acid

Ammonium nitrate is the most widely used fertiliser in Great Britain. It can be prepared by reacting ammonia solution and nitric acid.

ammonia + nitric acid ➡ ammonium nitrate

In the final stage, the solution of ammonium nitrate is evaporated. Solid ammonium nitrate is melted and sprayed down a tall tower (Fig 2). As the droplets fall they meet an upward flow of air. The fertiliser solidifies and forms small, hard pellets. These are easy to handle and to spread onto the fields.

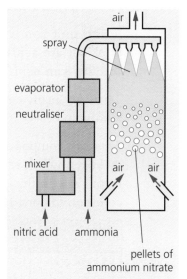

▲ **Fig 2** *Ammonium nitrate production*

3 Plan an experiment to prepare a sample of ammonium sulphate in the laboratory. Ammonium sulphate is a soluble salt.

Choosing the most suitable fertiliser

The factors which affect the choice of a nitrogen fertiliser include:

- *Percentage of nitrogen in the fertiliser.*
- *Solubility in water.* Plants absorb fertilisers in solution through their roots. If a fertiliser is very soluble in water, it will be quick-acting. However, a very soluble fertiliser is quickly washed off the field and into drainage ditches, brooks and rivers. This will cause **water pollution**.
- *Cost.* If two fertilisers have similar percentages of nitrogen and similar solubilities, the choice may be made on price.

▲ **Fig 3** *A tractor distributing solid fertiliser*

Words you should know

trace elements   **water pollution**

78 Acids and alkalis

In this unit you will learn the answers to these questions:
- What are acids, bases and alkalis?
- How can acids and alkalis be detected?

There are many examples of **acids** and **alkalis** in everyday life.

Acids are compounds which contain hydrogen which can be replaced by a metal to form a salt. In the laboratory there are three common mineral acids, as shown in the table.

acid

alkali

Acid	Formula	Salt produced
sulphuric acid	H_2SO_4	Na_2SO_4
hydrochloric acid	HCl	NaCl
nitric acid	HNO_3	$NaNO_3$

1 From your knowledge of apples, lemons and vinegar, suggest what kind of taste acids have?

2 Which element is present in all acids?

There are also many **organic acids** composed of carbon, hydrogen and oxygen. Examples are citric acid, tartaric acid and ethanoic acid. Many of these organic acids are solids.

A **base** is an oxide or hydroxide of a metal. It reacts with an acid to form a salt and water only. An alkali is a base which is soluble in water. A solution of an alkali contains an excess of hydroxide, OH^-, ions. The common laboratory alkalis are listed (right).

potassium hydroxide	KOH
sodium hydroxide	NaOH
calcium hydroxide	$Ca(OH)_2$
ammonia solution	NH_3 (aq)
(ammonium hydroxide)	or NH_4OH

Indicators

Acids and alkalis can be detected using indicators. Indicators are substances which change colour when acids and alkalis are added. Examples of good plant indicators are solutions from red cabbage, red roses, beetroot and elderberries.

In the laboratory the plant extract which is most commonly used to detect acids and alkalis is **litmus**. Litmus changes colour between red and blue.

in aci**d** solution – re**d**

in a**l**kali solution – b**l**ue

Solutions which are not acidic or alkaline are said to be **neutral**. Litmus is purple in neutral solutions.

Although litmus can detect acids and alkalis, it cannot compare the strengths of acids and alkalis. The comparative strengths of acids and alkalis is given by the **pH** scale. This is a scale from 1 to 14. A substance is an acid if it has a pH less than 7 or alkaline if it has a pH greater than 7. A neutral substance has a pH of exactly 7. The pH of a solution can be found in two ways.

1 *Using mixtures of indicators called* ***Universal Indicator***. This changes to a number of colours rather than just the one of a simple indicator such as litmus. The table gives the colours for a simple form of Universal Indicator.

For example, if Universal Indicator is added to a solution and the solution turns blue, the solution has a pH of 8 and is a very weak alkali.

2 *Using a pH meter.* A pH meter is a way of measuring the pH accurately. A glass probe is put into the solution being tested and the pH can be read from a dial or a digital readout immediately.

	pH	Colour of Universal Indicator	Examples in the home	Examples in the laboratory
STRONG ACIDS	1		car battery acid	mineral acids
	2			
	3	red		
	4		lemon juice, vinegar	ethanoic acid
WEAK ACIDS	5	orange		
	6	yellow	soda water	carbonic acid
NEUTRAL	7	green	water, salt, ethanol	
WEAK ALKALIS	8	blue	soap, baking powder	sodium hydrogencarbonate
	9	blue-purple		
STRONG ALKALIS	10			ammonia solution
	11		washing soda	
	12	purple	oven cleaner	
	13			sodium and potassium hydroxides
	14			

◀ *Fig 1 The glass probe of a pH meter measuring the pH of a solution*

Words you should know

acid   alkali   base   litmus   neutral   pH   Universal Indicator

79 Neutralisation

In this unit you will learn the answers to these questions:
- What is neutralisation?
- What examples of neutralisation are there in the world around us?

When an acid is mixed with an alkali, in the correct amounts, a neutral solution is formed. This process is called **neutralisation**.

One product of neutralisation is water.

These reactions are exothermic. There is a temperature rise when the two solutions are mixed.

Uses of neutralisation

1 Soil testing

A soil with a pH value between 6.5 and 7.0 is suitable for growing most plants. If the pH falls below 6.0, the soil will become too acidic for growing some plants. If the pH rises to 8.0 it will again be poor for plant growth because very alkaline soil is short of vital minerals necessary for plant growth.

The table shows plants which grow well in acidic and alkaline conditions.

Acidic conditions	Alkaline conditions
rhododendron	cherry
azalea	juniper
lavender	laburnum
wallflowers	lilac
stocks	birch
heather	broom
hydrangea	holly

You may be able to decide what the soil is like in your area by looking at the trees and plants which grow well in gardens around you. The pH of the soil can be found by mixing a sample of the soil with distilled water and adding pure, insoluble barium sulphate powder. The barium sulphate helps the solution to clear. Universal Indicator is then added and the colour of the solution compared with a Universal Indicator colour chart. Alternatively you could test the mixture of soil and distilled water with a pH meter.

Excess acidity of soils is an important cause of crop failure. It has been estimated that if this was always corrected properly there would be a one-fifth increase in food production.

Excess acidity of soils (or soil sourness) is caused by rainwater washing out alkalis from the soil and by rain containing acids. The excess acidity can be removed by neutralising it with alkalis.

Calcium oxide (or quicklime) and calcium hydroxide (or slaked lime) are frequently used to make the soil less acidic. They are made from limestone (calcium carbonate).

$$\text{calcium carbonate} \xrightarrow{\text{heat strongly}} \text{calcium oxide} \xrightarrow{\text{add water}} \text{calcium hydroxide}$$

Calcium hydroxide and calcium oxide are quick-acting. In order to correct excess soil acidity, these alkalis should be used in autumn or winter. Calcium carbonate can also be used. It is less soluble and acts more slowly.

2 Acids in digestion

There is about 1000 cm³ of dilute hydrochloric acid in your stomach. It is there to help you digest the food you eat. The food is broken down into simpler substances which can be used by your body.

Indigestion is caused by too much acid in the stomach. It can be cured by taking antacids such as bicarbonate of soda (sodium hydrogencarbonate). These substances are weak alkalis and neutralise excess acidity.

3 Insect bites and stings

Insect bites or stings involve the injection of a small amount of chemical below the skin. This causes irritation. Nettle stings and ant bites inject acid into the skin. Bee stings also involve the injection of an acid. The sting or bite should be neutralised by using calamine lotion (a suspension of zinc carbonate) or sodium hydrogencarbonate. Both are weak alkalis. In neutralising the acid they reduce the irritation.

▲ **Fig 1** *Close up of a wasp sting*

Wasp stings are different. They are best treated by applying vinegar (ethanoic acid) because the sting involves the injection of an alkali.

4 Removing acidic gases from gases leaving power stations

Coal-fired power stations produce sulphur dioxide which can affect the environment. The sulphur dioxide can be removed by passing the gases over limestone. The limestone neutralises the acidic gases in the gases escaping from the factory. Calcium sulphate is produced and can be used in making plasterboards.

1 Why is it important to remove acidic gases from power station gases?

Words you should know

neutral   neutralisation

80 Salt formation – 1

In this unit you will learn the answers to these questions:
- How can soluble salts be made?
- What are the rules for the solubility of salts?

Salts

A **salt** is made when hydrogen ions in an acid are replaced by metal or ammonium (NH_4^+) ions. For example:

hydrochloric acid ➡ sodium chloride

The hydrogen ion is replaced by a sodium ion.

nitric acid ➡ ammonium nitrate

Any metal carbonate, chloride, sulphate or nitrate will be a salt.

The method used to make a salt depends upon whether the salt is soluble in water or insoluble in water.

Solubility of salts

The table shows the solubility of a number of salts at room temperature.

Key: s soluble in water
    ss slightly soluble in water
    i insoluble in water

Metal	Chloride	Nitrate	Sulphate	Carbonate
sodium	s	s	s	s
calcium	s	s	ss	i
zinc	s	s	s	i
barium	s	s	i	i
magnesium	s	s	s	i
lead(II)	i	s	i	i
potassium	s	s	s	s
iron(II)	s	s	s	i
ammonium	s	s	s	s
copper(II)	s	s	s	i
silver	i	s	ss	i

1 Copy and finish the following sentences by putting in the correct metals.
All salts of potassium, sodium and ammonium are soluble in water.
All nitrates are soluble in water.
All chlorides are soluble in water except _____ and _____.
All sulphates are soluble in water except _____ and _____.
All carbonates are insoluble in water except _____, _____ and _____.

These are the solubility of salt rules. They need to be used when deciding which method you should use to make a particular salt.

Making soluble salts

There are four possible starting materials for making each soluble salt:

1 the metal;

2 the metal oxide (a base);

3 the metal hydroxide (an alkali);

4 the metal carbonate.

You will also need an acid.
- hydrochloric acid to make chlorides;
- nitric acid to make nitrates;
- sulphuric acid to make sulphates.

For example, magnesium sulphate can be made using dilute sulphuric acid and magnesium, magnesium oxide, magnesium hydroxide or magnesium carbonate (Fig 1).

1 solid added in small amounts

HEAT

2 glass rod

mixture stirred until some solid remains unreacted (all acid used up)

3 excess unreacted solid

solution of soluble salt

evaporating basin

4 glass rod dipped into solution at intervals crystals form on the glass rod on cooling in the air

gauze

tripod

HEAT

5 allow basin to cool as soon as crystals form on the end of the glass rod

crystals form on cooling

▶ **Fig 1** *Preparation of magnesium sulphate – a soluble salt*

The following word equations summarise the possible reactions.

metal	+ acid	➡	salt	+	hydrogen
metal oxide	+ acid	➡	salt	+	water
metal hydoxide	+ acid	➡	salt	+	water
metal carbonate	+ acid	➡	salt	+	water + carbon dioxide

2 Write word equations for the four reactions which can be used to make magnesium sulphate.

Words you should know

          salt   **solubility**

81 Salt formation – 2

In this unit you will learn the answers to these questions:
- How can insoluble salts be made?
- What can insoluble salts be used for?

Unit 80 listed the rules for solubility of salts at room temperature.
These are:

> **All salts of potassium, sodium and ammonium are soluble in water.**
>
> **All nitrates are soluble in water.**
>
> **All chlorides are soluble in water except lead and silver.**
>
> **All sulphates are soluble in water except barium and lead.**
>
> **All carbonates are insoluble in water except potassium, sodium and ammonium.**

Making insoluble salts

Insoluble salts are made by **precipitation**. Two suitable solutions are
mixed together so that the insoluble salt precipitates (see Fig 1).

To prepare barium sulphate, choose a salt containing barium which is
soluble in water to make one solution, e.g. barium nitrate or barium
chloride. (Remember that all nitrates are soluble in water and nitrates
are often the best salt to use.) The other solution could be sodium
sulphate or potassium sulphate.

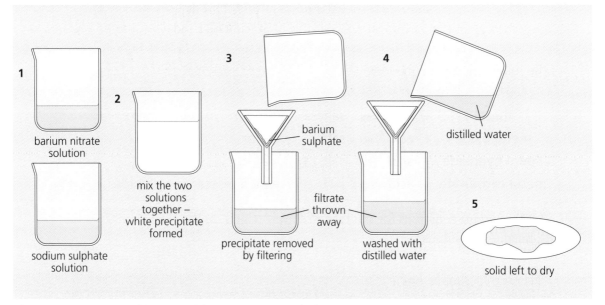

▲ **Fig 1** *Preparation of barium sulphate – an insoluble salt*

The following word equations summarise the reactions which take place:

barium nitrate + sodium **sulphate** ➡ **barium sulphate** + sodium nitrate

barium nitrate + potassium **sulphate** ➡ **barium sulphate** + potassium nitrate

barium chloride + sodium **sulphate** ➡ **barium sulphate** + sodium chloride

barium chloride + potassium **sulphate** ➡ **barium sulphate** + potassium chloride

The method used to make barium sulphate is summarised in Fig 1.
The barium sulphate made is pure and dry.

The progress of a precipitation reaction

Barium sulphate can also be made by mixing solutions of barium hydroxide (containing barium ions) and sulphuric acid (containing sulphate ions).

barium hydroxide + sulphuric acid ➡ barium sulphate + water

A solution of barium hydroxide has a pH value of 13. It is a strong alkali.

When sulphuric acid is added to the barium hydroxide solution, two things happen.

> **1** Suggest solutions which can be mixed together to make each of the following insoluble salts
> **a)** lead chloride
> **b)** zinc carbonate
> **c)** lead sulphate

1 A white precipitate of barium sulphate is formed.

2 The pH of the solution is reduced from 13 to 7. This happens when all of the barium sulphate has been precipitated and all of the acid and alkali have been used up. Adding more acid will reduce the pH below 7 as excess acid will remain. The course of the reaction could be followed using indicators or, better, a pH meter.

Uses of insoluble salts

Many insoluble salts are used in the paint industry. They are used to give paints their colour and are called **pigments**. Many insoluble salts have characteristic colours, e.g. copper carbonate is green.

Toxic materials in waste water are removed by precipitation followed by filtration. Heavy metals such as lead and cadmium are removed by precipitating insoluble salts.

> *Words you should know*
>
> **pigment**   **precipitation**

82 Measuring current

In this unit you will learn the answers to these questions:
■ How do we use an ammeter to measure current?
■ How does the current in a series circuit differ from that in a parallel circuit?

Using an ammeter

Ammeters measure electric current in **amperes** (amps). The direction of a current is from the positive to the negative terminal. Fig 1a shows a simple electrical **circuit** with an ammeter (A) to measure the current that enters the lamp. Fig 1b shows the ammeter being used to measure the current that leaves the lamp. The results show that the current passing into the lamp is the same as the current passing out of the lamp. This shows that lamps, and other electrical components, do not use up any electricity.

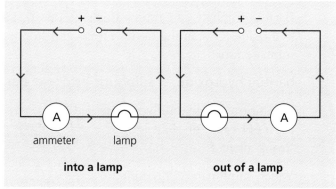

into a lamp   **out of a lamp**

▲ **Fig 1** *Measuring the current into and out of a lamp*

Current in a series circuit

Fig 2 shows a circuit where the current passes through one thing after another. This is a series circuit and the current is the same everywhere. The ammeter shows the same reading, 0.2 A, wherever it is placed. A switch, used to turn the current on and off, can be placed anywhere in this circuit.

Some Christmas tree lights use a series circuit. If one lamp filament "blows" it breaks the circuit. Then all the lamps go out.

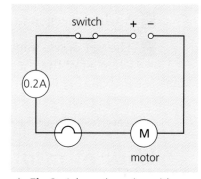

▲ **Fig 2** *A lamp in series with a switch, an ammeter and a motor*

1 The ammeter shows that the current entering the lamp is 0.2 A.
  a) How much current leaves the lamp?
  b) How much current enters the motor?
  c) How much current leaves the motor?
  d) If two more ammeters were added to the circuit, one between the lamp and the motor and one between the motor and the negative power supply terminal, what would you notice about all three ammeter readings?

Current in a parallel circuit

Most of the mains-operated circuits that we use at home are **parallel circuits**. In a parallel circuit each component can be switched on and off without affecting the others. Fig 3 shows how you can measure the current at different points in a parallel circuit.

Using the parallel circuit, you can switch the lamp and the motor independently; you do not have to have them both on or both off.

The black spots on the circuit diagram are junctions in the circuit. At these points the current divides as it goes into the two separate branches and rejoins after some has travelled through the lamp and some through the motor.

Measurements of electric current in a parallel circuit show that, unlike the series circuit, different size currents can pass in different components. In Fig 3, all the current passes through ammeter A_1 before splitting at the junction, some passing through the lamp and some through the motor. The currents then rejoin before returning to the power supply.

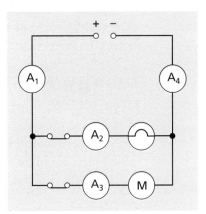

▲ *Fig 3* Measuring current in a parallel circuit

An important rule for parallel circuits is that the current that passes into a junction is equal to the current passing out. For the circuit in Fig 3, this means that the reading on ammeter A_1 is equal to the sum of the readings on A_2 and A_3. Ammeter A_4 reads the same as A_1 because it measures the current after it has rejoined.

2 List the ammeters A_1 to A_4. Next to each one write down its reading in amps.

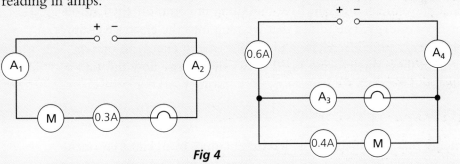

Fig 4

Words you should know

        ammeter   ampere   circuit   parallel   series

83 Circuits and energy transfer

In this unit you will learn the answers to these questions:
- How is energy transferred from a battery or power supply to components in electric circuits?
- What effects do electric currents have on lamps, motors and heaters?

In Unit 82 you learned that components such as lamps and motors in electric circuits do not use up any current. This unit examines the job that electric currents do in circuits and the energy transfers that take place.

▲ **Fig 1** *Four electrical appliances*

Energy from electricity

Electricity is the energy source that we use the most in our everyday lives at work and at home. One reason for this is its ready availability; it can be switched on and off and can be easily supplied to wherever we want to use it. There are three important things that electricity can be used to provide: **heat**, **movement** and **light**. Toasters, sandwich makers and electric fires all give out heat. Televisions, filament lamps and fluorescent tubes give out light. The sound from a radio, television or hi-fi is caused by the movement of the loudspeaker cone and we also rely on movement from electricity when we use a vacuum cleaner or washing machine.

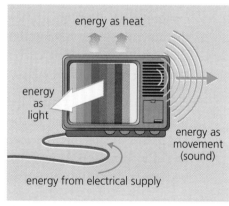

▲ **Fig 2** *Energy flow through a television*

Heat, movement and light have one thing in common; they are all forms of **energy**. The things that we plug into the electricity supply take energy from electricity and transfer it into energy in one or more of these three forms. Fig 2 shows the energy flow through a television set.

Where does the energy come from?

Energy that we obtain from electricity comes from batteries or the mains supply. In each case it comes from energy that is released when a chemical reaction takes place. The job of an electric current is to transfer this energy to where we want it. Electric currents have energy that they gain from the battery or mains supply and give up as they pass through the components in a circuit.

An electric circuit is just a means of moving energy from the energy source to wherever the energy is needed. The job of the current is to act as a go-between; it provides the link between the energy source and the device that then transfers the energy into movement, heat and light.

1 Name the appliances shown in Fig 1, and next to each write the source of electricity (mains or batteries) that it is likely to use.

2 Draw energy flow diagrams (like that in Fig 2) for the following devices:
   a) a kettle   **b)** a radio   **c)** a hairdryer

How does a current transfer energy?

An electric current is a movement of **charged particles**. In metals these particles are electrons, which carry a negative charge. In gases, such as in a fluorescent tube and sodium street lights, and in conducting liquids (electrolytes) there are both positively and negatively charged particles that move.

Think of a simple circuit consisting of a single cell, a lamp and two connecting wires. Metals contain lots of electrons that are free to move about. When the circuit is switched on, the electric force repels them from the negative terminal of the cell and attracts them towards the positive.

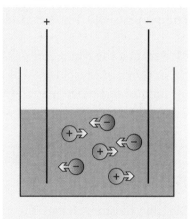

▲ **Fig 3** The movement of charged particles in an electrolyte

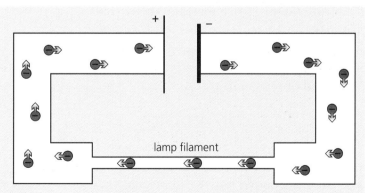

▶ **Fig 4** A model of charge flow in a circuit. Free electrons move in the direction negative to positive

lamp filament

Words you should know

energy

84 Current and its control

In this unit you will learn the answers to these questions:
- How is a voltmeter used in a circuit?
- What factors affect the current in a circuit?
- How does voltage differ in series and parallel circuits?

This unit examines the factors that determine the size of the electric current that passes in a circuit and how to measure voltage.

How easy?

You can compare the current that passes through different components in an electrical circuit. The same number of batteries or power pack settings must be used. The table shows the readings on a digital ammeter for three components and a power pack set at 4 volts.

Component	Current/A
heater	0.65
lamp	0.21
motor	0.36

1 Arrange the three components in order of resistance with the highest resistance first and the lowest last.

Components oppose a current passing. The bigger the **resistance** the less current passes. More current can pass through a component with a small resistance.

The variable resistor

Fig 1 shows a circuit that uses a **variable resistor**.

Variable resistors change the current that passes in a circuit by changing the resistance. Increasing the resistance causes less current to pass so the lamp dims or the motor slows. Reducing the resistance increases the current that passes in a circuit. Variable resistors, along

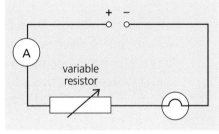

▲ *Fig 1* Using a variable resistor

with other components, are used in light-dimming circuits at home and in theatres. A variable resistor also forms the basis of the volume control circuit on a radio or television.

Changing the voltage

Current only passes through a component such as a lamp or a motor when there is a **voltage** across it. Fig 2 shows how to connect a **voltmeter** to measure the voltage across a lamp in a simple circuit. A voltmeter is always connected in parallel with a component.

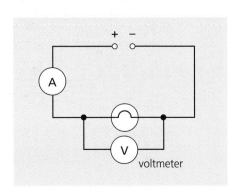

▶ *Fig 2* Using a voltmeter

By increasing the number of batteries or the power supply setting, you can see how the current and the brightness of the lamp depend on the voltage.

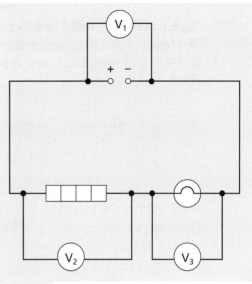

▲ *Fig 3*

2 Fig 3 shows how you can use a voltmeter to measure voltages in a circuit that has two components in series. V_1 measures the power supply voltage, V_2 and V_3 measure the voltages across the heater and the lamp. What do you notice about V_1, V_2 and V_3?

3 Make a circuit with two components in parallel. Connect a voltmeter first across the power supply, then across each component in turn. What do you notice about the readings?

The results of your measurements show that components in parallel always have the same voltage across them. In a series circuit the voltages across the individual components add up to equal the power supply voltage.

Series or parallel?

In a parallel circuit different currents can pass in individual components and each one can be switched independently of the others.

◀ *Fig 4*

Also, no matter how many components are switched on, the voltage stays the same. If you have your bedroom light on and someone puts the kettle on it doesn't affect the brightness of your light.

4 Explain why twenty 12 V lamps on a Christmas tree can be safely connected to the mains supply if they are connected in series, but not if they are connected in parallel.

Words you should know

resistance   resistor   variable resistor   voltage   voltmeter

85 Measuring resistance

In this unit you will learn the answers to these questions:
- How is resistance related to current and voltage?
- Does the resistance of a component depend on the current passing?

Calculating resistance

The more **resistance** a component has, the less current passes for a given voltage. When connected to the mains supply, the current in a filament lamp is 0.25 A but that in a kettle element is 10 A. The kettle element allows more current to pass because it has less resistance than the filament lamp.

Resistance is calculated using the equation

$$\textbf{resistance = voltage} \div \textbf{current} \quad \text{or} \quad R = \frac{V}{I}$$

The unit of resistance is the **ohm** (Ω).

Example

Calculate the resistance of a kettle element if the current is 10 A when it is connected to the 240 V mains.

Answer

$R = V \div I$

$\quad = 240\,\text{V} \div 10\,\text{A}$

$\quad = 24\,\Omega$

1 Use the resistance equation to complete the table.

	Device	Voltage/V	Current/A	Resistance/Ω
a	60 W household lamp	240	0.25	
b	iron	240	4.6	
c	1 kW (1000 W) heater	240		57.6
d	60 W car headlamp	12		2.4

Measuring resistance

The resistance of a wire-wound resistor or a piece of resistance wire can be measured using the circuit shown in Fig 1. The variable resistor is used to adjust the current. Then the resistance of 'X' can be measured over a range of values of current and voltage. Provided that the resistor or wire is not allowed to get hot, the resistance is the same.

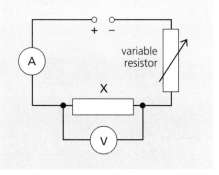

▲ **Fig 1**

Fig 2 shows two graphs of the results of an experiment to investigate the resistance of a metal wire 'X' at a constant temperature. Graph (a), of voltage against current is a straight line through the origin. This shows that voltage and current are in direct proportion to each other. These graphs show the typical behaviour of a metallic conductor. Provided the temperature does not change, the resistance has a constant value.

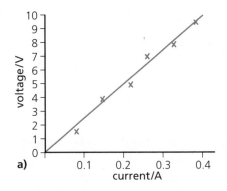 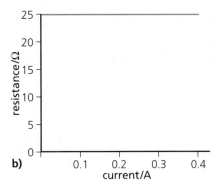

▲ **Fig 2** *Voltage, current and resistance at constant temperature*

Changing the temperature

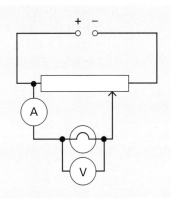

When a filament lamp is first turned on, the heating effect of the current causes the temperature of the filament to rise very rapidly. As the temperature changes, so does the resistance. The potential divider circuit shown in Fig 3 can be used to increase the voltage across a filament lamp gradually and note how the current changes. The results can then be used to plot graphs of voltage against current and resistance against current.

▶ *Fig 3*

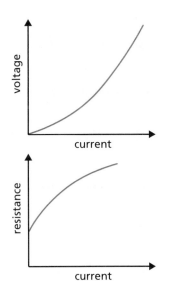

The graphs look very different to those for a metal kept at a constant temperature. Fig 4 shows typical results for a filament lamp.

The increasing gradient of the voltage–current graph shows that the resistance of the lamp filament increases as more current passes. The resistance–current graph shows the way in which the resistance changes.

◀ *Fig 4* *Voltage, current and resistance at changing temperature*

Words you should know

ohm **resistance**

86 Power in circuits

In this unit you will learn the answers to these questions:
- What determines the power of an appliance?
- What is a diode?
- How is power calculated?

The diode

A potential divider circuit similar to the one used in Unit 85 can be used to investigate the current in a **diode** as the voltage is varied. Unlike most circuit components, a diode has two different patterns of behaviour depending on how it is connected into a circuit. Current can pass in the direction shown by the arrow in the circuit symbol provided that the voltage is above a minimum value, 0.6 V in the case of a silicon diode. In the opposite direction it has a very high resistance, allowing no current at all to pass.

▲ **Fig 1** The circuit symbol for a diode

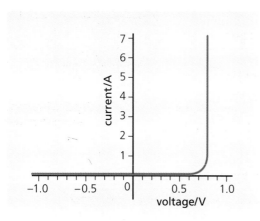

▲ **Fig 2** Current and voltage in a silicon diode

The graph, Fig 2, shows how the current in a silicon diode varies with the voltage. After it starts to conduct when the voltage is 0.6 V, the resistance of the diode decreases and continues to decrease as more and more current passes.

Diodes are used, along with transformers and other components, to produce a low voltage direct current, suitable for powering electronic equipment such as radios, keyboards and computers, from the high voltage alternating current mains.

Comparing the energy transfer

The electricity meter that you have at home does not measure the current or the voltage. It measures the energy that is delivered to your home by the current passing in the wires. You can use a **joulemeter** in a similar way to measure the energy provided from a power supply to a low voltage lamp, heater or motor.

The table compares the energy transferred in one minute from the mains supply to a kettle, a vacuum cleaner and a lamp.

The kettle is the most powerful of the devices shown because it transfers energy at the greatest

Device	Energy transfer in one minute/J
kettle	15 000
vacuum cleaner	4800
lamp	360

rate. **Power** is the energy transfer per second It is calculated using the equation:

$$\text{power} = \text{energy transfer} \div \text{time taken} \quad \text{or} \quad P = \frac{E}{t}$$

Power is measured in **watts** (W) when the energy is in joules and the time in seconds.

> 1 Use the equation to calculate the power of the kettle, the vacuum cleaner and the lamp.

Current, voltage and power

Energy transfer is the job of electric current. The more current that passes in a circuit the more energy is transferred each second. The other factor that affects the rate of energy transfer is the voltage (the amount of energy transferred by each coulomb of charge as it passes round a circuit).

Fig 3 shows an ammeter and voltmeter being used to measure the electrical power supplied to an electric motor (M). The meter readings show that 3 coulomb (C) of charge pass through the motor each second and each one transfers 12 J of energy. The total energy transfer each second is therefore three lots of 12 J, i.e. 36 J. Power is being supplied to the motor at the rate of 36 J/s or 36 W.

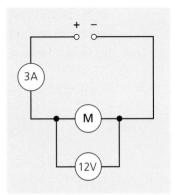

▲ **Fig 3** Measuring electrical power

For any electrical device, the power is calculated by multiplying the current and the voltage:

$$\text{power} = \text{current} \times \text{voltage} \quad \text{or} \quad P = IV$$

> 2 Use the equation $P = IV$ to fill in the blanks in the table.

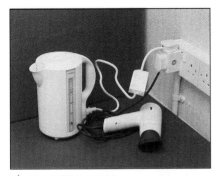

▲ **Fig 4** *This could cause overheating in the mains cable*

	Device	Voltage/V	Current/A	Power/W
a	torch lamp	3	0.15	
b	toaster	240	6.5	
c	car headlamp	12	5	
d	electric train	1500	1000	

Words you should know

      diode   joulemeter   power   watts

87 Using electricity safely

In this unit you will learn the answers to these questions:
- What do the live, neutral and earth wires do?
- Why are earth wires, fuses and circuit breakers necessary?

The mains supply

Mains electricity can kill if it is not used safely. There must be a complete circuit for an electrical appliance to work. The current needs a route to pass from the source to the appliance and then to return. Fig 1 shows where mains electricity enters a home. The incoming cable has three wires. The live wire supplies the house with energy from the source. The neutral wire completes the circuit. Normally no current passes in the **earth** wire. It is only used if there is a fault.

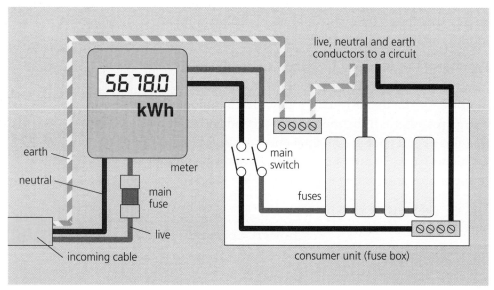

▲ **Fig 1** Mains electricity supply

The live and neutral cables are very thick. They can carry more than 100A of current without overheating. A fault could make the current too large. This could overload the cables and cause a fire. The main **fuse** in the live wire protects against fire. If the current is too large it melts and breaks the circuit.

▲ **Fig 2** A cartridge fuse

Fuses or circuit breakers

A house has several circuits, one or two for the sockets and separate ones for lighting, a cooker, a shower and an immersion heater. The live wire is connected to each house circuit in the consumer unit or fuse box. Each circuit is protected by a fuse. The fuse melts and breaks the circuit if the current is too large.

New houses have **circuit breakers** instead of fuses. They are more reliable. They cannot be tampered with and are easy to re-set when a fault has been repaired.

▲ **Fig 3** *Consumer unit fuse and circuit breaker*

Protecting the user

Fig 4 shows the connection between the mains supply and a heater with a metal case. The fuse does two jobs:

1 If the current is too large it melts, this breaks the circuit and prevents a fire.

2 Together with the earth wire it prevents electrocution.

Suppose the live wire became frayed and came into contact with the metal casing

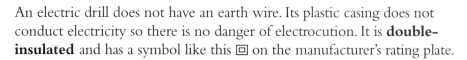

▲ **Fig 4**

or, through repeated movement, the cable became damaged where it enters the heater. This would cause the casing to become live. Anyone touching this would receive a severe shock as current passed through them to earth. The earth wire prevents this from happening by providing a low-resistance path to earth. If the casing does become live, a large current passes from the live wire straight to earth, causing the fuse wire to melt and break the circuit.

An electric drill does not have an earth wire. Its plastic casing does not conduct electricity so there is no danger of electrocution. It is **double-insulated** and has a symbol like this ▣ on the manufacturer's rating plate.

1 What is the colour of the insulation on the live wire, the neutral wire and the earth wire?

2 Describe the **two** functions of an earth wire.

Words you should know

      circuit breaker   **double insulation**   **earth**   **fuse**

88 Paying for electricity

In this unit you will learn the answers to these questions:
- How much does electricity cost?
- What are the different ways in which we use electricity for heating?

Once every three months, householders receive a bill from their electricity supply company. The bill is for the energy supplied through the mains.

Another unit of energy

The energy transferred when an appliance is used can be calculated using:

energy transfer = power × time   or $E = Pt$

You can work out that a 2500 W kettle which takes four minutes (240 seconds) to boil some water transfers 2500 W × 240 s = 600 000 J of energy. If you multiply this by the number of times the kettle is used in three months and add the energy transfer from all the other appliances – you get a very large number!

Electricity supply companies use a larger unit of energy, the **kilowatt-hour** (kWh), which is equivalent to 3 600 000 J. It is calculated using the equation above, but instead of using the watt and the second for units of power and time, it uses the kilowatt and the hour, as its name implies.

▲ **Fig 1** This electricity meter measures the energy in kWh

energy in kWh = power in kW × time in h

Example
Calculate the energy transfer, in kWh, by a 2.5 kW immersion heater which is used for 30 minutes each day for a week.

Answer
time = 30 mins × 7 = 210 mins = 3.5h
energy = power × time
= 2.5 kW × 3.5 h
= 8.75 kWh

The cost of energy from electricity is, including tax, about 8p per kWh so the cost of using the immersion heater is 8.75 × 8 = 70p per week.

1 Use the equation

energy in kWh =
power in kW × time in h

to complete the table.
Assume that each kWh
of electricity costs 8p.

	Appliance	Power/kW	Time used/h	Energy transfer/kWh	Cost/p
a	vacuum cleaner	0.8	0.5		
b	lamp	0.06	8		
c	kettle	2.5	0.75		
d	television set	0.12	5		

Electrical heating

We use electricity to provide heating, lighting and movement. Heating appliances (see Fig 2) are the most powerful and cost the most to use. Some appliances heat water and others heat the air around them.

Kettles, immersion heaters and convector heaters all use convection currents (see Unit 115) to transfer the heat away from the heating element into the surrounding air and water. Heating of the element takes place when a large current of about 10 A passes in it. Most electric kettles switch themselves off when they have boiled but immersion heaters are fitted with a thermostat, usually set to about 50°C, to switch off the current when the water has reached the desired temperature.

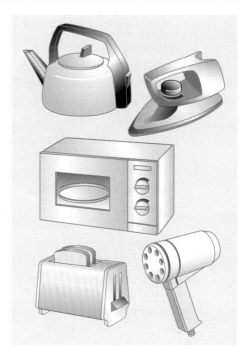

▲ *Fig 2*

Ovens and hairdryers also use heating elements. Like the immersion heater, an oven has a **thermostat** that switches off the current when a certain temperature has been reached. Many electric ovens also have a fan to give an even temperature throughout the oven. Hairdryers need fans to give a large air flow. It would take too long to dry your hair if you relied on convection currents from a hairdryer!

2 a) Why should the air inlet to a hairdryer never be covered?
  b) What is the purpose of the thermal cut-out fitted to a hairdryer?
  c) What do thermostats do and why are they useful?

Words you should know
  kilowatt-hour   **thermostat**

89 Static charge

In this unit you will learn the answers to these questions:
- How do balloons and other objects become charged?
- Why do some charged objects attract each other while others repel?
- How can static electricity be hazardous?

Electric currents are due to forces that make charges move. When a quantity of electric charge is isolated so that it cannot move, it can cause large forces on the charges in nearby objects.

Separating charges

Rubbing a balloon on a jumper or rubbing a polythene rod with a duster causes both objects to become charged. Polythene takes electrons from the duster and becomes negatively charged. The duster becomes positively charged because it has lost electrons.

The duster and the rod are both charged. They both affect uncharged objects. For example, they will attract the hairs on your head, pick up small pieces of paper and deflect a stream of water from a tap. These effects are due to the charged rod and duster exerting forces on the charges in other objects.

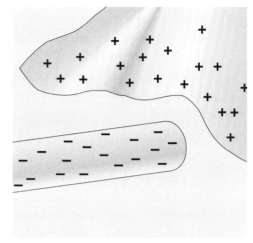

▲ **Fig 1** The charges on a polythene rod and a duster

Attraction and repulsion

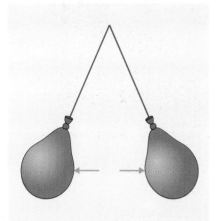

Two charged balloons or polythene rods push away from each other. A balloon charged by rubbing with the duster is attracted to the duster. These observations show that two objects with the same type of charge, both negative or both positive, repel each other. A negatively charged object is attracted to a positively charged one.

◄ **Fig 2** Objects with the same type of charge repel each other

1 A polythene rod becomes negatively charged when rubbed with a duster. Explain how you could use a charged polythene rod to find out the type of charge on a balloon that has been rubbed with a duster.

Insulators such as rubber, polythene and nylon can attract and repel each other when they are charged. They all attract small pieces of paper and the hair on your head. This is known as **induction**. It is caused by the movement of small amounts of charge carried by positive and negative ions. A perfect insulator does not allow any movement of charge. The moisture in paper contains both positive and negative ions, and these ions can move.

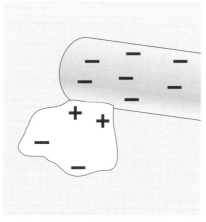

▲ **Fig 3** *How a piece of paper is attracted to a charged polythene rod*

Fig 3 shows how the negatively charged polythene rod attracts positive ions in the paper and repels negative ions. The positively charged part of the paper is attracted to the rod.

Static electricity can be dangerous. Refuelling is just one example.

2 Use diagrams to explain how hair can be attracted to a positively charged acetate rod.

Dangers of static charge – Refuelling

Petrol and other liquid fuels are very good insulators. When a car or aircraft is being refuelled the flow of liquid into the fuel tanks can cause **charge separation**. If you watch an aircraft being refuelled at an airport you will see that an **earthing lead** is always attached to the aircraft body before any fuel is put in. This allows charge to pass safely to earth. It prevents sparks that would be caused by static charge creating a high voltage and ionising the air.

▲ **Fig 4** *Refuelling an aircraft needs earth bonding*

Words you should know
  charge separation   **induction**   **insulator**   **static electricity**

90 Electromagnetism

In this unit you will learn the answers to these questions:
- ■ What pattern of magnetic field is produced by the current in a coil of wire?
- ■ What makes an electromagnet strong?
- ■ How do bells and relays work?

The field of a coil

Every electric current has its own magnetic field. We do not often notice the effects of the magnetic fields due to electric currents because they are very weak. Fig 1 shows the magnetic field pattern around a single current-carrying wire. (The direction of a magnetic field is the direction of the force on the N-seeking pole of a compass or other magnet.)

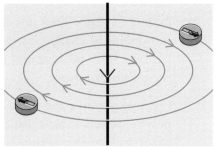

▲ *Fig 1* The magnetic field due to a current-carrying wire

A stronger magnetic field can be obtained by winding the wire into a **coil**. Using an arrangement like that shown in Fig 2a you can investigate the field pattern both outside and inside a coil of wire. Fig 2b shows the results of such an experiment.

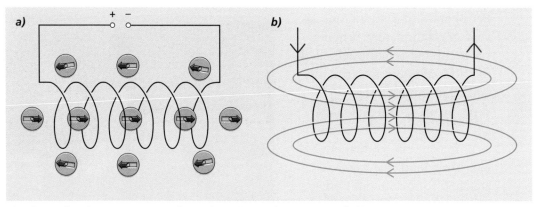

▲ *Fig 2* **a)** *Using compass needles to investigate the magnetic field due to a current in a coil of wire*
b) *The field due to a current in a coil of wire*

The field becomes much stronger if an iron nail is used as a **core** in the centre of the coils. This forms an **electromagnet** which can do simple jobs like lifting iron and other magnetic materials.

The strength of the field can also be affected by the size of the current passing in the wire and the number of turns of wire in the coil.

1 What are electromagnets used for?

The electric bell

When the bell push is pushed it completes the circuit. The electromagnet attracts the soft iron **armature**, the small gong is struck by the hammer and the bell "dings". This movement of the armature breaks the circuit at the contact screw. The electromagnet is turned off and no longer attracts the armature so it falls back into the position shown in Fig 3. This completes the circuit again and the process is repeated so long as the bell push is switched on.

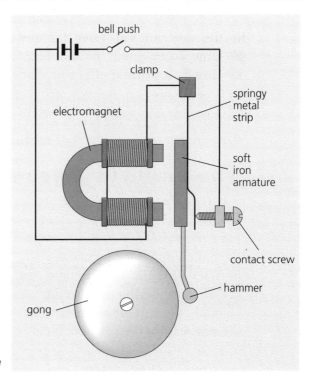

▶ *Fig 3 An electric bell*

An electromagnetic switch

A **relay** is a magnetic switch. An example of a relay is shown in Fig 4. When the d.c. source is switched on the coil becomes an electro-magnet and attracts part A of the armature. Part B then presses the switch contacts together and the mains lamp is turned on. Only a small current is needed for the relay to work. It switches on a larger current. Relays are used in cars to switch on starter motors and heaters. They enable thin wires to be used for the switches that the driver operates while thick wires are used between the relay and the high-current devices.

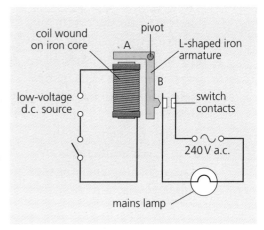

▲ *Fig 4 A relay circuit*

2 Write down the order of events that causes the lamp to be switched on when the current to the relay coil in Fig 4 is switched on.

Words you should know

      armature   **coil**   **core**   **electromagnet**   **relay**

91 The d.c. motor

In this unit you will learn the answers to these questions:
- ■ How do magnetic fields exert forces?
- ■ How is a turning effect produced in a motor?

Motors use electromagnetism to produce forces that cause rotation. This unit examines the forces when magnetic fields interact and how these are put to use in the **d.c. motor**.

The magnetic force

A current that is at right angles to a magnetic field experiences a force. Fig 1 shows how you can investigate the force using some wire and a horseshoe magnet. You should record the effect of varying the current, reversing the current and reversing the direction of the magnetic field.

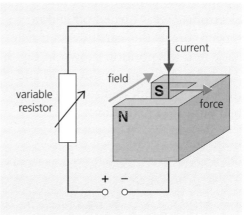

▲ *Fig 1*

The motor

The magnetic force is used in motors to produce a turning effect or moment. Fig 2 shows the forces on each side of a loop of wire in a magnetic field. Each force has a moment about an axis through the centre of the loop; these moments both have a turning effect in the anticlockwise direction.

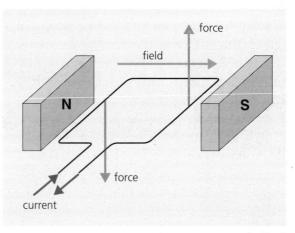

▲ *Fig 2*

The loop experiences the greatest turning force when it is horizontal and no turning force when it is vertical. You can feel this by making a loop out of copper wire and holding it between the poles of a horseshoe magnet or between opposite poles of a pair of slab magnets while passing a current in the loop.

> **1** Sketch the loop in a vertical position and draw the direction of the forces on the sides of the loop. Is there still a turning effect?

Practical motors

Although the motors we use at home are designed to operate from the alternating current mains rather than direct current, they work on the same principle. Motors such as those used to power electric trains use direct current since d.c. motors can produce much bigger forces than a.c. motors.

▲ **Fig 3** *A practical motor*

There are three main differences between a practical motor and the simple motor studied in this unit. Instead of using a loop, motors use a coil to produce a greater turning effect. They also have several coils wound on a single **armature**. This enables just one coil to be used at a time, when its position is such that the turning effect is at its greatest. The third difference is the magnets – practical motors use electromagnets instead of permanent ones.

▲ **Fig 4** *This train has a d.c. motor to drive it. What are the advantages of this?*

Words you should know

armature   **d.c. motor**   **left-hand rule**

92 Electromagnetic induction

In this unit you will learn the answers to these questions:
- What causes an induced voltage?
- What factors affect the size and direction of the voltage?
- How does a dynamo work?

Electricity can be produced by changing magnetic fields. This is called electromagnetic induction and is very important to our lifestyle. In around 1800 Volta invented the battery as a source of electric current. In 1831 Faraday generated a current by changing a magnetic field. Fifty years later the first power station was opened in Great Britain, at Godalming in Surrey.

Inducing a current

Fig 1 shows an arrangement that can be used to investigate what happens when the magnet is moved in the coils of wire:

1 the magnet could be moved quickly or slowly

2 the magnet could be reversed

3 the magnet could be kept still

4 the movement could be reversed.

The results show that tiny currents are generated when the magnet is moving.

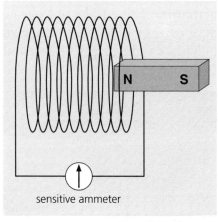

▲ *Fig 1*

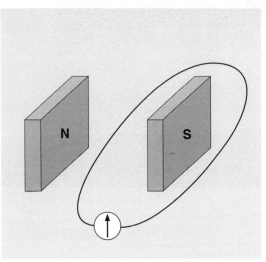

▲ *Fig 2*

It does not have to be the magnet that moves to generate a current. You can achieve similar results using a coil of wire and a horseshoe magnet or pair of slab magnets, as shown in Fig 2. Careful observation shows that current is generated when the wire is moved at right angles to the magnetic field. Again, you should experiment by varying the speed and direction of motion as well as the number of turns of wire on the coil.

Induced currents and voltages occur when magnetic fields change in size or direction. This can be caused by a changing current, as in a transformer (see Unit 93). Another way of changing a magnetic field is to use a spinning magnet; this happens in a cycle dynamo and a power station generator. Spinning a coil between the opposite poles of a magnet has the same effect as changing the magnetic field. Small generators usually use this method.

The dynamo

A **dynamo** on a bicycle and a **generator** in a power station both work on the principle that a magnetic field rotating inside a coil generates a voltage in that coil. Fig 3 shows the structure of a dynamo. The cylindrical magnet creates a magnetic field in the iron core. With the magnet in the position shown, the left-hand part of the iron core acts as a N-seeking pole and the right-hand part acts as a S-seeking pole. These poles are reversed when the magnet has turned through half a revolution.

As the cycle wheel turns the magnet rotates, causing the magnetic field in the iron core to change direction. Repeated reversal of this magnetic field generates an alternating voltage in the coil of wire.

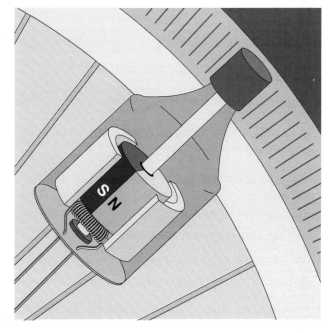

▶ *Fig 3* A dynamo

1 Describe the advantages and disadvantages of using a dynamo for cycle lights.

Words you should know

dynamo   **generator**   **induction**

93 Transformers

In this unit you will learn the answers to these questions:
- What do transformers do?
- How do the numbers of turns on transformer coils affect the current and voltage?

Changing fields

A voltage is induced in a conductor when the magnetic field around it changes. Fig 1 shows how the induced voltage can be investigated when an electromagnet is switched on or off. Switching on the current in the left-hand coil causes a pulse of current in the right-hand coil. A pulse of current passes in the opposite direction when the current in the left-hand coil is switched off.

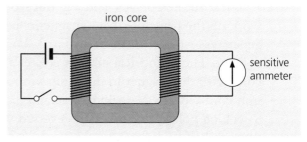

▲ *Fig 1 Investigating induced voltages*

The table summarises this:

Current in left-hand coil	Current in right-hand coil
a switch on	pulse of current passes
b switch off	pulse of current passes in opposite direction
c leave switch on so steady current passes	no current passes

The results can be explained using the principles of electromagnetic induction:

a Switching on makes the left-hand coil an electromagnet which has its own magnetic field. The field passes through the iron core and the air. The right-hand coil experiences a change in magnetic field within and around it so a voltage is induced.

b The reverse of a) happens. The magnetic field collapses, inducing a voltage in the opposite direction from when the field was created.

c There is no change in the magnetic field so no voltage is induced.

The transformer

Replacing the d.c. source with an a.c. source, as shown in Fig 2, gives a magnetic field in and around the iron core which is changing all the time. This causes an alternating voltage to be induced in the right-hand coil. A lamp or an a.c. voltmeter is needed to detect this induced voltage.

A **transformer** has two coils of wire, usually wound on an iron core. An alternating voltage applied to the **input**, or **primary**, **coil** induces an alternating voltage in the **output**, or **secondary**, **coil**. Energy is transferred from the input to the output through the changing magnetic field.

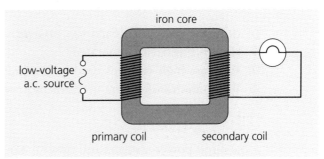

▲ **Fig 2** A transformer

1 Make a list of electrical appliances in the home that have transformers.

Changing the voltage

The effect of the number of turns on the input and the output coil can be investigated. The brightness of a lamp or an a.c. voltmeter could be used to indicate the output voltage. The number of turns on the wire on the coils has an important effect which is used in transformers. There are two types of transformer, step-up and step-down.

A **step-up transformer** has more turns on the secondary coil than on the primary and the output voltage is bigger than the input. **Step-down transformers**, used to make an alternating voltage smaller, have fewer turns of wire on the secondary coil than on the primary coil.

Transformers are very efficient devices. Some energy is wasted as heat in the wires and the core, but this is usually neglected. It is assumed that all the power in the primary coil is transferred to the secondary coil.

A transformer cannot provide more power from the output than it takes in at the input. When a transformer is used to increase the voltage there is a decrease in the current.

▲ **Fig 3** These trains use transformers to step down the voltage from the overhead power lines

Words you should know

transformer

94 Power transmission

In this unit you will learn the answers to these questions:
- How is electricity generated?
- Why are high voltages used to transmit electricity?
- What are transformers used for in power transmission?

The generator

Coal-fired power stations and nuclear power stations generate high-pressure steam to drive the **turbines**. In modern gas-fired power stations the turbines are driven by the high-energy waste products from the burning gas.

Fig 1 shows the turbines in a hydroelectric power station. The generator in a power station has three sets of wire coils, inside which an electromagnet rotates fifty times each second. This generates alternating current at 25 000 V with a frequency of 50 Hz. A 500 MW generator produces a large current, so very thick wire is used for the coils.

▶ *Fig 1* *Water-driven turbines*

Power into the grid

We do not receive our electricity from any one particular power station. All the electricity generated is fed into the **national grid**, a network of cables that links together the whole country. The electric current in these cables transfers energy as heat, which results in power losses.

To minimise the power losses in transmission, the current has to be kept as small as possible. A typical coal-burning power station has four generators, each producing 500 MW of power at 25 000 V. Using step-up transformers, the voltage is increased at the power station. The power is fed into the national grid at a reduced current.

Power around the country

Most of the national grid uses overhead cables to take the power from the power stations to the users. These cables do not need electrical insulation because the air gap between them and the ground is big enough to prevent sparking. Apart from cost, another advantage of not using insulation is that the air also acts as a coolant and prevents the cables from overheating. The cost of using underground cables is very high for two main reasons. Very good electrical insulation is required for cables at such high voltages.

This electrical insulation is also a good thermal insulator, so the cables have no natural coolant. Underground cables are cooled by oil flowing through them, increasing both the cost of the cable and the running costs.

Power to the consumer

Before going to consumers, the voltage of the electricity supply has to be reduced. Fig 3 shows how this is done in stages. Some industry uses electricity at a high voltage, 11 kV or 33 kV, but 240 V is supplied to domestic users. The last stage in the stepping-down process is at a substation close to your home. Power is supplied to these substations and travels to your home through underground cables.

▲ **Fig 2** *These pylons are ugly, but the alternative is expensive*

You can see from Fig 3 that, for efficient distribution of electrical power, transformers are widely used. They provide a cheap way of increasing the voltage for transmission and reducing it again to a safe level for consumers. The need to use transformers is the reason for using a.c. rather than d.c. for our mains electricity supply.

1 What are the advantages and disadvantages of using underground cables rather than overhead cables for the national grid?

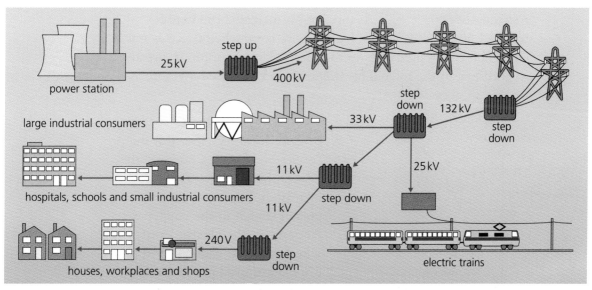

▲ **Fig 3** The national grid

Words you should know

national grid   turbine

95 Changing shape

In this unit you will learn the answers to these questions:
- Do all materials stretch in a regular way?
- Which materials are elastic?
- What is the difference between the 'elastic limit' and the 'limit of proportionality'?

Some materials are useful because they stretch easily. Rubber bands are stretched when they are used to hold things together. Socks often contain a material such as nylon so that they stretch when you put them on. Rubber and nylon are both **elastic** materials; they return to their original shape when the stretching force is removed. Plasticine is easy to stretch but it keeps its new shape; it is a **plastic** material.

Investigating stretching

Fig 1 shows how you can compare the stretchiness and elasticity of different materials. Suitable materials to use include 32 swg copper wire, nylon fishing line and rubber. Safety goggles must be worn in case the material being tested breaks.

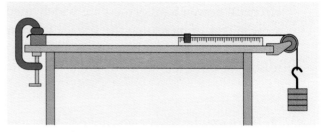

▲ **Fig 1** Comparing materials

Fig 2 shows the relationship between the force (or load) and the stretching of copper wire. As the force is increased the wire is stretched. If the force is doubled the wire is stretched twice as much. The graph is a straight line up to point P. The extension is directly proportional to the force. This is known as **Hooke's Law**. Other metals also obey this law.

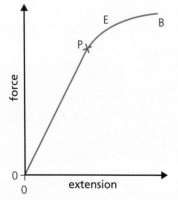

▲ **Fig 2** Stretching of copper wire

Point P is the **limit of proportionality**. After this the copper becomes less stiff and the relationship changes. The same increase in force now causes a greater stretch in the copper wire. At point E (the **elastic limit**) the wire has lost its elasticity and if the force is removed it will not return to its original size and shape. Increasing the force beyond this causes the wire to break (point B).

Storing energy

The force that stretches a material does work on it, causing energy to be stored in it. Archers use this energy to fire an arrow at a target. Bungee-jumpers and trampolinists use the energy stored in stretched elastic to bounce back up after falling down.

▲ *Fig 3*

1 Describe the energy transfer that takes place when the girl shown in Fig 3 bounces on the trampoline.

Designing car tyres

Unlike metal wires, rubber does not obey Hooke's law. The graph (Fig 4) shows the pattern of stretching for a sample of rubber. The slope of the graph indicates the stiffness of the rubber.

2 How does rubber change when it is stretched?

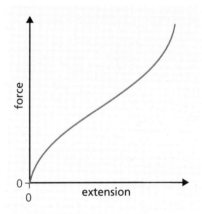

Fig 4 *Stretching of rubber* ▶

Rubber absorbs some energy each time it is stretched. You can demonstrate this by repeatedly stretching and relaxing a rubber band – it becomes warm.

Tyres on a car travelling at 60 mph are deformed and returned to their original shape about 20 times each second, causing heating. If the tyre pressure is low, more deformation and heating occurs. This raises the pressure of the air inside the tyre and can cause a 'blow-out'. This is the result of high air pressure in the tyre causing the tyre to explode.

The ideal car tyre has a stretchy tread so that it adjusts to the shape of the road and gives a good grip. The tyre wall does not need to change shape and so it should be made of a stiffer material which does not stretch so much.

Words you should know

elastic   plastic

96 **Under pressure**

In this unit you will learn the answers to these questions:
- How is pressure affected by the area that a force acts on?
- Under what circumstances does a force exert a high or a low pressure?
- How is pressure worked out?

High pressure

A force acting on a small area can pierce or cut through things. Cutting cheese with wire, food with a knife and paper with scissors all depend on this. The effectiveness of a force depends on the area it acts on. A small force can have a big effect if the area it is acting on is small. It is difficult to push a nail into a piece of wood. It is easier to push a drawing pin into wood because the pushing force acts on a smaller area and creates a greater **pressure**.

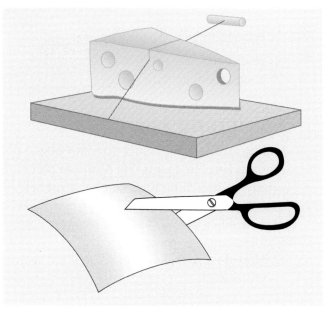

▲ *Fig 1* Forces used for cutting

1 Write down three other examples of a force acting over a small area being used to pierce an object.

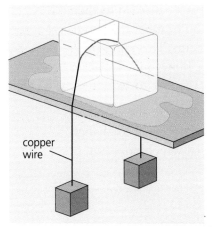

copper wire

▲ *Fig 2* Cutting ice using pressure

Fig 2 shows how a high pressure can melt ice. Ice skaters also use high pressure. The blades of their skates melt the ice so they can skate on the water produced. They leave traces where they have skated. These form as ice melts under the pressure and then re-freezes when the skate has passed.

Low pressure

Skiers need to exert a low pressure so that they do not sink into the snow. Skis do their job by spreading the downward push of the skier on the snow over a large area. The pressure is small. This enables the skier to ski on the top of the snow, unlike the skater who skates in the ice.

Heavy machinery such as tanks and cranes also need to exert a small pressure so that they do not become stuck in the ground or damage the roads that they travel over. The solution in these cases is to use caterpillar tracks that have a larger area than wheels.

▲ *Fig 3* *Caterpillar tracks reduce pressure*

2 Write down three examples of things that use a large area of contact to reduce the pressure caused by a force.

Calculating pressure

The pressure caused by a force is calculated using the formula:

$$\text{pressure} = \frac{\text{force}}{\text{area}} \quad \text{or} \quad p = \frac{F}{A}$$

The pressure is measured in **pascal** (Pa). This unit is the same as a **N/m^2**.

Example

An elephant weighs 5 tonnes, which is equivalent to 50 000 N. When standing on four feet, the area in contact with the ground is $0.4\,m^2$. Calculate the pressure on the ground.

Answer

pressure = force ÷ area = 50 000 N ÷ $0.4\,m^2$
    = 125 000 Pa

This may seem to be a large pressure, but the answer to question **3** shows that humans can exert much larger pressures than elephants!

3 A (slim) young lady weighs 600 N. As she walks wearing stiletto heels, there are times when all her weight rests on one heel. The area of a stiletto heel is $1\,cm^2$, or $0.0001\,m^2$. Calculate the pressure she exerts on the ground in Pa.

Words you should know

pressure   pascal

97 Hydraulics

In this unit you will learn the answers to these questions:
- What are the advantages of using liquids in machinery?
- How are the pressure transmitted by a liquid and the force it exerts worked out?

Fluids under pressure

Gases and liquids behave very differently under pressure. If you put your finger over the end of an air-filled syringe you can easily push the plunger in, squashing the air. Let go, and the plunger springs back. If the syringe is filled with water the plunger

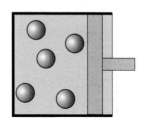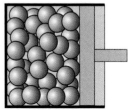

▲ *Fig 1* The gas particles can be pushed closer together, but the liquid particles cannot

cannot be pushed in. Gases are squashy because there are relatively large spaces between the particles. Liquid particles are close-packed and cannot be forced any closer together.

Solids exert a downward pressure on surfaces due to their weight. Liquids and gases exert pressure equally in all directions. The pressure in a liquid is caused by the movement of the particles and the force they exert on the walls of the container. Because the particles have equal movement in all directions, the pressure is exerted equally in all directions.

Liquids are useful because they can transmit a pressure round corners. You can demonstrate this with two syringes and some plastic tube as in Fig 2. Pushing in the plunger of one syringe causes the plunger of the second syringe to be pushed out.

The hydraulic lift

Liquids can be used to increase the size of a force because they can transmit pressure. Hydraulic car jacks and the lifts found in garages use a liquid to raise a heavy weight by the application of a small force. This can be demonstrated by using two unequal-sized syringes as shown in Fig 3. A force acting on the smaller syringe creates a pressure that is transmitted through the liquid. This pressure then acts on the greater area of the larger syringe, exerting an upward force. The upward force at the large syringe is greater than the downward force at the small syringe because the liquid pressure is acting over a large area.

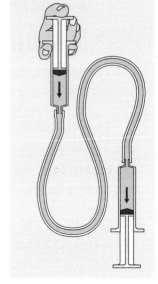

▲ *Fig 2*
Transmission of pressure

Example

In Fig 3, a downward force of 50 N acts on a piston of area 2 cm².

a) Calculate the pressure transmitted by the liquid.

b) The area of the piston in the large syringe is 12 cm². Calculate the upward force on the piston.

Answer

a) pressure = force ÷ area

= 50 N ÷ 2 cm² = 25 N/cm²

b) force = pressure × area

= 25 N/cm² × 12 cm² = 300 N

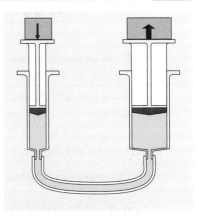

▲ *Fig 3* *Making a larger force*

1 a) In an arrangement similar to that shown in Fig 3, a force of 80 N pushes down on a piston of area 4 cm². Calculate the pressure transmitted by the fluid.

b) This pressure acts on a large piston of area 25 cm². Calculate the force that the liquid exerts on the large piston.

Hydraulic machinery

When the driver presses the brake pedal, pressure is transmitted from the master cylinder to the slave cylinder. The slave cylinder moves the brake pads and shoes which causes the car to slow and stop. Part of a car braking system is shown in Fig 4.

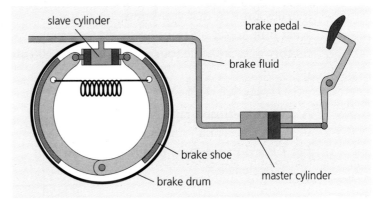

▶ *Fig 4* *Car braking system*

2 a) In the braking system shown in Fig 4, a force of 200 N is exerted on a piston of area 25 cm² in the master cylinder. Calculate the pressure transmitted by the brake fluid.

b) The brake fluid transmits this pressure to four slave cylinders, each of which has a piston of area 3 cm². Calculate the force on each piston.

c) It is important that the fluid used in a car braking system does not contain any air. Explain why the brakes are not as effective if an air bubble is trapped in the brake fluid.

Words you should know   **hydraulic**

98 How fast?

In this unit you will learn the answers to these questions:
- What is the relationship between speed, distance travelled and time taken?
- What information does a distance–time graph give?
- How are displacement–time graphs interpreted?

Calculating speed

The equation linking speed, distance and time is:

average speed = distance travelled ÷ time taken   or $v = d/t$

Using the symbols v for speed, d for distance and t for time, the speed formula can be written in three different ways:

$$v = d/t, \quad d = v \times t \text{ and } t = d/v.$$

If you are going on a long journey by car you need to be able to make an estimate of your journey time so that you know what time to set off from home. At an average speed of 60 mph on a motorway, a 300 mile journey should take 300 miles ÷ 60 mph = 5 hours.

1 Use the speed formula to calculate the average speed of:
   a) a bus that travels 60 miles in 2 hours,
   b) a sprinter who runs 100 m in 12.5 s.

2 Calculate the time taken to travel:
   a) 150 miles at an average speed of 40 mph,
   b) 300 m at an average speed of 12 m/s,
   c) 6000 miles at an average speed of 500 mph.

Using graphs

A **distance–time** graph can be used to represent a journey. Fig 1 is a distance–time graph of a bicycle ride.

You can gain a lot of information about the journey by looking at the slope, or **gradient**, of the line. This gradient represents the speed of the cyclist.

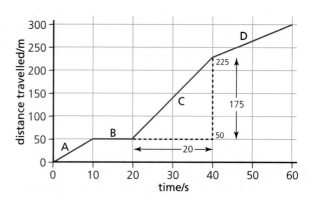

▲ *Fig 1 A distance–time graph*

3 Without doing any calculations, write out a brief description of the bicycle ride.

Calculating the gradient of the line gives the actual speed of the cyclist at any point on the journey. The gradient of part C of the graph is (225 − 50)/20, representing a speed of 8.75 m/s.

4 Calculate the speed of the cyclist at parts A and D of Fig 1, and the average speed for the journey.

One important piece of information that the graph does not give is where the journey ended. You can tell that the cyclist travelled a total distance of 300 m but there is no information about the direction in which the cyclist was travelling.

A **displacement–time** graph gives more information than a distance–time graph. **Displacement** is the distance an object moves from a certain position. It can have both positive and negative values to show movement in opposite directions. Fig 2 is a displacement–time graph for a child on a swing. It shows her swinging away from the mid-point of the swing, then returning and swinging away in the opposite direction.

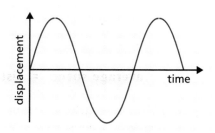

▲ **Fig 2** *A displacement–time graph of a swing*

The gradient of the graph can also be positive or negative. If the positive value represents speed in one particular direction, then the negative value represents the speed in the opposite direction. So the gradient of a displacement–time graph gives information about both the speed of an object and the direction in which it is moving. These two quantities together, the speed and the direction, are called the **velocity**.

Fig 3 is a displacement–time graph that represents the movement of a lift. Part A of the graph represents the lift travelling from the eighth to the fifteenth floor of a building. The gradient of each part of the graph represents the velocity of the lift, i.e. its speed and direction. You can tell therefore that the lift was moving down during part C. The gradient of this part of the graph is −2, representing a velocity of 2 m/s downwards.

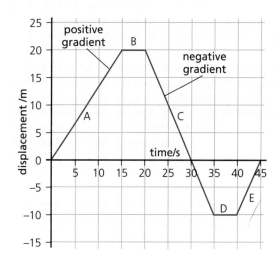

▲ **Fig 3** *A displacement–time graph of a lift*

5 a) Describe the movement of the lift that Fig 3 represents.
  b) Calculate the velocity during parts A and E of the graph.
  c) How far did the lift travel altogether, and where was it after 45 s?

Words you should know

displacement   speed   velocity

99 Coming to a halt

In this unit you will learn the answers to these questions:
■ What are the factors that affect stopping distance?
■ How does stopping distance depend on speed and the driver's reaction time?

Drivers of vehicles need to judge how fast it is safe to drive in different conditions. If they drive too fast then they may not be able to stop the vehicle when something unexpected happens; this can lead to accidents.

Braking distance

The speed limit on roads where there are a lot of houses is usually 30 mph, equivalent to a speed of 14 m/s.

On a dry road in good conditions, a car travelling at 14 m/s takes about 2 s to stop after the brakes are applied. The average speed while braking is 7 m/s (this is the average of the initial speed and the final speed).

> **1** Show that a car that brakes from a speed of 14 m/s and stops after 2.0 s travels 14 m.

A **braking distance** of 14 m is quite a long way, and yet cars travelling at motorway speeds are often to be seen with a shorter distance than this between them.

▲ **Fig 1** A braking distance of 14 m

> **2** The braking time from a speed of 28 m/s is twice that from a speed of 14 m/s, so the car in question **1** would take 4.0 s to brake from a speed of 28 m/s. Calculate the distance the car travels in braking from this speed. (Do not forget to use the car's average speed in your calculation.)

If you compare the answers to questions **1** and **2**, you can see that when the speed of a car doubles, its braking distance *becomes four times as big*. Not only does it take twice as long to stop, its average speed is also twice as great.

Some of the factors that can affect braking distance are the type of road surface, weather conditions, the weight of the vehicle and the condition of its tyres and brakes. Water acts as a lubricant and a film of water between a tyre and the road would cause the vehicle to slide over the road surface. Tread on tyres is very important because it allows the tyre to push water out from underneath the tyre, so the tyre stays in direct contact with the road.

▲ **Fig 2** *Tyre tread*

Stopping distance

Good drivers are always ready for the unexpected. If a child steps out from between two parked cars the driver's reaction time, that is the time between the driver seeing the child and pressing the brake pedal, is very important.

An alert driver can react in 0.6 s, but this time is lengthened if the driver is tired or has been drinking alcohol. During the time it takes the driver to react, the car carries on moving at a steady speed. The distance travelled by the car in this time is referred to as '**thinking distance**' in the Highway Code.

Stopping distance is the total distance travelled by a vehicle while the driver is reacting and braking.

▶ **Fig 3** *Small children stepping out from behind parked cars present particular problems to drivers*

3 **a)** Assuming a reaction time of 0.6 s, calculate the 'thinking distance' for a car travelling at 14 m/s and one travelling at 28 m/s.

   b) Use the braking distances you calculated in questions **1** and **2** to calculate the total stopping distances from these speeds.

Words you should know
braking distance   **stopping distance**   **thinking distance**

100 Forces in and out of balance

In this unit you will learn the answer to this question:
■ How is an object's motion affected by the forces acting on it?

Unless you are travelling downhill, if you want to keep a bicycle moving you have to keep pedalling. This unit is concerned with the forces that act on objects that are slowing down, speeding up or travelling at a constant speed.

What makes a bicycle go?

Like buses, trains, cars and lorries, bicycles are driven by **friction**. Anyone who has ever ridden a bicycle onto a patch of ice realises that without friction there is no propulsion. When a cyclist pushes on the pedals the force is transmitted through the chain to the rear wheel. The rear wheel pushes backwards against the road, as shown in Fig 1. Friction between the road surface and the tyre prevents the tyre from sliding. The friction force pushes forwards on the tyre, propelling the cycle in the forwards direction.

▲ **Fig 1** The push of a bicycle wheel on the road surface

▲ **Fig 2** The push of the road surface on the wheel

The backward push of the wheels on the road or track is matched in size by the forward push of the friction force that acts between the two surfaces. This friction force is the **driving force**.

1 We rely on friction to walk. Describe the forces between the floor and a shoe when a person walks.

What slows a bicycle down?

There are several forces that combine together to slow you down when you stop pedalling a bicycle. One of them is the **air resistance**. You have to exert a force to push the air out of the way so that your body and bicycle can pass. Racing cyclists crouch to reduce the effect of air resistance.

▶ **Fig 3** This racing cyclist crouches to reduce the effect of air resistance

200

Resistive forces also act on the tyres. This is called **rolling resistance** and is caused by the tyres changing their shape as they go round. You can minimise the effects of rolling resistance by keeping the tyres pumped up to the recommended pressure.

A third resistive force comes from the **friction** in the wheel bearings, but provided that these are kept lubricated they do not offer much resistance to motion.

2 What are the three forces slowing you down when cycling?

Going on a bicycle ride

Resistive forces only act when a bicycle is moving, so at the instant a cyclist sets off the only force acting is the driving force. Once the cyclist is moving the resistive forces start to act. If the total resistive force is smaller than the driving force the forces are unbalanced and the cyclist accelerates.

As the cyclist goes faster, the resistive forces increase. The further the cyclist travels each second, the more air has to be pushed out of the way and the more times the tyres change their shape. Eventually the resistive forces are equal to the driving force. The cyclist now travels at a constant speed. Because the forces are equal in size but act in opposite directions, they are said to be **balanced forces**.

Cyclists usually stop pedalling when they brake, so as a cyclist slows down and stops the resistive force is the only force acting. Fig 4 shows the forces acting on a cyclist when speeding up, travelling at constant speed and braking.

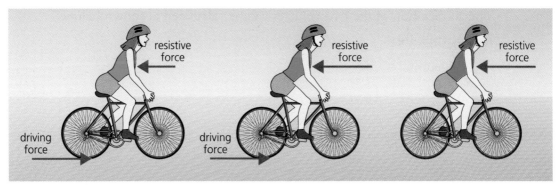

▲ **Fig 4** *The cyclist on the left is speeding up, the one in the centre is travelling at a constant speed and the one on the right is slowing down*

Words you should know

air resistance   **balanced forces**   **friction**   **rolling resistance**

101 Acceleration

In this unit you will learn the answers to these questions:
- What does acceleration mean?
- What is a negative acceleration?
- How is acceleration calculated?

When the forces acting on a moving object are unbalanced, the result is a change in velocity.

Speeding up

Imagine a milk float and a small car setting off together from some traffic lights. The milk float reaches its top speed of 8 m/s after a time interval of 5 s. The car accelerates to a speed of 14 m/s in 7 s. Which has the greater acceleration?

For an object moving in a straight line, **acceleration** is how much it speeds up by each second.

> **The definition of acceleration is:**
> **increase in velocity / time   or**
> $$a = (v_2 - v_1) / t$$

1 Use the definition to calculate the acceleration of:
  a) a cyclist who speeds up from 0 m/s to 10 m/s in 4 s,
  b) a car that speeds up from 15 m/s to 30 m/s in 9 s,
  c) an aircraft that speeds up from 10 m/s to 60 m/s in 10 s.

▶ **Fig 1** This aircraft needs a large acceleration to reach its take-off speed before the end of the runway

The acceleration of the two vehicles can be calculated as shown below.

For the milk float:

$$\text{acceleration} = \frac{v_2 - v_1}{t}$$

$$= \frac{8\,\text{m/s} - 0\,\text{m/s}}{5\,\text{s}}$$

$$= 1.6\,\text{m/s}^2$$

For the car:

$$\text{acceleration} = \frac{v_2 - v_1}{t}$$

$$= \frac{14\,\text{m/s} - 0\,\text{m/s}}{7\,\text{s}}$$

$$= 2\,\text{m/s}^2$$

Fig 2 is a speed–time graph for part of a car journey:

   A shows steady speed
B & E shows speeding up/ accelerating
   C shows slowing down/ decelerating/ negative acceleration
   D shows stopped.

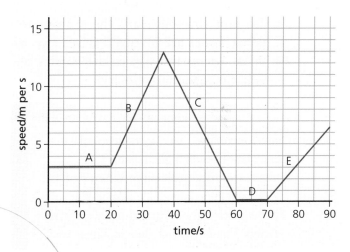

▲ **Fig 2** *A speed–time graph*

The gradient of a speed–time graph represents the size of the acceleration of an object. A positive gradient means that it is speeding up and a negative gradient represents a slowing down.

2 Work out the acceleration (gradient) of the graph for each section B, C and E.

Information about the direction of travel can be obtained by studying a **velocity–time graph**. You learned in Unit 98 that the velocity of an object describes both its speed and its direction, so velocity can have negative as well as positive values.

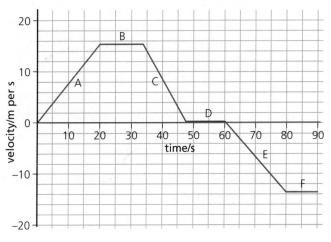

▲ **Fig 3** *A velocity–time graph*

Fig 3 shows a velocity–time graph for part of a car journey:

   A shows acceleration
B & F shows steady speed
   C shows slowing down
   D shows stopped
   E shows accelerating in the opposite direction.

3 a) Calculate the value of the acceleration represented by parts A, C and E of the graph.
  b) Use the speed equation to calculate the distance travelled by the car on the outward part of its journey.
  c) After 90 s, how far is the car from the place it set off from?

Words you should know

acceleration

102 Falling down

In this unit you will learn the answers to these questions:
- What forces are involved when two objects interact?
- What affects the size of the Earth's pull on an object?
- What is terminal velocity?

The Earth's pull

Newton realised that gravitational forces act between all masses. The effects are only noticeable when one of them is very massive. We notice the effects of the gravitational forces due to planets, but not those due to ourselves!

Another of Newton's important discoveries was that objects exert forces on each other, so if one object pulls or pushes a second, then the second object pulls or pushes the first with an equal-sized force in the opposite direction. You came across this idea in Unit 100 when considering the force that propels a bicycle.

▲ **Fig 1** *The forces between you and the Earth are equal in size but opposite in direction*

The Earth is pulling you towards it and you are pulling the Earth towards you with an equal-sized force. The effect of your pull on the Earth's mass is negligible so rather than it moving to meet you, you move towards the Earth.

The size of the Earth's pull is called its **gravitational field strength**, or *g* for short. Close to the surface of the Earth this has a value of 10 N/kg. Each kg of your body mass is pulled towards the centre of the Earth with a force of 10 N. This downward pull is the force called weight, which can be calculated using the formula:

weight = mass × gravitational field strength   or $W = mg$

1 Why is it incorrect to say that 'a bag of sugar weighs 1 kg'?

2 Potatoes can be bought in 50 kg sacks.
   a) How much does a sack of potatoes weigh on the Earth?
   b) The Moon's gravitational field strength is 1.5 N/kg. How much would a sack of potatoes weigh on the Moon?

Terminal velocity

The diagram shows a skydiver falling. There are two forces acting on her. The Earth pulls her down and air resistance acts upwards.

▲ *Fig 2 A skydiver falling*

As she continues to fall her velocity increases.
As her velocity increases so does the air resistance.

When the air resistance is equal to the force of attraction of the Earth, the two forces are **balanced**. At this point her velocity remains constant. This is called the **terminal velocity**.

3 Copy the diagram twice.
   Label your diagrams A and B.
   On diagram A draw the forces when the skydiver is speeding up, before she opens her parachute.
   On diagram B draw the forces when she is travelling at terminal velocity before she opens her parachute.
   Finally, draw a diagram showing the forces when she has opened her parachute and is slowing down.

Words you should know
gravitational field strength   **terminal velocity**

103 Turning forces

In this unit you will learn the answers to these questions:
- ■ What are the factors that determine the turning effect of a force?
- ■ How is the moment of a force calculated?
- ■ What is the principle of moments?

We use forces to turn things round whenever we move an arm or a leg, cut with scissors or ride a bicycle.

Turning round

You steer a bicycle with your hands placed at the end of the handlebars rather than near the middle, and when you push open a swing door it opens easily if you apply your push as far away from the hinge as possible. The effect that a force has in causing an object to move in a straight line depends on the size of the force. When forces are used to turn things round both the direction of the force and its point of action need to be considered.

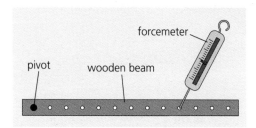

Fig 1 shows an experiment using a forcemeter to make a wooden beam turn round.

◀ **Fig 1** *Experimenting with turning forces*

1 List six everyday examples of forces being used to turn objects round.

The results of this experiment show that the force has the greatest turning effect when it is applied as far away from the pivot as possible and at right angles to a line from the point of action to the pivot.

The measurement of the effectiveness of a force in causing rotation is called its **moment**. The moment of a force is calculated using the formula:

> **moment = force × perpendicular distance to pivot**

The force shown in Fig 2(a) has a moment of 15 N × 0.8 m = 12 Nm. The moment of that on the right is 0 since the perpendicular distance from the force line to the pivot is zero.

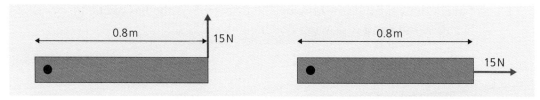

▲ **Fig 2(a)** *This force has the greatest turning effect*

Fig 2(b) *This force has no turning effect at all*

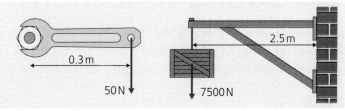

2 Calculate the moments of the forces shown in Fig 3.

▲ *Fig 3*

A question of balance

When we turn on a tap, we want the forces we exert to rotate the tap. Machines such as cranes have to be designed so that they are stable. This means that any force that has a turning effect has to be counterbalanced with a force that has an equal turning effect in the opposite direction.

The **principle of moments** applies to situations where there are two or more turning forces in balance. It states that:

> **when an object is in equilibrium the sum of the clockwise moments about a pivot must equal the sum of the anticlockwise moments.**

When you hold a drink in your hand there are two turning forces acting on your forearm, as shown in Fig 4. The weight of the drink has a clockwise moment that is counterbalanced by the upward pull of the biceps. Because the biceps are positioned very close to the pivot, they have to exert large forces to counterbalance the effect of forces at the hand. The principle of moments can be used to calculate the size of the force needed to counterbalance the weight of the drink. Each force has the same moment, so

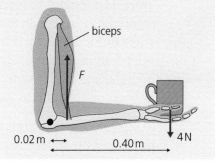

▲ *Fig 4* Turning forces acting on your forearm

$$F \times 0.02\,\text{m} = 4\,\text{N} \times 0.40\,\text{m} \quad F = \frac{(4\,\text{N} \times 0.40\,\text{m})}{0.02\,\text{m}}$$

$$F = 80\,\text{N}$$

3 The arm shown in Fig 4 is an example of a lever. Does it magnify force or distance?

Using levers

Levers use forces to turn things round. A lever used to remove a tight lid from a tin does so by **force magnification**. In this case the force exerted by the lever is much closer to the pivot then the force that the person exerts.

Other levers **magnify distance**. When an angler uses a fishing rod a small movement near the base of the rod produces a large movement of the fish.

Words you should know

      equilibrium   **force magnification**   **moment**

104 **Sound reflections**

In this unit you will learn the answers to these questions:
- How do reflections of sound affect the acoustics of rooms?
- How is ultrasound used at sea and in medicine?

Hearing yourself speak

When you talk in a room that has been emptied of furniture, you can hear your voice make a 'ringing' sound. Without furniture in the room to absorb the energy of the sound, the large flat surfaces of the walls are excellent reflectors of sound waves. Like a ball bouncing between the walls, the sound is reflected several times before it becomes inaudible. The effect is known as **reverberation**. It can cause speech to sound unclear as each sound is mixed with **echoes** of sounds made a fraction of a second earlier. The control of reverberation is very important in large halls, particularly those where music is played. If there is too much reverberation the music sounds 'fuzzy', but too little gives a 'flat' tone, as the individual notes do not blend into each other.

> **speed equations:**
> $$speed = \frac{distance}{time}$$
> $$distance = speed \times time$$

▲ **Fig 1** The acoustics of the Albert Hall have been improved by using large baffles in the ceiling. These absorb the sound, reducing the reverberation time

To separate a sound from its echo, a large distance is needed between the sound source and the reflecting surface. Fig 2 shows a girl shouting her name and hearing the echo.

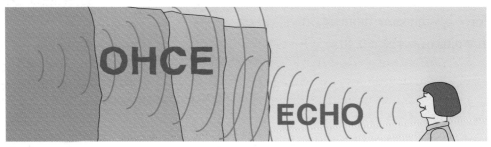

▲ Fig 2

1 A girl, standing some distance from a large brick wall, shouts her name and hears the echo 0.6 s later.
   a) The speed of sound in air is 330 m/s. Use the speed equation to work out how far the sound travelled between the girl calling her name and hearing the echo.
   b) How far was the girl from the brick wall?

Using echoes

Echoes are used in many ways.

1 At sea to locate shoals of fish and wrecks on the sea bed.

2 By geologists to study the structure of the Earth and locate minerals.

3 By surgeons to study body organs.

Short bursts of high-frequency waves, called **ultrasound** because the frequency is above the human audible range, are used to search for shoals of fish and wrecks on the sea bed.

▲ **Fig 3** Using sound to search for a wreck

2 Sound travels in water at a speed of 1500 m/s. A pulse of sound is sent out from a ship and the echo from the sea bed returns 0.44 s later.

a) Use the speed equation to calculate the distance travelled by the sound.

b) How deep is the sea?

c) What would be noticed if a shoal of fish swam under the ship?

Sound in medicine

Ultrasound is used extensively by doctors and surgeons to 'see' inside the body without using X-rays. It is considered to be safer than X-rays because, provided a low power is used, there is no damage to body cells or tissue. Sound scans can be used to examine delicate organs such as the brain and the eye. Sound scans are routine for pregnant women to check on the size and development of the fetus. Fig 4 shows an ultrasound of a 12-week-old fetus in the womb.

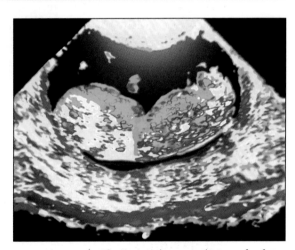

▲ **Fig 4** An ultrasound scan of a fetus

The picture is built up by the reflection of ultrasound whenever there is a boundary between body tissues. In this case the fetus reflects more energy than the surrounding amniotic fluid does. The fetus shows up lighter than the fluid.

3 Describe the advantages of using ultrasound to scan body organs.

Words you should know

echo   reverberation   ultrasound

105 Reflecting light

In this unit you will learn the answers to these questions:
- How do surfaces reflect light?
- How does a plane mirror form an image?
- What are the properties of the image in a plane mirror?

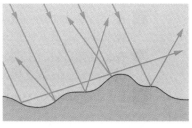

▲ **Fig 1** *Light is reflected from a rough surface*

Seeing

You can see the page of this book because of the way in which light is reflected. Light comes from light sources such as the Sun, flames and lamps. Surfaces that are not perfectly smooth scatter this light by reflecting it in all directions. The surface of this page may look smooth to you, but under a microscope it would appear rough, covered in small hills and valleys.

Fig 1 shows how a rough surface scatters the light that falls on it, making it possible for the light to be detected by eyes in different positions in a room.

Fig 2 shows a band. The audience can see them because light from the lamps is reflected in all directions.

◀ **Fig 2** *The band*

Regular reflection

Mirrors and other smooth surfaces reflect light in a regular way. The light is reflected from a mirror surface at the same angle as it hits it. Fig 3 shows two pairs of angles that are equal. The angles between the rays and a line drawn at right angles to the surface, marked i and r, are known as the **angle of incidence** and the **angle of reflection**.

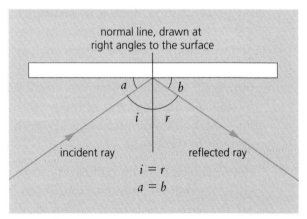

normal line, drawn at right angles to the surface

a b

i r

incident ray   reflected ray

$i = r$
$a = b$

▲ **Fig 3** *The angles of incidence and reflection*

> **1** Mirrors can be used in periscopes to turn light through 90°. Draw a diagram to show how two mirrors can be used to make a periscope. Trace the path of light as it passes through the periscope.

Images

When you look into a mirror, you see a likeness of yourself. This likeness is called an **image**. You also see images when looking at the picture on a television or cinema screen. Images do not have to be exact copies. That on a cinema screen is a **magnified** image and when you use a camera to take a photograph the image captured on the film is **diminished** (smaller than the object). The images made by projectors and cameras are upside down (inverted) and they are examples of **real** images. A real image is one that can be caught on a screen. If an image cannot be caught on a screen then it is **virtual**, it is not really there.

The image in a mirror

Is the image in a mirror real or virtual? Upside down or upright? Magnified or diminished? Whereabouts is the image?

You may be able to answer some of these questions from your everyday experience of looking into mirrors. Fig 4 shows how you can use three **ray streaks** from a lamp to locate the position of the image formed by a plane mirror. Once you have found the position of the image, you can use a piece of paper as a screen to test whether the image is real or virtual.

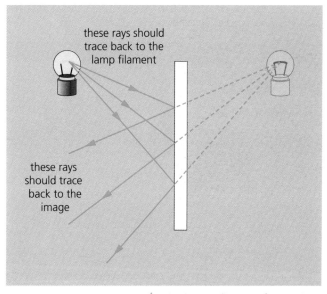

these rays should trace back to the lamp filament

these rays should trace back to the image

▲ **Fig 4** Ray diagram for a mirror

The image formed by a plane mirror is virtual, and it is formed straight behind the mirror, as far back as the object is in front. It is also upright and the same size as the object.

2 In tracing back the ray streaks to find the position of the lamp and the image of the lamp, what did you assume about the way in which light travels?

Words you should know

image   real   virtual

106 **Different waves**

In this unit you will learn the answers to these questions:
- How are sounds produced and transmitted through the air?
- What is the difference between a transverse wave and a longitudinal wave?

Sound and light travel as waves. Waves transfer energy from a source to another place, without the transfer of matter.

Making sounds

All sounds are made by vibrations. You can see an elastic band vibrate if you pluck or 'twang' it. A signal generator can be used to make a loudspeaker cone vibrate at different frequencies. The speaker cone moves in and out repeatedly. This can be shown to affect a piece of cling film stretched over a frame (see Fig 1) – it also moves in and out.

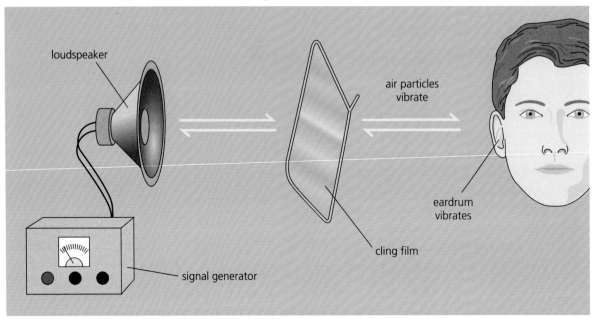

▲ **Fig 1** *Vibration of a loudspeaker*

The air particles do not travel from the loud speaker to the ear. They only vibrate. The vibrations of the air particles cause the air to be squashed and stretched alternately as the sound wave passes.

A wave model

A slinky spring can be used to show how a sound wave travels. If the spring is stretched and then squashed (pushed and pulled) as Fig 2 then a longitudinal wave is sent down the spring as in Fig 3.

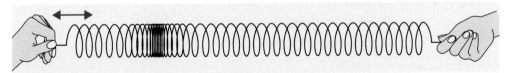

▲ *Fig 2 Slinky spring can show how sound wave moves*

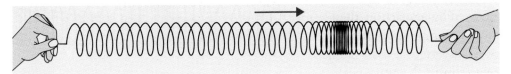

▲ *Fig 3 A longitudinal wave moves along the spring*

Each part of the spring vibrates in the direction of wave travel. The compressions and rarefactions travel through the air to the ear.

1 What is the effect on a sound when the amplitude of the vibrations of the loudspeaker cone is increased?

2 Name three sources of sound waves.

Another type of wave

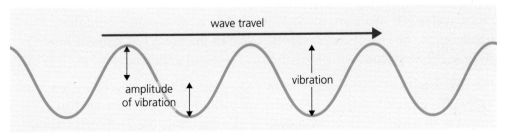

▲ *Fig 4 Vibrations of a transverse wave*

Surface water waves, light, radio and other electromagnetic waves (see Unit 110) are transverse waves. In a **transverse wave** the vibrations are at right angles (perpendicular) to the direction of travel. A rope or a slinky spring can be used to study the vibration of a transverse wave. Fig 4 shows the vibrations of a transverse wave.

Words you should know
       amplitude   longitudinal   transverse

107 Wave measurements

In this unit you will learn the answers to these questions:
■ What is the meaning of wavelength and frequency?

The difference between longitudinal and transverse waves was studied in Unit 106. The amplitude of a wave motion is the measurement of the greatest displacement from the mean position.

The long and short of it

A wave motion is a repetitive motion. A longitudinal wave consists of compression followed by rarefaction, then another compression, and so on. Transverse waves are similar. They consist of a wave peak, then a trough, followed by another peak. One complete cycle is a compression and rarefaction in the case of a longitudinal wave, and a peak and trough in the case of a transverse wave. The whole wave motion is formed by repetitions of this cycle.

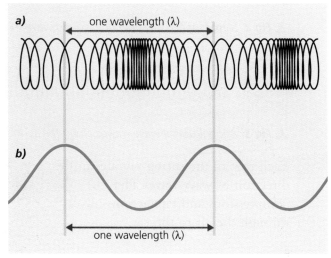

▲ **Fig 1** Wavelengths of a) longitudinal and b) transverse waves

The **wavelength** of a wave motion (symbol λ) is the distance from the beginning to the end of one complete cycle of the wave. Fig 1 shows how to measure the wavelength of a longitudinal wave and a transverse wave.

The wavelength of sound ranges from a few centimetres to several metres, but is typically around 1 metre. Light has a wavelength of approximately half a millionth of a metre and the wavelength of radio waves used for broadcasting varies from three metres (VHF) to two thousand metres (long wave).

How often?

The **frequency** of a wave (symbol f) is the number of cycles of the wave that go past any point each second. It is measured in hertz (Hz). Audible sounds range in frequency from approximately 20 Hz to 20 000 Hz. Using the arrangement shown in Unit 106, Fig 1, you can watch the effect on the loudspeaker cone when the frequency of the a.c. supply is increased.

1 How does increasing the frequency affect the pitch of a sound?

The effect on the wavelength when the frequency of a wave motion is increased can be studied using a slinky spring or rope. Fig 2 shows two waves travelling at the same speed in a rope. You can see that when the frequency of the wave is increased, the wavelength gets shorter.

a wave on a rope   a higher frequency wave

▲ *Fig 2*

High-pitched sounds have a higher frequency and shorter wavelength than low-pitched ones. Light also varies in frequency and wavelength. Blue light has a higher frequency than red light. When they are travelling at the same speed the wavelength of blue light is shorter than that of red.

Tuning in a radio

Radio waves cover a wide range of wavelengths and frequencies. Radio programmes are broadcast on one of three wavebands; long wave, medium wave and VHF (very high frequency). As its name implies. VHF uses the highest frequencies and the shortest wavelengths. It is used to broadcast high quality stereo programmes, but can only be received within 40 to 50 km of

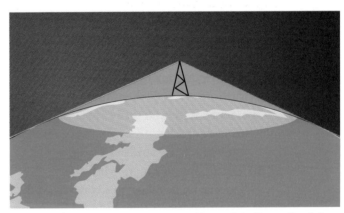

▲ *Fig 3* VHF waves travel in straight lines. The lighter shaded area shows where they can be received

a transmitter. Long wave broadcasts have the lowest frequency. Unlike shorter radio waves, long wavelength waves follow the Earth's curvature. This means that broadcasts from just one transmitter can be received everywhere in the country as well as on the continent.

Words you should know

frequency   wavelength

108 Refraction of light

In this unit you will learn the answers to these questions:
- What happens when a wave crosses a boundary?
- When does a change of speed result in a change of wave direction?
- How does refraction cause virtual images to be formed?

Changing the speed

Whenever a wave passes from one substance into another, there is a change of speed. The consequences of this speed change can be seen by studying water waves in a ripple tank. Fig 1 shows what happens when water waves are slowed down as they pass into a shallow water region.

Notice how the parts of the waves in the shallow water lag behind those travelling in the deeper water. This change in wave speed is called **refraction**. When the waves emerge from the shallow water they speed up again.

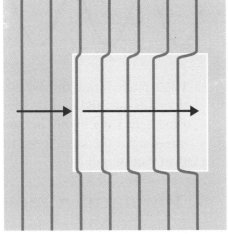

▲ *Fig 1 Using a ripple tank*

> **1 a)** The frequency of the waves in the shallow water is the same as that in the deeper water. Describe what happens to the wavelength of the waves when they enter the shallow water.
> **b)** On a copy of Fig 1, finish the picture by drawing the waves as they speed up when they emerge from the shallow water.

When the waves meet the shallow water region at an angle each wave is slowed down and the waves change direction. Fig 2 shows the change in direction of water waves as they enter and leave a shallow water region.

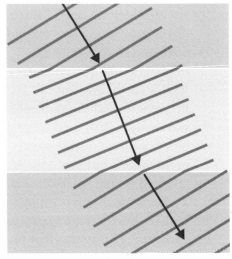

▲ *Fig 2 Refraction causes waves to change direction*

Refracting light

You can use a block of glass to study the effect of light being slowed down as it passes from air into the glass. The change in direction of the light depends on the angle at which it meets the surface. Fig 3 shows these changes. You will also notice that some light is reflected at each boundary.

The lower diagram in Fig 3 shows the angles of incidence and refraction drawn relative to a normal line (a line drawn at right angles to the surface). The change in direction is towards this normal line when the light slows down and away from it when the light speeds up.

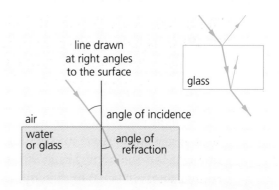

▶ **Fig 3** *Refraction in glass*

Image formation

If you look at the bottom of a swimming pool while standing on the poolside, the pool looks to be shallower than it really is. You can see the same effect if you examine the printing in this book, looking at it through a glass block or a beaker of water. Fig 4 shows how you can locate the image formed when light passes through glass.

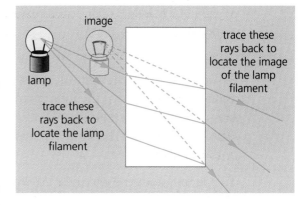

▶ **Fig 4** *Ray diagram for a block of glass*

2 **a)** Is the image formed by the glass real or virtual ? Explain how you can tell.
   b) Choose words from the list to describe the other properties of the image formed by glass. *diminished   inverted   magnified   same size   upright*

The change in direction as light leaves water or glass can be used to explain why the bottom of the swimming pool appears to be nearer than it really is. As light leaves the water it changes direction, moving away from a line drawn at right angles to the water surface. Fig 5 shows how this leads to the formation of a virtual image.

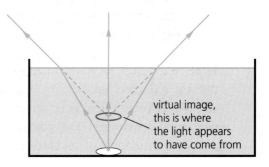

▲ **Fig 5** *Refraction produces a virtual image*

3 Imagine that you are swimming under water, looking at someone standing at the poolside. Draw a diagram to show how light from the person would reach your eye. Whereabouts would the person look to be?

Words you should know
refraction

109 **Using total internal reflection**

In this unit you will learn the answers to these questions:
- When is light totally internally reflected at a boundary?
- What is total internal reflection used for?

Light getting faster

When light passes from a transparent substance such as glass or perspex into air, it speeds up. Unless the light hits the boundary at 90°, this change in speed causes a change in direction. As always when a wave passes from one substance to another, some of the light is reflected at equal angles. This is shown in Unit 108, Fig 3.

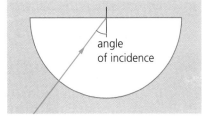

▲ *Fig 1*

Using a semicircular glass block allows you to investigate this effect by changing the angle at which the light meets the glass–air boundary. Fig 1 shows a suitable arrangement. Provided the light is aimed at the centre of the flat face of the semicircle, it does not change direction as it enters the block. This arrangement enables you to vary the angle of incidence of the light at the glass–air boundary in the range 0° to 90°.

You should compare the light leaving the block and the light reflected as you change the angle of incidence. Fig 2 gives some typical results.

For small angles of incidence most of the light leaves the block by refraction, but some is reflected internally. As the angle of incidence is increased, the proportion of the light reflected increases and there is a reduction in the brightness of the refracted light. At an angle of incidence of around 40° the reflected light is very bright and the dim refracted light splits into a spectrum. When light only just emerges by refraction the angle of incidence is called the **critical angle**. For angles of incidence greater than the critical angle, around 42° for glass and perspex, all the light is reflected internally. This is known as **total internal reflection** (TIR).

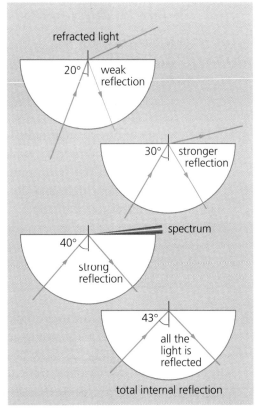

▶ *Fig 2 Showing total internal reflection*

Seeing round corners

Periscopes, bicycle reflectors and binoculars all use 45°-45°-90° prisms to turn light through an angle of 90° or 180°. Bicycle reflectors consist of hundreds of these prisms made as a single moulding. Fig 3 shows how light enters a prism and undergoes two internal reflections, each one at an angle of incidence that is greater than the critical angle. At each reflection the light is turned through an angle of 90°. The result is that light from the headlamps of a car travelling behind the cyclist is reflected back to the car driver.

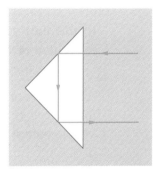

▲ **Fig 3** *Ray diagram for a prism*

1 **a)** On a copy of Fig 3, mark in the angles of incidence and reflection at the first internal reflection.
   b) Explain how the light is turned through 90° at each reflection.

2 Fig 4 shows the arrangement of two prisms in a periscope. On a copy of the diagram, trace the path of two rays of light from the ship, through the periscope, and into the eye.

▶ **Fig 4** *Using prisms in a periscope*

Fibre optics

A thin fibre of glass or plastic can be used to transmit light round bends and corners with very little energy loss. In a simple fibre, whenever the light hits the boundary it does so at an angle that is greater than the critical angle, so all the light is reflected back into the fibre. Fig 5 shows how light can travel round a bend in a fibre by travelling in a series of straight lines.

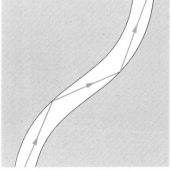

▲ **Fig 5** *Ray diagram for a fibre*

Optical fibres are used by surgeons to see inside the body using natural openings such as the mouth or anus or small incisions made for the purpose. Such an instrument used for medical purposes is called an **endoscope**. It consists of two bundles of fibres. One carries light into the body, the other transmits the reflected light to a small camera which then displays the picture onto a monitor like a television screen. Endoscopes allow surgeons to detect problems that would have have required major surgery.

3 Describe the benefits that endoscopy has brought to medicine.

Words you should know

critical angle   **endoscope**   **total internal reflection**

110 A family of waves

In this unit you will learn the answers to these questions:
- Where does each type of electromagnetic radiation occur within the spectrum?

A spectrum of visible light is obtained by sorting the waves that make up white light into an order according to wavelength and frequency. Visible light is only a small part of a large **spectrum** of waves that have some similar properties and some important differences. In this unit you will learn about the properties of electromagnetic waves. Later units will examine some of the uses of waves from different parts of the electromagnetic spectrum.

The visible spectrum

The visible part of the electromagnetic spectrum ranges from red to a deep blue or violet colour. The colour that light appears to the eye depends on the frequency of the wave motion. Blue light has a higher frequency than red light. In a vacuum, light (and other forms of electromagnetic radiation) travels at a speed of $300\,000\,000$ m/s, usually written as 3×10^8 m/s. When light changes speed as it passes through different substances the frequency does not change, only the wavelength changes. Fig 1 shows the range of frequency of the visible spectrum and the wavelength for light travelling in air or a vacuum.

	red	orange	yellow	green	cyan	blue	violet
frequency / 10^{14} Hz	4.3	5.0		6.0		6.7	7.5
wavelength / 10^{-6} m	0.7	0.6		0.5		0.45	0.4

▲ **Fig 1** The visible spectrum

The whole family

You can see from Fig 1 that the electromagnetic radiation detected by our eyes extends over a narrow range of frequencies and wavelengths. The whole electromagnetic spectrum covers a vast range of wavelengths and frequencies. Radio waves have the longest wavelength, extending up to thousands of metres. At the opposite end of the spectrum, X-rays and gamma rays can have wavelengths shorter than a millionth of a millionth of a metre (1×10^{-12} m).

The whole family of waves includes **infrared** and **ultraviolet** radiation, as well as **microwaves**. Fig 2 shows the position of each type of wave in the spectrum and the range of frequencies and wavelengths. The wavelengths apply to waves travelling in air or a vacuum.

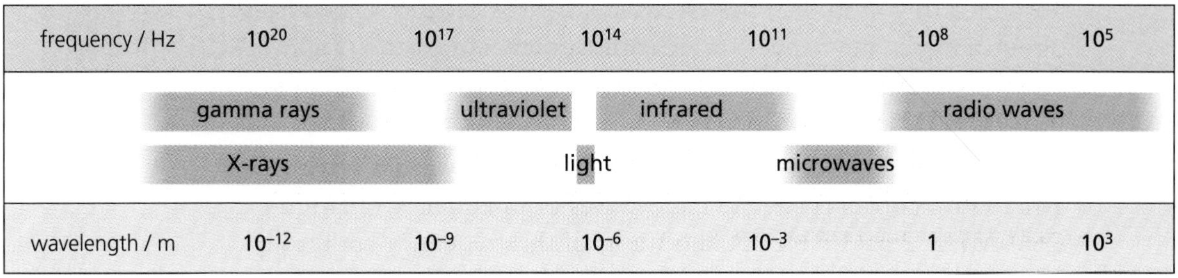

frequency / Hz	10^{20}	10^{17}	10^{14}	10^{11}	10^{8}	10^{5}
	gamma rays	ultraviolet	infrared		radio waves	
	X-rays		light	microwaves		
wavelength / m	10^{-12}	10^{-9}	10^{-6}	10^{-3}	1	10^{3}

▲ **Fig 2** *The electromagnetic spectrum*

2 a) Which type of wave has a wavelength shorter than microwaves but longer than light?

b) Which type of wave has a wavelength just beyond the shortest wavelength of the visible spectrum?

Family trends

All electromagnetic waves are transverse waves, they can all be reflected and refracted and they travel at the same speed in a vacuum. The most dangerous to humans are those with a wavelength shorter than that of light. Short wavelength electromagnetic radiation has a higher energy and can be more penetrative than longer wavelength radiation.

3 Choose words from this list for the letters A–G:

gamma rays   **infrared**   **microwaves**   **radio waves**
ultraviolet   **visible light**   **X-rays**

A	B	C	D	E	F	G

High frequency   Low frequency
Short wavelength   Long wavelength

Words you should know

infrared   **microwave**   **spectrum**   **ultraviolet**

111 At home with waves

In this unit you will learn the answer to this question:
■ **What are the uses and dangers of microwave, infrared and ultraviolet radiation?**

In Unit 110 you studied the electromagnetic spectrum. This unit is about the uses and dangers of electromagnetic radiation.

Cooking by radio

Microwaves are short-wavelength, high-frequency radio waves. Microwave cookers generate radio waves at a frequency of around 2500 MHz (2.5×10^9 Hz). Radio waves of this frequency are readily absorbed by water and salt particles in food. As these particles absorb the energy, they become heated and vibrate with a bigger amplitude. Some of the energy is passed on to nearby particles, so all the food becomes hot.

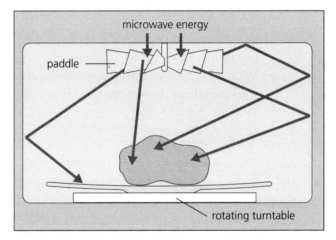

▶ **Fig 1**
A microwave cooker

Fig 1 shows a microwave cooker. The metal sides and the metal grid on the glass door reflect microwaves that hit them. The turntable moves food through the regions of high and low energy, so that the heating is even.

Vegetables take a long time to cook in boiling water or in a normal oven. The outer layers are heated first. Then heat is transferred through the food by conduction. Microwaves heat food quickly. They penetrate several centimetres before being absorbed. Food cooks evenly. Vegetables cook in a few minutes.

Microwaves can quickly defrost food taken straight from a freezer. The food is then ready for cooking.

1 **a)** How does a metal grid prevents microwaves from travelling through the glass door?
   b) Why is it important that microwaves do not leave the cooker?

Using infrared

Infrared radiation is the electromagnetic radiation with a wavelength between that of visible light and that of microwaves. It can be used for cooking, heating and in the remote controls for TV and Hi-fi systems.

Thermograms are produced by infrared radiation given out by a body (see Fig 2). They provide information about the tissues. All objects give out infrared radiation. The hotter the object the more radiation is given out.

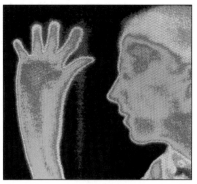

▲ **Fig 2** A thermogram

2 Wrapping hot objects in aluminium foil reduces the energy loss through infrared radiation. What property of infrared radiation does this rely on?

Using ultraviolet

We cannot see ultraviolet radiation. It is used in lighting. Fig 3 shows a fluorescent tube. An electric current passes through the mercury vapour, causing ionisation. When the positive and negative ions recombine together energy is given out as ultra–violet radiation. This radiation is absorbed by the fluorescent coating and re-emitted as light.

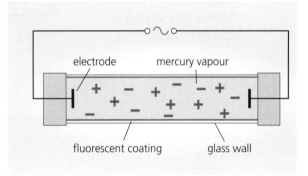

▲ **Fig 3** A fluorescent tube

Fluorescent lamps are more efficient than ordinary filament lamps. They do not rely on heating so less energy is lost when the lamp is used. The energy efficient lamp, Fig 4, is a fluorescent tube in a coil.

Sunbeds use mercury vapour lamps, without a fluorescent coating. They emit ultra–violet radiation. This can give skin a suntan. Exposure time should be limited because ultraviolet radiation can cause skin cancer.

▶ **Fig 4** An energy-efficient lamp

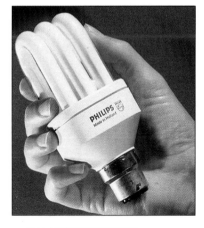

Words you should know

infrared   microwaves   ultraviolet

112 Using X-rays and gamma rays

In this unit you will learn the answer to this question:
■ How are X-rays and gamma rays used in medicine?

Short-wavelength electromagnetic radiation can have damaging effects on human tissue and it needs to be used with care.

X-ray pictures and X-ray therapy

X-rays are produced by firing high-speed electrons at a metal target, as shown in Fig 1. Although X-rays are absorbed to some extent by all body tissue, bone absorbs more X-ray energy than flesh does.

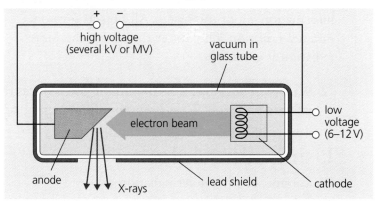

▲ **Fig 1** Producing X-rays

X-rays are passed through the body, forming an image on a photographic plate or fluorescent screen. Fig 2 shows a radiographer examining an X-ray plate. Notice how the bone shows up white on the black-and-white negative. The darker the area on the plate, the more X-radiation it has been exposed to.

▲ **Fig 2** Examining an X-ray

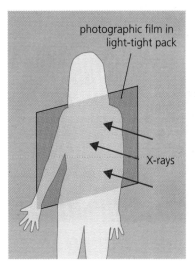

▲ **Fig 3** Having a chest X-ray (lead protection not shown)

When X-rays are absorbed by body tissue, they can cause ionisation by removing electrons from atoms. This can damage molecules that control vital aspects of a cell's behaviour or, if water molecules are ionised, cause the production of hydrogen peroxide which can damage or destroy parts of the cell. The effects on the body of exposure to X-radiation include gene mutations, damage to the central nervous system and cancer. Radiographers who operate X-ray equipment do so from behind a lead screen and lead is also used to protect parts of the subject's body that are not being X-rayed.

As well as causing cancer, X-rays can be used to destroy cancer cells. Cancer cells absorb more energy from an X-ray beam than healthy cells do. Fig 4 shows how the body is exposed to X-ray beams from several directions which overlap at the area being treated. This ensures that the cancer receives a high dose of X-rays but the surrounding tissue only gets a low dose.

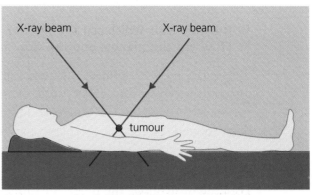

▲ **Fig 4** Using X-rays in cancer treatment

1 The X-rays used to kill cancer cells are of shorter wavelength than those used to take X-ray photographs. Explain why long-wavelength X-rays are used for photographs but short-wavelength X-rays are used for therapy.

Using gamma rays to trace and treat

Like X-rays, **gamma rays** can be used to treat cancers. Gamma rays emitted from cobalt-60 are used in a similar way to the X-rays shown in Fig 4.

Gamma rays are used to treat cancers by using sources inside the body. The body sends certain chemicals to particular organs and this can be used to concentrate radioactive materials in a chosen part of the body. Cancers of the thyroid can be treated using iodine-131, which emits both beta and gamma radiation when it decays. In this treatment the patient drinks a solution containing the isotope and the body sends the iodine to the thyroid gland. Here it decays and the radiation emitted destroys cancer cells.

Gamma rays are more commonly used as **tracers**, to detect cancers, tumours or blood flow in various parts of the body. The isotope used is an unstable form of technetium-99. The isotope emits gamma radiation only and has a half-life of 6 hours. This gives time for the isotope to reach its target while the activity is still high and it is also short enough so that the patient is not exposed to unnecessary radiation. By using technetium-99 in conjunction with other chemicals, it is possible to concentrate the radiation in a particular body organ.

2 Why is it important that tracers have a short half-life?

Words you should know

gamma rays   **tracer**   **X-rays**

113 The Earth and the Universe

In this unit you will learn the answer to this question:
- ■ How are the planets and the Sun arranged in the Solar System?

The Earth is a small **planet** orbiting a small star on one of the spiral arms of the Milky Way **galaxy**, one of an uncountable number of galaxies that make up the Universe. This unit is about the planets in the Solar System.

The inner planets

Looking from above the north pole of the Earth, motion in the Solar System is mainly anticlockwise. The nine known planets move in anticlockwise elliptical orbits around the Sun and, except for Venus, Uranus and probably Pluto, each planet spins anticlockwise about its own axis. Venus has a very slow clockwise spin. Uranus spins on its side, with one pole facing the Sun. Pluto and its moon, Charon, both spin around a common axis.

The four innermost planets are the dense planets. The closest planet to the Sun is **Mercury**. Mercury has the greatest speed of all the planets and the shortest distance to travel to complete an orbit, so it races around the Sun. The further a planet is from the Sun, the slower it moves and the further it has to move to complete an orbit. Consequently, planetary years increase in length with increasing distance from the Sun.

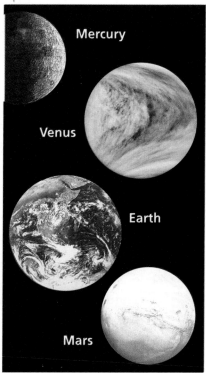
▲ **Fig 1** The inner planets

The orange planet **Venus** is the second planet out. Then comes the blue planet **Earth** with its **satellite**, our Moon. **Mars**, the red planet, is similar to Earth in some ways. They have similar length days and white clouds and, because of their tilt, they both have seasons.

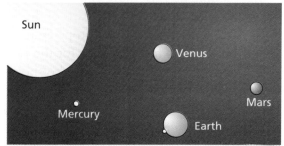
▲ **Fig 2**

Asteroids, fragments of rock ranging in size up to 100 km in diameter, orbit the Sun in a belt between the four inner planets and the five known outer ones.

1 **Craters** are the result of impacts with lumps of rock called **meteors**. Several meteors reach the Earth each day, but few of them reach the surface as they burn up in the atmosphere. Most of those that do reach the surface hit water rather than land. Neither Mercury nor the Earth's moon has an atmosphere. Explain why both are covered in impact craters and why many of these craters have been undisturbed for millions of years.

The outer planets

The five known outer planets lie beyond the asteroid belt. Our knowledge of **Jupiter** and **Saturn** is much greater now than 20 years ago because of pictures sent back to Earth from the Voyager space probes.

Jupiter and Saturn are the largest planets in the Solar System. Jupiter is more than three hundred times the mass of the Earth and it has sixteen moons.

While the inner planets are dense and rocky, the outer, cooler planets are composed largely of gases and ice. Saturn, the sixth planet out from the Sun, has thousands of small rings made up of ice, dust and small pieces of rock. The yellow appearance of Saturn is due to its ammonia-rich atmosphere.

Uranus and **Neptune** are very similar in size and mass. Both have several moons in orbit around them. They are thought to have a rocky core surrounded by a liquid mantle and an outer atmosphere composed of hydrogen, helium and methane.

▲ **Fig 3** Four of the five known outer planets

Little is known about **Pluto**, the ninth known planet. It has not yet been visited by a space probe and so there are no close-up pictures. Pluto is a tiny planet with a relatively large moon, Charon.

2 Write down the names of the planets in order, starting with the one closest to the Sun.

Words you should know

asteroid   crater   galaxy   meteor   planet   satellite

114 **Gravitational forces**

In this unit you will learn the answer to this question:
■ How do gravitational forces affect the motion of planets and comets?

Planetary orbits

Moons orbit planets and planets orbit the Sun following paths that have the shape of an **ellipse**, or a squashed circle. For most planets and their satellites, the ellipses are very close to being circles. The exceptions are the innermost and outermost planets, Mercury and Pluto. Motion in a circle requires a constant pull or push towards the centre. In the case of planets and their satellites the force pulling the object towards the centre of the circle is the **gravitational force**. Gravitational forces are always attractive, they can only pull. They act between all objects, but they only have noticeable effects when one of the objects is very massive.

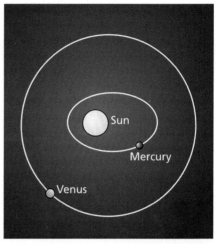

▲ **Fig 1** The path of Mercury is an ellipse but Venus follows an almost perfect circle

1 Most planets have near circular orbits. Which two planets have elliptical orbits?

The size of the Sun's gravitational pull on a planet depends on the distance of the planet from the Sun and the mass of the planet. Jupiter is approximately five times as far from the Sun as the Earth is. Because of the way in which gravitational forces decrease with distance, the force pulling each kilogramme of the Earth towards the Sun is twenty-five times as big as the force pulling each kilogramme of Jupiter to the Sun. However, Jupiter is more than three hundred times as massive as the Earth so although the force on each kilogramme of Jupiter is smaller, the total force pulling Jupiter is bigger than that pulling the Earth.

The seven planets whose orbits are almost circular maintain an almost constant speed in their journeys around the Sun. The speed of a planet in its orbit depends only on its distance from the Sun. Venus has an average speed of 35 km/s, but that of Neptune is only 5.4 km/s. Mercury, being nearest the Sun, has the greatest average speed of all at 48 km/s but its speed varies considerably due to the shape of its orbit.

Comets

Comets travel round the Sun in elliptical orbits. The nucleus of a comet can be anything between 100 m and 10 km in size, and probably consists of frozen water and gases. Comets become visible when they are close enough to the Sun for the water and gases to be vaporised, forming a glowing head and a tail. Fig 2 shows the spectacular appearance of a comet as it passes close to the Sun.

▲ **Fig 2** Comet West

As a comet approaches the Sun the increasing gravitational pull causes it to speed up. It passes round the Sun very quickly, slowing down again as it moves further away. So fast is their passage close to the Sun that comets are usually only visible for a few weeks.

Unlike the planets, which all orbit the Sun in one plane, comets can orbit in any plane and any direction. A comet orbit is shown in Fig 3. Comets can sometimes be thrown off course by the gravitational pull of the planets as they pass close by.

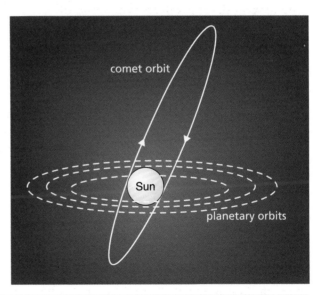

comet orbit

Sun

planetary orbits

▶ **Fig 3** Orbits of the planets and a comet

2 Use a diagram to describe how the Sun's gravitational force on a comet changes during one orbit. Explain how the changing gravitational force affects the speed of a comet.

Words you should know

comet   **ellipse**   **gravitational force**

115 Using convection currents

In this unit you will learn the answers to these questions:
- What happens in convection currents?
- How do we make use of convection currents?

Everything is continually transferring energy to its surroundings and receiving some back. When hot drinks cool they lose energy faster than they gain it. Cold drinks taken out of a fridge take in energy faster than they give it out. There is not just one simple way in which cold things warm up and hot things cool down. The four different ways in which energy is transferred are called **conduction**, **convection**, **evaporation** and **radiation**. A hot cup of tea is losing energy in all four ways at once, as is a human body!

Moving fluids

You can feel the effect of a **convection current** when you open the door of an upright freezer. The cold air inside the freezer is denser than the warmer air in the room, so it sinks underneath the warm air, making your feet feel cold. The cold air is denser because the slower-moving molecules are, on average, closer together than those in the warmer air.

You can also feel the warm air rising from a central heating radiator. When the air is warmed the molecules become faster moving, making the air expand and become less dense.

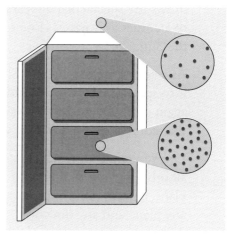

▲ **Fig 1** The cold air in a freezer is denser than the warm air in the room

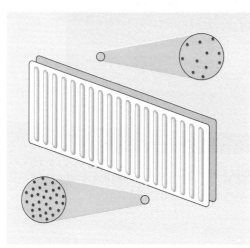

▲ **Fig 2** The molecules in the warm air are more widely spaced than those in the cold air, making it less dense

Convection currents are examples of floating and sinking. When part of a liquid or gas is made warmer than its surroundings it expands and rises because it is less dense. The air next to the ice box in a fridge is cooled and so it contracts. The cold air sinks because it is denser than the warmer air below it. This movement of air is called a **convection current**. A dye in the form of a crystal or an ice cube can be used to see convection currents in water.

Convection involves the movement of molecules and so it can only occur in **fluids** (liquids and gases), where the molecules can move within the body of the fluid.

1 Copy the diagrams in Fig 3 and label them to explain water movement.

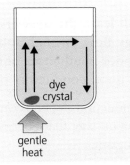 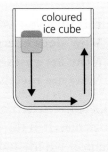

▶ **Fig 3** *Convection currents when water is heated and cooled*

Convection and the fridge

When a fridge is working, energy is being removed from the inside of the fridge and transferred to the room. Convection currents are needed to do both jobs. Fig 4 shows the inside of a fridge. Air is cooled at the top of the fridge and downwards-driven convection currents keep the food cool.

Convection currents are also important in removing energy at the back of the fridge. Fridges work by pumping a fluid through pipes both inside and outside. Inside the fridge, the fluid is made to evaporate and this causes cooling (see Unit 118). Outside the fridge, a compressor turns the vapour back into a liquid, which causes heating. The excess heat has to be lost before the fluid can be pumped back inside the fridge. Most of this heat is lost through convection currents. The air that has been warmed by being in contact with the pipes rises and is replaced by colder air. This upwards-driven convection current forces a continuous flow of cooling air over the warm pipes.

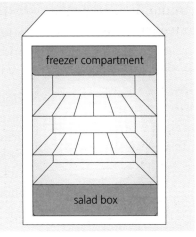

▲ **Fig 4** *Inside a fridge*

2 a) Describe the movement of air inside a fridge.
  b) Explain why the fridge does not work efficiently when it is packed tightly with food.
  c) Suggest why the salad box is covered with a solid shelf.

3 Explain why a fridge should not be positioned too close to a wall.

Words you should know

convection current **fluid**

116 Thermal conduction

In this unit you will learn the answers to these questions:
- How does energy flow through solids?
- Why are gases poor conductors of thermal energy?
- Why are metals good conductors of thermal energy?

Like convection, conduction depends on the movement of atoms and molecules. It is the main way that energy transfer occurs in solids. It can also occur in liquids and gases.

What makes conduction work?

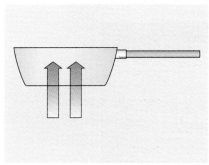

▲ **Fig 1** *Energy passes easily through the base of the pan*

Food in a saucepan gets hot because the pan is a good **conductor**. The handle is a poor conductor so you can touch it without getting burnt.

Good conductors are needed to transfer the energy of the hot water in a radiator to the air outside and the energy from the heating element of a kettle into the water. Bricks and building blocks for houses need to be made from poor conductors, as do our clothes and containers that keep food hot.

When one part of a material is hotter than another, the molecules in the hotter part have more energy than the surrounding ones. Heating a substance causes increased motion of the atoms and molecules. In a gas this means that the average speed of the atoms and molecules increases, but in a solid or a liquid it leads to increased vibration. Atoms and molecules do not exist in isolation, and they are continually interacting and swapping energy with their neighbours. The transfer of energy from energetic molecules to those with less energy is responsible for **conduction**.

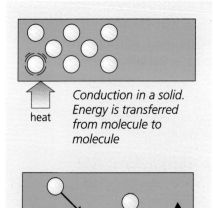

Conduction in a solid. Energy is transferred from molecule to molecule

heat

The molecules of a gas are more widely spaced so conduction is a much slower process than in a solid

◀ **Fig 2**

Gases are poor at transferring energy in this way because the molecules are relatively far apart, compared to a solid or liquid. The more energetic molecules in part of a gas that has been heated travel large distances, in molecular terms, between collisions and so it takes them longer to transfer energy to other molecules.

1 Some gases are better conductors of thermal energy than others. What other factor, apart from the average spacing of the molecules, affects the conduction of energy in a gas?

Comparing conductors

Fig 3 shows how to compare the rate at which energy flows along solid materials. The results of this comparison show that metals are very good conductors, the heat-sensitive paper changing colour within a few minutes. Non-metals such as glass are very poor conductors in comparison.

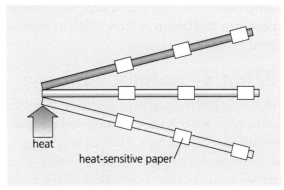

heat

heat-sensitive paper

▲ **Fig 3** *Comparing conduction rates in solids*

A brick made out of copper would conduct energy at five hundred times the rate of a normal house brick! The table lists some common materials in order of their conductivity, the best being at the top of each list. Foam is at the bottom of the list of poor conductors because it contains a very poor conductor – air! The insulating properties of air are discussed in Unit 119.

Good conductors	Poor conductors	Very poor conductors
silver	concrete	hydrogen
copper	glass	helium
aluminium	brick	oxygen
brass	wood	air
iron and steel	foam	carbon dioxide

2 **a)** Most saucepans are made of aluminium, but some cooks prefer to use saucepans with copper bases. Why do some cooks prefer copper saucepans?

b) Suggest why silver saucepans are not very common.

Words you should know

conductor   conduction

117 Radiant energy

In this unit you will learn the answers to these questions:
- What sort of things radiate energy?
- How does the emission and absorption of radiant energy depend on the nature of the surface?

Convection and conduction depend on the movement of particles. Energy transfer by **radiation** is most efficient when there are no particles present, i.e. in a vacuum.

What is radiant energy?

All of the electromagnetic spectrum (see Unit 110) from short-wave X-rays to long-wave radio waves are radiated by the Sun. All transfer energy, but not all of it travels through the Earth's atmosphere. All the waves are of the same type. However, they have different wavelengths and frequencies so they have different effects on the objects that absorb them.

Infrared radiation has a heating effect. Infrared radiation from the Sun heats our skin, and that from grills and toasters heats our food. Everything radiates energy in the form of infrared radiation. The hotter something is the more energy it radiates.

▲ **Fig 1** The coals of the barbecue radiate energy to the food being cooked

Giving and receiving

The properties of electromagnetic waves depend on their wavelength. Infrared radiation is close to light in the spectrum and it behaves in a similar way. Fig 2 shows a demonstration that, like light, infrared radiation is reflected by shiny surfaces and absorbed by dark ones.

You can use a similar arrangement, using two blackened probes, to compare the energy radiated by different surfaces at the same temperature. The results of these experiments show that **dark, dull surfaces emit and absorb more radiant energy than light, shiny ones**.

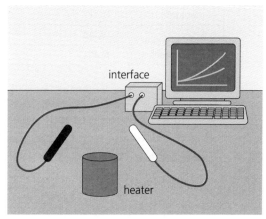
▲ **Fig 2** A blackened temperature probe absorbs more energy from the heater than a shiny one does

1 Why is black the best colour for cooling pipes at the back of a fridge?

2 Explain how:
- **a)** Foil containers keep take-away food hot long enough for it to be taken home.
- **b)** Foil-wrapped ice cream remains frozen for longer than ice cream wrapped in paper

Using radiant energy

Solar heated water panels (see Fig 3) are common in southern Europe. Energy from the Sun heats water that passes through pipes in the panel. Hot water is then stored in a tank above the panel. To absorb the maximum energy the panel is painted black and it has a glass cover.

▲ **Fig 3** *Solar-heated water panel*

The Sun is very hot and gives off radiation of all wavelengths. Glass is transparent and light passes through it. Short-wavelength infrared radiation behaves like light. It passes through the glass and heats the water. Black is the best absorber of radiant energy. It is also the best emitter, so heat could be lost from the pipes. The glass reduces this energy loss. The black panel is very much cooler than the Sun, and only emits long-wavelength infrared radiation. This can not pass through the glass so the water remains hot.

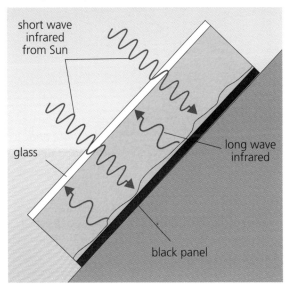

◀ **Fig 4** *Short-wavelength radiation from the Sun passes through the glass and heats the water. The longer wavelength radiation cannot pass through*

3 Why is the hot water tank shown in Fig 3 shiny on the outside?

Words you should know

radiation

118 Evaporation and insulation

In this unit you will learn the answers to these questions:
- Why does evaporation cause cooling?
- How can energy losses be minimised?
- How does a vacuum flask keep food hot?

Keep cool

Evaporation is the process by which particles from a liquid form a vapour (see Unit 45). Perfumes are designed to evaporate over a time period of several hours. The appetising smell of cooking food is due to evaporation.

Liquids need energy to evaporate. Energy is taken from the surroundings and so there is a cooling effect. You can feel this if you put a drop of surgical spirit on your hand. It evaporates quickly leaving a cold patch. Water takes longer to evaporate because it takes a lot of energy to change water into water vapour. We sweat a lot in hot climates. This helps to keep us cool, because evaporating watery sweat removes a lot of heat from our body.

Attractive forces hold molecules together in a liquid. A molecule needs energy to move away, against these forces. Only the most energetic molecules near the surface can escape. When this happens the average energy of the remaining molecules is reduced, so the liquid cools.

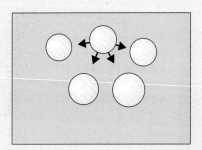

The attractive forces from neighbouring molecules make it hard for a molecule to evaporate

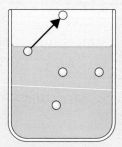

This molecule is near the surface and has enough energy to evaporate

▲ **Fig 1**

Evaporation only applies to liquids or objects that contain a large proportion of liquid, such as human beings and other animals. When a hot drink cools, the main energy loss is through evaporation. A lid reduces the energy loss.

1 Explain why hot liquids evaporate at a greater rate than cold ones.

2 A hot drink can be cooled down by blowing across the surface. Explain how this increases the energy loss from the liquid.

Using evaporation

Fridges, freezers and air-conditioners use the evaporation of a liquid to cause cooling. When a liquid evaporates it takes in energy from its surroundings, causing them to cool. In a fridge the fluid is pumped round and forced to evaporate by being squirted through a jet into a wide tube in the freezer compartment. The vaporising liquid cools rapidly. It absorbs energy as it passes through the freezer compartment.

Keeping food hot

Hot food can lose energy in all four of the ways described so far. The most effective insulator for food is the **vacuum** flask. This minimises energy transfer by conduction, convection, evaporation and radiation so it can keep food hot for several hours. Fig 3 shows the important parts of a vacuum flask. Vacuum flasks are not only used for keeping things hot – they are equally good at keeping things cold. Chiropodists use liquid nitrogen at a temperature of –200°C to kill verrucas. By keeping the nitrogen in a vacuum flask, they can keep it cold for weeks before it all evaporates and a fresh supply is needed.

3 The important features of a vacuum flask are the stopper, the vacuum between the walls and the silvering on the walls. Explain how these features together reduce energy transfer by convection, conduction, radiation and evaporation.

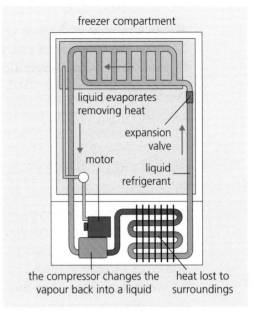

▲ **Fig 2** *Evaporation and condensation in a fridge*

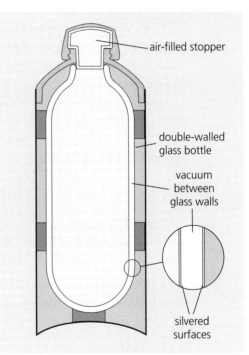

▲ **Fig 3** *A vacuum flask*

Words you should know

evaporation   vacuum

119 Insulating a house

In this unit you will learn the answers to these questions:
- How can the loss of energy from houses be reduced?
- How does house insulation work?

Warm things can lose energy to the surroundings in four ways. Only **conduction** and **convection** are important in house insulation. Houses need to be able to lose moisture to prevent them being damp.

Why insulate?

No matter how much energy you put into heating a house, it all leaves through the floor, walls, windows, doors and roof. When a warm house has reached a steady temperature, energy flows out of it at the same rate as it flows in. The diagram (Fig 1) shows the ways in which energy flows out of an uninsulated house.

Insulating a house means that less energy flows out of it, and so less energy needs to be supplied to maintain a comfortable temperature. Reduced fuel bills are not only good for the householder, they also save the nation's fuel resources!

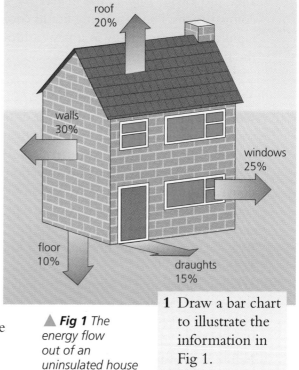

▲ *Fig 1* *The energy flow out of an uninsulated house*

1 Draw a bar chart to illustrate the information in Fig 1.

Where to insulate

The first place to start with the house shown in Fig 1 would be to stop the draughts! However, it is important to remember that human beings and gas-burning appliances need a constant supply of oxygen. So draughts should not be stopped completely.

The three common ways of reducing energy losses are **loft insulation**, **cavity wall insulation** and **double glazing**. All these rely on using the insulating properties of air.

Loft insulation is the most cost-effective form of domestic insulation. The cost for an average-sized house is less than £100 and that money is easily saved with reduced heating bills. In an uninsulated loft, energy conducted through the ceiling is transferred to the roof by convection currents. Fibreglass insulation traps pockets of air. The trapped air cannot form convection currents so energy can only be transferred through the fibre-glass by conduction, and air is a very poor conductor.

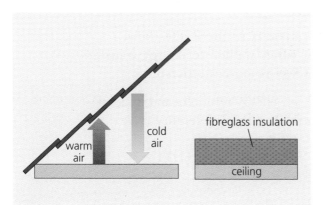

▲ *Fig 2* *An uninsulated loft and an insulated loft*

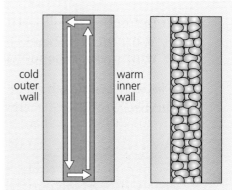

▲ *Fig 3* *The convection currents in a cavity wall are stopped by insulating foam*

Cavity wall insulation involves insulating the walls of a house. Houses are double-walled. In older houses both walls are brick. In modern houses building blocks, which are better insulators than brick, are used for the inside walls. The gap between the walls is called a cavity. If there is only air in this cavity then convection currents transfer energy from the inside wall to the outside wall. Filling the cavity with mineral wool or foam stops the convection currents. This halves the rate at which energy is transferred through the walls. For an average house cavity wall insulation costs a few hundred pounds.

Double glazing an average house is likely to cost several thousand pounds. The energy flow through a single-glazed window is about ten times that through the same area of uninsulated cavity wall. This is because windows are much thinner than walls. Double glazing uses twice the thickness of glass, because there are two panes, and also traps air. If the air gap between the inner and outer panes is thin then convection currents cannot flow over the surfaces of the glass. A thin air gap is a better insulator than a wide one.

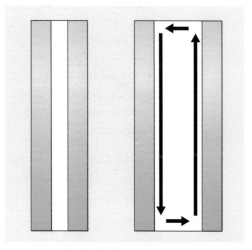

▲ *Fig 4* *Convection currents make a wide air gap less effective than a narrow one in double glazing*

2 Despite the cost, a lot of houses now have double-glazed windows. What are the benefits to a householder?

3 Some householders put a layer of kitchen foil on the walls behind central heating radiators. Explain whether you think this is a good idea or not.

Words you should know

conduction   **convection**
insulate

120 Using energy resources

In this unit you will learn the answers to these questions:
- What does efficiency mean when applied to energy transfer?
- Why do we need to use energy resources efficiently?

This unit examines how we use our energy resources and looks at alternative sources of energy for the twenty-first century.

Where our energy comes from

We rely on a number of energy resources in our daily lives. Petroleum (crude oil) products include petrol, diesel and paraffin. These are burnt in the engines used for road, sea and air transport. Each year there are more vehicles on the road. People travel more, and take more foreign holidays, so more fuel is used.

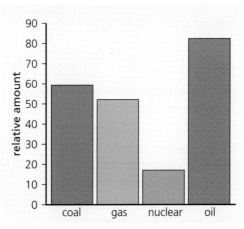
▲ **Fig 1** *Energy use in the UK*

Gas, coal and oil are burnt to heat our homes and work places. Most of our electricity is produced by burning these fuels. Electricity is an energy source for heating, lighting and electric motors. Fig 1 compares the amounts of each energy source that we use each year. The small amounts of energy from wind and hydroelectric power are not included.

> **1 a)** Which of the fuels shown is not a fossil fuel?
> **b)** Which fuel is only used to generate electricity?
> **c)** Use the information in the bar chart to draw a pie chart showing the proportions of each fuel used.

Using resources efficiently

If you boil a pan of water on a gas ring, not all of the energy from the gas goes into the water. Some of it goes into the air in the room. Boiling water in a kettle is a more **efficient** process because less energy is wasted. The **efficiency** of an energy transfer is the percentage of the available energy that is transferred to where you want it. Fig 2 illustrates the efficiencies of some common energy transfers.

A car engine transfers 20% of the energy in the fuel to the drive mechanism

A filament lamp transfers 5% of the energy from the electricity into light

A microwave cooker transfers 55% of the energy from the electricity to the food

◀ *Fig 2*

2 a) Describe what happens to the 80% of the energy from fuel that is not transferred to a car's drive mechanism.

b) A 60 W lamp takes in energy from electricity at the rate of 60 J per second. How much of this energy is transferred to light?

Electricity is generated from a variety of fuels, the main ones being coal, gas, nuclear and oil. Energy is lost as heat at all stages in the process. The major loss occurs when steam from the turbines is condensed back into water. Fig 3 shows the energy flow through a coal-burning power station.

The efficiency of renewable resources

Photovoltaic cells transfer energy from the Sun into electricity with an efficiency of around 17%. This seems low compared to the efficiency of a power station, but power plants of this type are helping to conserve our fuel resources. **Solar panels** at the moment have a high capital cost and a low efficiency. If both these factors were to be improved they could be a major energy resource in the twenty-first century.

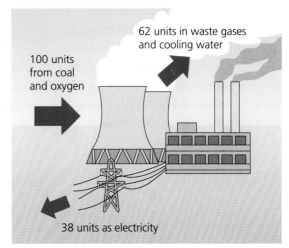

100 units from coal and oxygen

62 units in waste gases and cooling water

38 units as electricity

▲ *Fig 3* Energy flow through a power station

3 Coal could be used more efficiently if some of the energy wasted in a power station were used in the local community. Suggest some possible uses for this energy.

4 Describe the advantages and disadvantages of using solar panels to provide electricity for a home.

Words you should know

efficiency   solar panel

121 Forces and work

In this unit you will learn the answers to these questions:
- When are forces working and when are they not working?
- How much work does a working force do?
- What is the link between work and energy transfer?

Measuring work

A **force** that causes movement is doing **work**. Some forces and the movement they cause are easily recognised – others are less obvious.

Some forces do not work. The upward force from your chair is a very useful force because it is supporting you, but it is not causing any movement so it is not working.

The amount of work a force does when it causes movement is calculated using the formula:

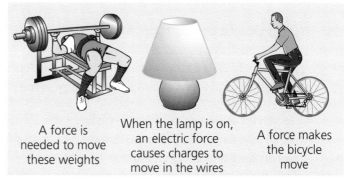

A force is needed to move these weights

When the lamp is on, an electric force causes charges to move in the wires

A force makes the bicycle move

▲ **Fig 1** *Forces working*

1 Which of the following forces are working and which are not working?
   a) the friction force supporting a shelf on a wall
   b) the force used to push a lawnmower
   c) the Earth's pull on a falling parachutist
   d) the Earth's pull on a floating ship

---

work done = force × distance moved in its own direction   or $W = F \times d$

Work is measured in **joules** (J).

Example	Answer
A 65 N force is used to push a supermarket trolley for 180 m. How much work does the force do?	$W = F \times d$ $= 65\,\text{N} \times 180\,\text{m}$ $= 11\,700\,\text{J}$

2 Calculate the amount of work done by the following.
   a) A crane lifts a 3000 N load through a height of 15 m.
   b) A high-jumper lifts her own weight of 600 N through a height of 1.8 m.
   c) A man uses a 45 N force to push a pram a distance of 1500 m.

Work and energy transfer

Nothing can work unless it has energy. People get their energy from food. Motorised transport obtains energy from the fuel and oxygen supply. A lot of our work is done with energy from electricity. When something or someone is at work, energy is on the move! Fig 2 shows how you can measure the energy that passes through a motor when it lifts a weight or drags it up a slope to the same height.

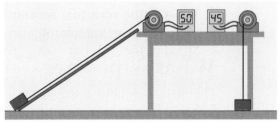

▲ **Fig 2** *Comparing energy transfer*

As the weight moves up, it is gaining energy due to its position. The motor is doing the work to lift or drag the weight up, using energy from electricity. All the time the motor is working, it is transferring energy from electricity to the weight. Not all of the energy from the electricity goes to the weight, some of it stays in the motor as heat in the wires.

It takes more energy to drag the weight up the slope than to lift it. It does not matter which way the job is done, the weight gains the same amount of energy because it has been moved through the same vertical height. More energy is needed to drag the weight because of the frictional forces opposing the motion up the slope. Movement against these frictional forces causes a small amount of heating.

When work is done energy is transferred. The amount of energy transferred is equal to the work done. Fig 3 shows the energy transfer from the motor when it is lifting and dragging the weight uphill.

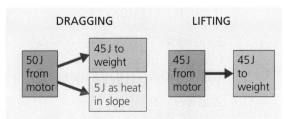

▲ **Fig 3** *The motor does more work when it drags the weight up the slope than when it lifts it straight up*

3 **a)** Which process is more efficient, lifting the weight or dragging it? Explain your answer.

   b) Even though it takes more energy, people prefer to drag heavy things up a ramp rather than lift them. Explain why this is.

Words you should know

       force   joule   work

122 Power

In this unit you will learn the answers to these questions:
■ What is the scientific meaning of power?
■ How is power calculated?

What is power?

The diesel engine that drives a train has to be more powerful than that of a car because there is a lot more mass to be accelerated. A 36 W fluorescent light fitting uses less electricity than a 100 W lamp but it gives out more light each second because it transfers energy more efficiently.

Power is the rate of working or transferring energy. If two cars of the same weight race for one mile the winning car is described as the more powerful. The amount of work (F × d) is the same for both cars, *but the time taken is different*. Power is the amount of work done, or energy transferred, each second.

The equation for calculating power is:

$$\text{power} = \frac{\text{work done}}{\text{time taken}} \quad \text{or} \quad P = \frac{W}{t}$$

Power is measured in **watts** (W) when the energy transfer is in **joules** (J) and the time is in seconds (s).

▲ **Fig 1** *Both of these kettles can boil a pint of water, but the one that does it faster is more powerful*

Example
Calculate the power of a cyclist who transfers 105 000 J of energy to the pedals in 300 s.

Answer
$$\text{power} = \text{energy transfer} \div \text{time}$$
$$= 105\,000\,\text{J} \div 300\,\text{s} = 350\,\text{W}$$

▶ **Fig 2** *A jet aircraft needs very powerful engines to accelerate it to take-off speed in only a few seconds*

1 Calculate the power of the following.
   a) A kettle that transfers 750 000 J of energy into heat in the 300 s it takes to boil some water.
   b) A weightlifter who does 12 000 J of work to lift some weights in 1.5 s.
   c) A clock that transfers 240 J of energy from the mains supply each minute.

Measuring your own power

Human beings are not the most powerful creatures on Earth. They can work at a low power of a few hundred watts for long periods of time. They can work at a higher power over short time periods. Footballers and marathon runners need to be able to work at a steady rate for long periods of time. Sprinters and cricket fast bowlers work at a higher power for shorter times.

You can measure your own power by getting someone to time you as you do a job such as running up some stairs. The work that you do to run upstairs is equal to your *weight × change in height*.

The person in Fig 3 weighs 600 N. He climbs the stairs in 4.0 s. To calculate his power you first of all need to calculate how much work he does:

work = weight × change in height
= 600 N × 1.5 m = 900 J

1.5 m

Next divide by the time to calculate the power:

power = work done ÷ time taken
= 900 J ÷ 4.0 s
= 225 W

▶ **Fig 3**

2 In the following examples, first calculate the work done or energy transfer. Then calculate the power by dividing the work or energy transfer by the time.
   a) A boy who stacks shelves in a supermarket lifts 500 N weight of sugar through a height of 0.8 m in 16 s.
   b) A father pushes a pram for a distance of 1500 m with a force of 80 N. The journey takes 20 minutes (1200 s).
   c) A swimmer pushes on the water with an average force of 150 N as she swims 200 m in 75 s.

Words you should know

joule   power   watt

123 Radioactive emissions

In this unit you will learn the answers to these questions:
- Where do radioactive emissions come from?
- What are the differences between the three main types of radioactive emission?

Many radioactive materials are as old as the Earth. Others are very short-lived. Radioactive materials are used to generate electricity on a small scale in heart pacemakers and on a large scale in nuclear power stations. The first atomic bomb, used more than 50 years ago, and the Chernobyl disaster in 1986 caused long-lasting damage to the Earth. Radioactive materials bring many benefits to humans, but they need to be used with great care.

Why are some materials radioactive?

Substances which are radioactive have nuclei that are not stable. When they change or decay to a more stable state, they give out particles or electromagnetic radiation or both. Unstable substances include radium-226, americium-241, strontium-90 and cobalt-60.

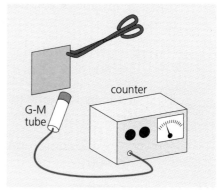

▲ **Fig 1** Detecting radioactive decay

A Geiger-Müller tube connected to a counter can detect emissions from radioactive decay. Fig 1 shows how to compare the emissions from different substances. Experiments such as this show that while substances containing elements such as uranium are strongly radioactive, those containing copper and sodium are not.

Different types of emission

Fig 2 shows how a Geiger-Müller tube and counter can be used to compare the penetration of emissions from different sources. Emissions from radioactive materials are classified according to their penetration. There are three distinct types, named alpha (α), beta (β) and gamma (γ) after the first three letters of the Greek alphabet.

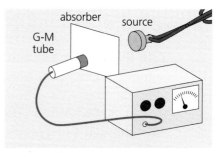

▲ **Fig 2** Comparing the penetration of radioactive emissions

Alpha radiation is easily stopped by paper or thin card and it cannot penetrate more than a few centimetres of air. **Beta radiation** is more penetrative. It is absorbed by a thin sheet of aluminium or any other metal. **Gamma radiation** is the most penetrative of all. It is partially absorbed by lead but some radiation will always penetrate even a ten centimetre thick lead wall.

Do not be fooled into thinking that alpha radiation is harmless because it is not very penetrative. It is the most intensely ionising radiation. Damage to human tissue is due to ionisation, and alpha radiation can be particularly dangerous to humans if breathed in.

The nature of the emissions

Alpha particles are the largest of the three types of radioactive emission. Because of their size, they undergo frequent collisions when passing through air or other materials, slowing down at each collision until all their energy has been lost. Alpha particles consist of two protons and two neutrons, and they are often referred to as **helium nuclei**.

Beta particles are **electrons** that have been ejected from the nucleus of an atom when a neutron changes to a proton.

If you have previously studied Unit 110, you will already know that gamma radiation is **short-wavelength electromagnetic radiation**, given out when a nucleus loses excess energy.

The table summarises the properties of alpha, beta and gamma radiation.

Radioactive emission	Nature	Charge	Mass	Penetration	Affected by electric and magnetic fields	Causes ionisation	Detected by
alpha particle	two neutrons and two protons	positive	4x the mass of a proton	absorbed by paper or a few cm of air	yes	intensely	G-M tube photographic film spark counter solid state detector
beta particle	fast-moving electron	negative	1/2000 of the mass of a proton	absorbed by 3mm of aluminium	yes	weakly	G-M tube photographic film solid state detector
gamma ray	short-wavelength electromagnetic radiation	none	none	reduced by several cm of lead	no	very weakly	G-M tube photographic film solid state detector

1 Which type of emission, alpha, beta or gamma is:
   a) most penetrative?   **b)** most ionising?   **c)** deflected away from positive charge?

2 A radioactive source is placed next to a Geiger-Müller tube connected to a counter. When a piece of paper is inserted between the source and the tube the count-rate decreases from 60 counts per second to 40 counts per second. Inserting a sheet of aluminium has the same effect as a sheet of paper.
   a) What type or types of radiation is the source emitting?
   b) What further test could be done to confirm this? What would the result be?

Words you should know
   alpha radiation   **beta radiation**   **gamma radiation**

124 **Radioactive decay**

In this unit you will learn the answers to these questions:
- ■ What is 'background radiation'?
- ■ What does 'half-life' mean?

Background radiation

We live in a radioactive world. All living things are radioactive, as are all things that have been alive. Many rocks in the Earth's crust are radioactive, giving particularly high levels of radioactivity in areas built on granite. There is a constant stream of radiation from the Sun and space, although some of it is very difficult to detect. All this radiation is collectively referred to as '**background radiation**'.

If a Geiger–Müller tube and counter is set up away from any radioactive sources, it detects a random pattern of background radiation. It may go for a few seconds without detecting anything, and then there may be several 'pulses' in a short space of time. Counting the number of pulses over a period of 1 or 2 minutes results in an average background radiation of around 1 count per second. This may seem very low, but a more sensitive detector would record much higher levels of background radiation.

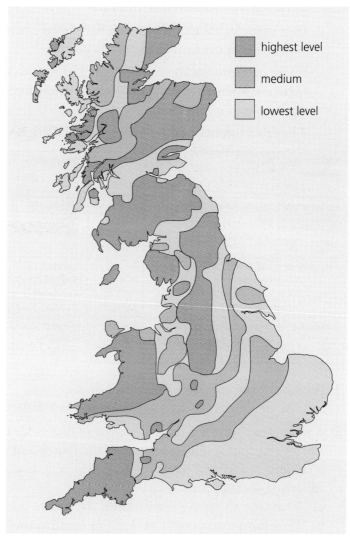

highest level

medium

lowest level

▲ **Fig 1** The background radiation in some areas of Britain is higher than in others due to the radioactivity of the rock

The decay pattern

Radioactive decay is a random process. There is no way of predicting when an unstable nucleus will change to a more stable form. For every radioactive substance, however, the rate of decay is fixed. The measure of the rate at which a radioactive material decays is called its **half-life**. This is the time taken for half of the atoms in a sample to decay. Substances which decay quickly have a short half-life. One which decays slowly has a long half-life.

> 1 A radioactive sample contains 4 million atoms. The time taken for half of them to decay is 70 seconds. How much longer will it take for the number of radioactive atoms to drop to ½ million?

Measuring activity

Routine tests are carried out on many materials to measure the level of radioactivity. Fig 2 shows a way of measuring the radioactivity of food samples. The detector is placed in the centre of a food container made of thick lead. The lead acts as a shield to absorb any background radiation that would affect the detector.

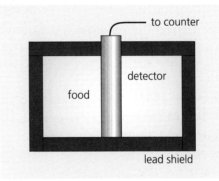

▲ **Fig 2** *Measuring the radioactivity of food*

When measuring the activity of radioactive samples, it is necessary to either shield the detector from background radiation or take it into account by subtracting the average level of background radiation from the measured count rate.

> 2 Explain why it is more important to take background radiation into account when measuring the activity of a sample with a low count rate of 10 counts/s than it is for a more active sample of 1000 counts/s.

Words you should know

background radiation   **half-life**

125 **Using radioactivity**

In this unit you will learn the answers to these questions:
- What are radioactive materials used for?
- How can radioactivity measurements be used to date rocks?

Gauging the thickness

Paper, cling film, aluminium foil and other sheet materials need to be produced to a constant thickness. In the manufacturing process, the thickness of the material is continually monitored by measuring the amount of radioactive emission from a

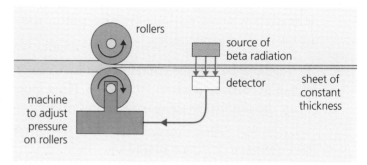

▲ **Fig 1** *Controlling the thickness of a sheet material*

source that penetrates the material. Strontium–90, a beta–emitting source with a half-life of 29 years, is used in an arrangement similar to that shown in Fig 1.

> **1 a)** Explain why a beta-emitting source is suitable for this purpose, but alpha-emitting or gamma-emitting sources would not be.
> **b)** Explain why sources with half-lives of 3 years or 300 years would not be suitable.

Some uses of tracers

Radioactive tracers can be used to follow the flow of fluid in pipes. It can be used to find leaks in a pipe. The principle is shown in Fig 2. Factors to be considered when choosing a suitable radioactive material to use as a tracer include how easily it mixes with the fluid, the type or types of radiation emitted and the half-life.

Plant biologists use radio-active tracers. Radio-active phosphorus-32 can be used to make a fertiliser for soil. Biologists can then study the flow of liquid in the plants grown in the soil and also their uptake of minerals.

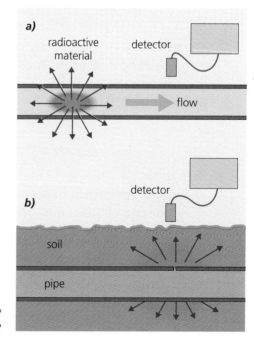

▶ **Fig 2** *a) Measurement of flow rate in a pipe*
b) Detection of a leak in an underground pipe

2 A tracer is to be used to detect a leak in an underground water pipe.
   a) What type of emission could be detected from a liquid leaking from a pipe underground?
   b) What factors should be considered when selecting a material with a suitable half-life?

Dating rocks

Rocks can be dated by measuring the relative amounts of radioactive material and the substance produced when the material decays.

Uranium-238 decays into lead-206 with a half-life of 4500 million years. This is similar to the age of the Earth, which is believed to be 4600 million years. Rocks formed at the same time as the Earth contain the same proportion of lead-206 and uranium-238 atoms, the lead having been formed by the decay of uranium. Rocks formed since then have a higher proportion of uranium-238 to lead-206.

Moon rocks have been dated, giving ages of up to 4400 million years. This suggests that the Moon was not formed at the same time as the Earth.

▲ **Fig 3** An astronaut gathering samples of Moon rock for radioactive dating

3 Uranium-235 decays to lead-207 with a half-life of 700 million years. Explain why uranium-235 cannot be used to date rock as old as the Earth.

Words you should know

half-life   tracer

GLOSSARY

A

acceleration – increase in velocity (or speed) per second

accommodation – process during which the shape of the lens and pupil size change to focus the eye on near or distant objects

acid – a substance that dissolves in water to form a solution with a pH below 7. An acid contains hydrogen which can be replaced by a metal to form a salt.

acid rain – rain that contains more than normal amounts of sulphur dioxide and nitrogen oxide gases

aerobic respiration – the release of energy from food in the presence of oxygen

air – air is a mixture of gases. Approximately one fifth is oxygen and four fifths nitrogen.

alkali – an alkali is a metal oxide or hydroxide (base) that dissolves in water to form a solution with a pH greater than 7. An alkali is neutralised by an acid to form a salt and water.

alkali metal – a metal in group 1 of the Periodic Table, e.g. sodium, potassium.

alkane – a family of hydrocarbons with a general formula of C_nH_{2n+2}. The simplest alkene is ethene, CH_4.

alkene – a family of hydrocarbons with a general formula of C_nH_{2n}. The simplest alkene is ethene, C_2H_4.

allotropes – different forms of the same element in the same physical state, e.g. carbon can exist as diamond, graphite and fullerenes

ammeter – instrument that measures electric current

ammonia – ammonia is a colourless gas which turns red litmus blue. It has a formula NH_3.

ampere – the unit of electric current

amplitude – the maximum displacement from the normal position

anaerobic respiration – the release of energy from food in the absence of oxygen

anode – the positively charged electrode in electrolysis

antibodies – proteins produced by lymphocytes which help to neutralise the effect of antigens

antigens – foreign cells or substances present in the body

assimilation – process which puts food chemicals to use in the body

atom – the smallest particle of an element which can exist

atomic number – the number of protons in the nucleus of an atom.

auxin – growth substance produced by plants (plant hormones)

B

balanced diet – all the necessary daily food requirements in the correct proportions for an individual

base – an oxide of a metal

bauxite – the common ore of aluminium containing aluminium oxide with impurities such as iron(III) oxide.

biomass – total mass of the body of a plant or animal after all the water has been taken away

blast furnace – a furnace used for extracting metals such as iron. Blasts of hot air are blown through the furnace.

boiling – a liquid turns rapidly to its vapour at a fixed temperature

braking distance – the time it takes for the brakes to bring a vehicle to rest

brine – a salt solution

burning (or combustion) – the combination of a substance with oxygen to produce energy

C

carbon dioxide – colourless gas produced when carbon or carbon compounds burn in a plentiful supply of oxygen. It is also formed when acid acts on a carbonate.

carbon monoxide – poisonous gas produced when carbon and carbon compounds burn in a limited supply of oxygen. Carbon monoxide is a good reducing agent.

carnivore – an animal which kills and feeds on an animal

catalyst – a substance which alters the rate of a reaction without being used up

cathode – a negatively charged electrode in electrolysis

cell – basic unit of life

chemical bond – the forces joining atoms together

chemical change – a permanent change which produces new substances

chloride – the ion formed when a chlorine atom gains an electron

chlorine – a reactive greenish-yellow gas of the halogen family (group VII)

chlorophyll – green pigment which traps light energy in photosynthesis

chloroplast – cell structure which contains chlorophyll

chromatography – a way of separating mixtures, especially coloured substances, by letting them spread across a filter paper. Each component in the mixture spreads at a different speed. The pattern of spots produced on the piece of paper is called a **chromatogram**.

chromosome – contains genetic information

cilia – microscopic hair-like structure

clone – a group of organisms with identical genetics

combination – the joining together (or **combining**) of atoms of different elements to form a compound

community – a group of populations of plants and animals living in a habitat

compass – small pivoted magnet that points towards magnetic North

compound – a substance formed by joining atoms of different elements together

condensation – changing a vapour (or gas) into a liquid. This change is accompanied by a giving out of energy.

conduction – mechanism of transfer of heat or electricity

consumer – an organism which feeds on ready-made food, i.e. other organisms, typical of animals

continuous variation – differences shown by organisms which can be affected by their environment

convection – movement of air currents due to differences in density

crude oil (or **petroleum**) – a complicated mixture of hydrocarbon produces by the action of high temperature and high pressure on the remains of sea creatures in the absence of air. It is trapped between impermeable rocks.

cryolite – a sodium aluminium fluoride used as a solvent for aluminium oxide in the extraction of aluminium

crystallisation – a process producing crystals. Crystals are formed when a molten substance is cooled or when a hot, saturated solution is cooled. Slow crystallisation produces large crystals and rapid crystallisation produces small crystals.

current – a flow of electric charge

D

decomposer – a microscopic organism e.g. bacterium or fungus which reduces organic matter to inorganic matter

decomposition – the splitting up of a substance by eating or by electrolysis or with a catalyst.

diatomic molecule – a molecule made up of two atoms, e.g. Cl_2

diffusion – the spreading out of a substance, due to the kinetic energy of its particles, to fill all of the available space

digestion – chemical and sometimes mechanical breakdown of food

discontinuous variation – differences shown by organisms which cannot be affected by their environment

displacement reaction – a reaction where one metal replaces another during a chemical reaction e.g. copper(II) sulphate + iron
$$\rightarrow \text{copper} + \text{iron(II) sulphate.}$$

dissolve – what happens when salt is added to water. The salt disappears but is still in the solution.

distillation – a process of purification involving boiling followed by condensation

double insulation – the casing of an electrical device is insulated as well as the wires

ductile – metals are said to be ductile because they can be drawn into fine wires

dyes – coloured substances

E

earth wire – a safety wire, connecting the metal case of an appliance to the earth

echo – a reflection of a sound

ecosystem – the sum total of all the living organisms and non-living factors in an environment

effector – a muscle or gland which brings about a change

egestion – the removal of undigested waste left in the gut

elastic – the property of regaining shape after deformation

elastic limit – the maximum force that can be applied to an object for it to remain elastic

electrolysis – the splitting up of an electrolyte, either molten or in aqueous solution, by electricity

electrolyte – a chemical compound which, in aqueous solution or when molten, conducts electricity and is split up by it. Acids, bases, alkalis and salts are electrolytes.

electromagnet – a magnet whose magnetic field is caused by a current passing in a coil of wire

electron – negatively charged particle in an atom that is responsible for electrical conduction in metals

element – a pure substance that cannot be split up into anything simpler

embryo – new individual that develops from a zygote

endocrine gland – releases hormones directly into the blood stream

energy – the ability to cause motion

energy level – electrons are around the nucleus in shells or energy levels. Each energy level can hold a maximum number of electrons.

environment – the surroundings of a cell or organism

enzyme – a protein molecule which acts as a biological catalyst

erosion – process where rocks are worn away

eutrophication – the result of the introduction of excessive amounts of nutrients, often nitrates and phosphates, into an aquatic ecosystem

evaporation – the process by which a liquid changes to a vapour, due to particles leaving the surface of the liquid. This happens at temperatures below the boiling point but is fastest when the liquid is boiling.

evolution – a theory which offers an explanation of the way organisms present on Earth today came to be there

excretion – removal of wastes manufactured by the chemical processes going on in an organism

exocrine gland – gland which releases its product into a duct which carries the substance to where it is needed

explosion – a very rapid reaction accompanied by a large expansion in gases

F

fermentation – the process in which enzymes in yeast change glucose into ethanol and carbon dioxide

fertilisation – the fusion of the nuclei of two different gametes (sex cells)

filtering (or **filtration**) – a method of separating a solid from a liquid

food chain – a sequence of organisms in a feeding relationship

food web – arises when one producer or consumer can be eaten by more than one consumer, i.e. interconnected food chains.

formula – a shorthand method of writing a chemical, e.g. H_2O is the formula for water.

fossil – the remains of plant and animal bodies which have not decayed and disappeared but have been preserved or replaced by rock. Fossils may be found in sedimentary and metamorphic but not igneous rocks.

fossil fuel – fuels such as coal, oil and natural gas produced in the Earth over long periods of time

fraction – this is formed during fractional distillation and is part of the original mixture but with a definite range of boiling point

fractional distillation – a method of separating liquids with different boiling points

free-fall – vertical motion with no resistive forces acting

freezing – when a liquid changes to a solid at the freezing point

friction – a force that opposes objects sliding over each other

fuel – a substance which burns to produce energy

fullerene – a recently discovered allotrope of carbon

fuse – thin wire that melts to cut off the supply to a circuit when the current exceeds a stated value

G

gas – a state of matter where the particles are widely spaced

gene – a section of the nucleic acid of a chromosome, which on its own, or with other genes, is responsible for a particular characteristic

generator – generates electricity by an electromagnet spinning inside a coil of wire

giant structure – this is a crystal structure in which all of the particles are linked together in a network of bonds extending throughout the crystal, e.g. diamond

greenhouse effect – caused by the increase in atmospheric carbon dioxide concentration, may result in global warming

group – a vertical column in the Periodic Table.

H

Haber process – industrial process used to manufacture ammonia from nitrogen and hydrogen

haematite – one of the common iron ores containing ion(III) oxide

haemoglobin – pigment which combines reversibly with oxygen, found in red blood cells

halogen – an element in group VII of the Periodic Table. The word halogen means salt producer.

herbicide – chemical which is poisonous to plants

herbivore – an animal which feeds exclusively on plant material

homeostasis – maintenance of a stable environment, steady state

hormone – chemical messenger

hydrogen halide – a compound of hydrogen and a halogen atom e.g. hydrogen chloride HCl

I

igneous – rocks that have cooled and solidified as crystals from molten rock, e.g. granite

immiscible liquids – *see* miscible liquids

impermeable rocks – rocks which do not allow water or gas to pass through them

in vitro fertilisation (IVF) – eggs taken from female are fertilised outside the body before being returned to a receptive uterus

ingestion – the way food is taken into the mouth

inhibitor – a catalyst that slows down the rate of a reaction

insulation – reduces the flow of heat or prevents the flow of charge

invertebrate – animals which have no vertebral column (backbone)

ion – a positively or negatively charged particle formed when an atom or group of atoms loses or gains electrons

ionic bonding – type of bonding involving complete transfer of one or more electrons from a metal atom to a non metal atom. Doing this forms ions.

isotope – atoms of the same element containing different numbers of neutrons, e.g. carbon-12 and carbon-14

J

joule – the unit of work and energy

K

kilowatt-hour – the domestic unit of energy from electricity

kinetic energy – energy due to the movement of an object

L

lattice – ionic bonding leads to a crystalline structure called a lattice

leaching – the removal of soluble material by a solvent e.g. removal of nutrients from soils by rainwater

liquid – a state of matter

litmus – an indicator used to test for acids and alkalis. It turns red in acids and blue in alkalis.

live wire – the wire that supplies energy to an electrical device

longitudinal – a wave in which the vibrations are parallel to the direction of motion

lymphocytes – white blood cells that produce chemicals to protect the body from infection

M

magma – semi-molten rock under the solid crust of the Earth

mantle – the part of the Earth between the crust and the core

marble – a metamorphic rock produced by the action of high temperatures and pressures on limestone

mass number – number of protons plus neutrons in an atom.

meiosis – cell division which produces cells which have half the number of chromosomes of the parent cell, achieved by the separation of the members of pairs, important in the formation of gametes (sex cells)

melting – a solid changes to a liquid at the melting point.

menstrual cycle – the pattern of changes that take place in the ovary and uterus

metamorphic – rocks that were originally either igneous or sedimentary and which have been altered by the effects of high temperatures and pressures, e.g. marble.

mineral – a naturally occurring substance of which rocks are made

miscible liquids – liquids which mix together to form a single layer, e.g. ethanol and water. Liquids which do not mix are said to be **immiscible**.

mitosis – cell division which produces two identical copies of the parent cell (replication)

mixture – a substance made up of several chemicals not combined together, e.g. air is a mixture of gases

molecular structure – a type of structure where the structure is built up of molecules. A substance with a molecular structure has a low melting and boiling point.

molecule – the smallest part of an element or compound which can exist on its own

monoculture – farming practice where large areas of land are used to grow one type of crop, often year after year, e.g. large areas of cereal

monomer – a small molecule which joins together with other molecules to produce a polymer

mutation – usually random process of genetic change, sometimes caused by a – factor known as a mutagen, product known as a mutant

N

national grid – the network of cables and transformers that distributes electricity around the country

negative feedback – by producing more of something, the source eventually causes its own shut-down

nephrons – microscopic tubes in the kidney that filter blood and make urine

neurone – nerve cell

neutral – a neutral substance has a pH value of 7

neutral wire – the wire that completes a mains circuit

neutralisation – a reaction in which an acid reacts with a base or alkali

neutron – a particle without a charge in the nucleus of an atom

noble gas – an element in group 0 of the Periodic Table

nucleus – site of the chromosomes, the control centre of the cell – centre of an atom where protons and neutrons are packed together

O

ore – a rock which contains a metal or a compound of a metal

organ – group of tissues with a specific function

organ system – group of organs with a specific function

osmosis – net movement of water through a selectively permeable membrane from a region of higher water concentration to one of lower water concentration

oxidation – a reaction where a substance gains oxygen, loses hydrogen or loses electrons. The opposite of oxidation is reduction.

oxide – compound of an element with oxygen

oxidising agent – substance which brings about the oxidation of another substance

ozone layer – gas found in the upper atmosphere that filters out some of the ultra-violet light from the Sun

P

parallel circuit – a circuit containing more than one current path

period – a horizontal row in the Periodic Table.

petrification – process of fossilisation where minerals are laid down over a long period of time in the tissues of a dead organism 'turning it to stone'

pH – a scale measuring acidity and alkalinity.

phagocytes – white blood cells that protect the body by 'eating' bacteria in the blood

phagocytosis – feeding process typical of phagocytes, which surround bacteria so forming a food vacuole

photosynthesis – process carried out by green plants to make food from carbon dioxide and water

physical change – a temporary change which can easily be reversed

pigment – an insoluble material used to give paint its colour

plankton – tiny sea creatures which have decomposed over long periods of time to form crude oil

plasma – solution of many chemicals dissolved in water that forms the liquid part of blood

platelets – bits of old red blood cells that are used to form a blood clot

polymer – a long chain molecule built up of a large number of small units, called monomers, joined together by a process called polymerisation

polymerisation – repetitive chemical combination of small molecules to form a large chain known as a polymer

power – the rate of energy transfer or doing work

precipitate – an insoluble substance formed in a chemical reaction involving solutions

precipitation – a reaction where a precipitate is formed

predator – carnivore which kills and eats, other animals

pressure – the effect of a force in piercing a surface

prey – animal which forms the food of a predator

producer – organism which produces organic compounds (food) from inorganic raw materials typical of green plants

proton – a positively charged particle in the nucleus of an atom

pyramid of number and biomass – the numbers of individuals or the total biomass at each trophic level of a food chain can be graphed, the results produce a pyramid shaped graph

R

reactants – the substances which react together to form products

reaction time – the time lapse between an event and a person reacting to it

reactivity series – a list of metals in order or reactivity with the most reactive metal at the top of the list

receptor – cell or organ which is sensitive to a stimulus

redox reaction – a reaction where both oxidation and reduction are taking place

reducing agent – substance which brings about the reduction of another substance. Common reducing agents are hydrogen and carbon monoxide.

reduction (see **oxidation**)

reflex action – a very rapid nervous response to a stimulus that does not involve any thought

refraction – the change in speed of a wave due to a change in the medium that the wave is travelling through

replication – process that provides an exact copy of DNA and a duplicate set of chromosomes prior to cell division

resistance – opposition to charge flow

reversible reaction – a reaction which can go forwards or backwards depending upon conditions

S

salt – a substance which is formed as a product of neutralisation

saturated hydrocarbon – a compound which contains only single covalent bonds, e.g. ethane C_2H_6. An **unsaturated** compound contains one or more double or single bonds.

saturated solution – a solution in which no more solute will dissolve providing temperature remains constant

sedimentary – rocks that are composed of compacted fragments of older rocks which have been deposited in layers of the floor of a lake or sea, e.g. sandstone.

selective breeding – artificial selection process used by Man to develop improved breeds of wheat, cattle, roses etc

selective reabsorption – process that allows some substances, filtered from the blood in the kidney, to be removed from the urine before it leaves the kidney tubules

selective weedkiller – chemical used to kill some plants and not others

series circuit – one in which there is only one current path

sexual reproduction – process that involves the fusion of the nuclei (fertilisation) of two, different, gametes in contrast to asexual reproduction where new individuals are formed from pieces of parent tissue

slag – waste materials from a furnace containing impurities

sodium chloride – the chemical name for common salt. It is found in the Earth as **rock salt**.

solubility – the number of grams of a solute dissolving in $100\,g$ of solvent at a particular temperature

solubility curve – a graph of solubility against temperature

solute – a substance which is dissolved in another substance

solution – the mixture of solute and solvent, e.g. salt solution is a mixture of salt and water

solution mining – a way of mining salt by pumping water underground. The salt dissolves and the salt solution (brine) is pumped to the surface.

solvent – the substance in which a solute dissolves

speed – the distance travelled per second

stimulus – a change in the environment that is registered and initiates a response

sublimation – a solid turns directly to a gas on heating without melting

synthesis *see* combination

T

target cell – cell that is sensitive to a particular hormone

Thermit reaction – the Thermit reaction is a displacement reaction where iron is obtained from iron(III) oxide using aluminium powder. This is an exothermic reaction.

tissue – group of cells of the same type having a specific function

tissue fluid – plasma which leaks from capillaries

toxin – poisonous protein produced by a pathogen

trace elements – elements such as magnesium and iron which are required in small amounts for plants to grow successfully

transformer – a device for changing the size of an alternating voltage

transpiration – evaporation of water from plant shoot systems

transverse – a wave motion where the vibrations are at right angles to the direction of wave travel

trophic level – level of feeding in a food chain, e.g. producers will be at level 1

tropism – plant growth response where the direction of the response is related to the direction of the stimulus

turgor – water pressure which inflates a cell, important in the support of plants

U

universal indicator – a mixture of indicators used for finding the pH of a substance

V

variable – something which changes

variation – differences which arise in the offspring of a sexually reproducing organism

vasoconstriction and **dilation** – changes shown by blood capillaries in the skin, involved in temperature regulation, decrease in diameter (vasoconstriction) and increase in diameter (vasodilation)

vegetative reproduction – asexual reproduction in plants

velocity – the speed and direction of a moving object

vertebrates – animals which have a vertebral column (backbone)

volt – the unit of voltage or potential difference

voltmeter – an instrument for measuring voltage

W

watt – the unit of power

wavelength – the length of one cycle of a wave motion

weathering – the action of wind, rain, snow etc. on rocks. These changes can be physical or chemical.

weight – the size of the Earth's gravitational pull on an object

work – is done when a force causes motion; it is always accompanied by an energy transfer

Z

zygote – cell formed by the fusion of two gametes, contains a diploid nucleus, cell divides to form an embryo

INDEX

A

absorption 22, 24–5
acceleration 202–3
accommodation, eyes 40–1
acid rain 83
acids 156–7, 159
aerobic respiration 34–5
air, breathing 30–1
air resistance 200–1
air sacs 32–3
alcohol 58–9
alkali metals 136–7
alkalis 156–7
alkanes 115, 116–17
allotropes 95
alpha radiation 246
aluminium 124–5
alveoli 32
ammeters 164–5
ammonia 152–3
ammonium nitrate 154–5
ammonium sulphate
  154–5
amoeba 12
ampere 164–5
amphibians 3
amplitude 213
anaemia 74, 75
anaerobic respiration 36–7
animal kingdom 2, 4
anodes 125, 127
antibodies 57
arachnids 4, 6
area 193
armature 181
arteries 26
asexual reproduction 15, 76
assimilation 22, 25
asteroids 227
atomic number 92, 134
atoms 92–5
atrium 26, 27
attraction 178–9
auxins 65

B

background radiation 248
baking 37
balanced forces 200–1,
  205, 207
bases 156–7
bauxite 124–5
bells 181
beta radiation 246
biological washing
  powders 151
biomass 85
birds 3
blast furnaces 126
blindspot 40
blood
  cells 28–9, 56
  circulation 26–7
  clotting 56, 74
  haemophilia 75
  sickle-cell anaemia 74
  white cells 56
boiling 102
bonding 94–5, 96–7
braking distance 198
breathing 30–1
brine 100
bromides 143
bronchioles 30, 32
bronchus 30, 32

C

camouflage 80–1
cancer 33, 225
capillaries 25, 26
carbohydrates 18, 20
carbon 95
carbon cycle 86–7
carbon dioxide 82–3, 86–7
cars
  hydraulic braking
  system 199
  tyres 191, 199
catalysts 118, 148–9,
  150–1
catalytic decomposition
  111

cathodes 125, 127
cavity wall insulation 238
cells 10, 12–17
  blood 28–9, 56
  homeostasis 50–1
cement 131
central nervous system
  (CNS) 38–9
ceramics 88–9
CFCs see
  chloro flouro carbons
charge separation 179
charges 178–9
chemical bonding 94–5
chemical change 110–11
chemical reactions 99
chlorides 143
chlorine 137
chloro flouro carbons
  (CFCs) 83
chlorophyll 60
chloroplasts 60
chromatography 106
chromosomes 14
cilia 33
circuit breakers 175
circuits 164–7
circulatory system 10,
  26–7
classification 2–5
cloning 77
CNS see
  central nervous system
coils 180
combustion 117
community 84
compounds 99
concentration 146
concrete 131
condensation 102
conduction 230, 232–3,
  238
conductors 233
consumers 84
continuous variation 70–1
contraceptive pill 49
convection currents
  230–1, 238

copper, electrolysis 127
core 180
cornea 40
cracking 119
craters 227
critical angle 218
crude oil 114, 121
crustaceans 6
cryolite 125
crystallisation 133
current 173, 184–5
  control 168–9
  measuring 164–5
cystic fibrosis 74
cytoplasm 12

D

Davy, Sir Humphrey 136
d.c. motor 182–3
decomposition
  biological 86
  chemical 111
deoxyribonucleic acid
  (DNA) 14
diabetes 48, 74
diamond 95
diaphragm 30
diatomic molecules 140
diet, humans 20–1
diffusion 91
digestion 22, 23, 159
digestive system 10, 22–3
diodes 172
discontinuous variation
  70–1
disease 74–5
displacement reactions 123
displacement–time graph
  197
dissolving 100
distance–time graphs 196
distillation 102, 103, 104,
  105, 114
DNA see
  deoxyribonucleic acid
double glazing 238
double insulation 175
driving force 200

drugs 58–9
dyes 107
dynamo 185

E

earth 174, 175, 179
echoes 208–9
ecosystem 84
effectors 39
efficiency 240–1
egestion 22
elasticity 190
electric bells 181
electricity 166, 176–7
electrolytic composition
  111
electromagnetic induction
  184–5
electromagnetic radiation
  247
electromagnetic spectrum
  220–1
electromagnetism 180–1
electromagnets 180
electrons 92–3, 96
elements 98
ellipse 228
embryos 72
emissions, radioactive
  246–7
endocrine glands 44–5
endocrine system 10, 44–5
endoscopes 219
energy
  food 34
  resources 240–1
  storage 191
  transfer 166–7, 176–7,
    230–7, 242–3
energy levels 93
enzymes 23, 150–1
epidermis 56
equilibrium 207
erector muscles 54
erosion 132
ethanol 36
eutrophication 63
evaporation 68, 69, 101,

230, 236–7
evolution 78
excretion 8–9, 10
exhalation 31
exocrine glands 45
external environment 50
eyes 40–1

F

fallopian tubes 11
fats 18, 20
feeding relationships 84–5
fermentation 36–7, 105
fertilisation 16, 72
fertilisers 154–5
fertility, human 49
fibre, dietary 19, 21
fibres 88–9
filtering 101
fish 3
fluids 194, 230–1
food
  chains 84
  chemistry 18–19
  energy 34
forces 193
  balanced 200–1, 205
  gravitational 204–5,
    228–9
  magnification 207
  turning 206
  work 242–3
formulas 99
fossils 78–9, 129
fovea 40
fractional distillation 103,
  104, 114
fractions 104, 115
freezing 90
frequency 214–15
friction 201
fridges 231, 237
fuel 117
fullerenes 95
fuses 174–5

G

galaxy 226
gamma radiation 225, 246
gas exchange 32–3
gases 90–1, 159
Geiger-Müller tube 246,
 248
generators 185, 188
genes 14
giant structures 94–5
glasses 88–9
global warming 82–3
glucagon 46
glucose 18, 46
glycogen 46
gradients 196–7
graphite 95
graphs 196–7, 202–3
gravity 64, 204–5, 228–9
greenhouse effect 82
grinding 101
groups, Periodic Table
 134–5
growth 15

H

Haber process 152–3
haemoglobin 29, 74
haemophilia 75
hair 54
half-life 249, 250
halogens 140–1, 142–3
heart 26–7
heat 166
heating, electrical 177
herbicides 66
herbivores 84
high pressure 192
homeostasis 50–1, 54–5
Hooke's law 190
hormones 46
 control 44–5
 medical uses 48–9
 plants 65, 66–7
 sex 46–7, 49
hydraulics 194–5

hydrocarbons
 alkanes 116–17
 cracking 118–19
 crude oil 114–15
 polymerisation 120–1
 reactions 117
hydrogen 141, 152–3
hydrogen halides 142–3
hydrogen peroxide 148,
 150–1
hydrolysis 18

I

igneous rocks 129
ileum 24
images 211
immiscibility 103
impermeable rocks 114
impurities 101
in vitro fertilisation
 (IVF) 49
indicators 156–7
induced voltages 186
induction 179, 184–5
infrared radiation 221, 223
ingestion 22
inhalation 30
inheritance 74–5
inhibitors 149
inorganic fertilisers 63
insects 4, 6, 159
insolubility 162–3
insulation 174–5, 237,
 238–9
insulators 179
insulin 46, 48
intercostal muscles 30
internal environment 50
invertebrates 2
iodides 143
ionic bonding 96–7
ions 94, 96–7
iris 41
iron 126–7
irritability 8
isotopes 93
IVF *see*
 in vitro fertilisation

J

joulemeters 172
joules 242

K

keys 6–7
kidneys 52–3
kilowatt-hour 176

L

lactic acid 36
lattices 97
leaves 61
left-hand rule 182
lens 40, 41
life processes 8–9
light 166
 reflection 208–9, 210–11
 refraction 216–17
 total internal reflection
  218–19
limit of proportionality
 190
liquids 90–1, 102
litmus 156–7
loft insulation 238
longitudinal waves 213
low pressure 193
lungs 30–3
lymphocytes 29, 56, 57

M

magnesium 62
mains electrical supply
 174–5
malnutrition 21
mammals 3
mass number 92
materials 88–9
medicine 209, 225
meiosis 16–17
melting 90
membranes 12
Mendeléev, Dmitri 134
menstruation 47

metals 88–9
  alkali 136–7
  extraction 124–7
  ores 124–5
  reactivity 122–3, 137, 141
metamorphic rocks 129
meteors 227
microscopes 13
microwaves 221, 222–3
minerals 128
  plant nutrition 62–3
  salts 19, 21
miscibility 103
mitosis 15, 17
mixtures 98–9
molecules 94–5
molluscs 4
moments 206–7
monoculture 62
monomers 120
motors 182–3
movement 8, 166
mucus 33, 56
muscles 34, 36
muscular dystrophy 75
mutagens 73
mutation 72–3
myriapods 6

N

national grid 188, 189
negative feedback 51
nephrons 52–3
nerve impulses 34
nervous system 10
neurones 38–9, 42
neutralisation 157, 158–9
neutrons 92–3
Newton, Isaac 204
nitric acid 155
nitrogen 62, 152–3
noble gases 96, 138–9
normal distribution 71
nuclei 12, 93
nutrition 9

O

offspring 9
ohms 170
oil 114
omnivores 84
optic nerve 40, 41
orbits 228
ores 124–5
organ systems 10–11
organic fertilisers 63
organs 10–11
osmosis 68
ovaries 11
oxidation 112–13
oxidising agents 113
oxygen 136
ozone layer 83

P

pain 42
palisade cells 61
pancreas 46
paper chromatography 106
paraffin 119
parallel circuits 165, 168–9
particle size 144–5
pascals 193
penis 11
perennating organs 76
Periodic Table 134–5
periods, Periodic Table 134–5
peristalsis 23, 24
petrification 79
pH 156–7
phagocytes 29, 56, 57
phloem 61
photosynthesis 9, 60–1
photovoltaic cells 241
physical change 110–11
pigments 163
planets 226–7, 228
plankton 114
plant kingdom 2, 5

plants
  fertilisers 154–5
  growth control 64–5
  hormones 65, 66–7
  nutrition 62–3
  photosynthesis 9, 60–1
  roots 65, 68–9
  runners 76
  soil testing 158–9
  water 69
plasma 28
plasticity 190
plastics 88–9
platelets 29
polymerisation 18, 120–1
polymers 120
potassium 62
power 172, 173, 176–7, 244
  generation 188
  transmission 188–9
practical motors 183
precipitates 143
precipitation 162–3
predators 80–1
pressure 192–3, 194–5
prey 80–1
principle of moments 207
properties, materials 88–9
proteins 18, 19
protons 92–3
pupils 40–1

R

radiation 230, 234–5
radioactive decay 248–9
radioactive emissions 246–7
radioactive tracers 225, 250–1
radios 215
rate of reaction 144–9
raw materials 88–9
reaction rates 144–9
reactivity series 122–3
real images 211
receptors 38–9, 42
redox reactions 113

reducing agents 113
reduction 112–13, 126, 127
reflection 208–9, 210–11
reflexes 42–3
reforming 118
refraction of light 216–17
relays 181
replication 15
reproduction 9, 72–3
reproductive system 10, 11
reptiles 3
repulsion 178–9
resin 148
resistance 168, 170–1
resistors 168
respiration 8, 34–7
respiratory system 10, 30–3
response, nervous 39
retina 40
reverberation 208–9
reversible reaction 152–3
rock salt 100
rocks
    cycle 132–3
    dating 251
    types 128–9
    uses 130–1
rolling resistance 201
rooting powders 66
roots 65, 68–9
runners, plants 76

S

safety, electricity 174–5
salts
    formation 160–3
    insolubility 162–3
    rock salt 100
    sodium chloride 100, 108–9
    solubility 160
satellites 227
saturated hydrocarbons 116
saturated solution 108
scabs 56
sedatives 59

sedimentary rocks 128–9
seedless fruit 67
seeds 5
selective breeding 77
sense organs 38
sensitivity 8
sensory nerves 42
separating mixtures 100–7
series circuits 164, 169
sex hormones 46–7, 49
shape 190
sickle-cell anaemia 74
skin
    defence 56–7
    homeostasis 54–5
slag 126, 127
slate 130
smoking 33, 58
sodium chloride 100, 108–9
soil testing 158–9
solar power 235, 241
solids 90–1, 102
solubility 108–9, 160–1
solutes 108
solution mining 100
solvents 58, 108
sound 208–9
spectrum 220–1
speed 196–7, 198–9, 208
sperm tubes 11
spinal cord 42
starch 18
static electricity 178–9
statistics 71
stills 105
stimuli 38
stings 159
stomata 61, 69
stone see rocks
stopping distance 199
stretching 190
sublimation 90
sulphur 62
surface area 144–5
sweat glands 54–5
switches 181
synthesis 99

T

target cells 45
temperature 54–5, 147
terminal velocity 205
testes 11
thermal conduction see conduction
thermal decomposition 111
Thermit reaction 123
thermostats 177
thinking distance 199
TIR see total internal reflection
tissue 10, 11
total internal reflection (TIR) 218–19
trace elements 154
tracers 225, 250–1
transformers 186–7
transition metals 134–5
transpiration 68–9
transverse waves 213
trophic levels 85
tropisms 64
tumours 73
turbines 188
turgidity 69
turning forces 206
twins 72
tyres 191

U

ultrasound 209
ultraviolet radiation 221, 223
Universal Indicator 157
universe 226–7
urea 52–3
urine 53
uterus 11

V

vacuole 12
vacuum 237
vagina 11
valves 26, 27
variable resistors 168

variables, chemical
  reactions 146–7
variation 17, 70–1
vasoconstriction 55
vasodilatation 55
veins
  human 26
  leaves 61
velocity 197, 202–3
ventricles 26, 27
vertebrates 2, 3
vibration 212–13
villi 24–5
virtual images 211
visible spectrum 220–1
vitamins 19
voltage 168–9, 173, 186–7
voltmeters 168–9

W

washing powders 151
water
  diet 21
  plants 69
  pollution 155
  reactions 136–7, 140–1
watts 244
wavelength 214–15
waves
  amplitude 213
  light 210–11, 216–17,
    218–19
  measurements 214–15
  types 212–13
weathering 132
weedkillers 66
weight 204
white blood cells 56
work 242–3

X

X-rays 224–5
xylem 61

Y

yeast 36–7

Z

zygotes 14, 16, 72